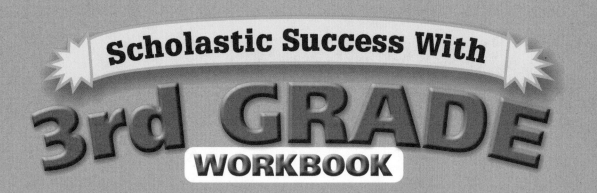

Scholastic Success With
3rd GRADE
WORKBOOK

SCHOLASTIC

NEW YORK • TORONTO • LONDON • AUCKLAND • SYDNEY
MEXICO CITY • NEW DELHI • HONG KONG • BUENOS AIRES

Cover design by Anna Christian; Cover art by Rob McClurkan
Interior illustrations by Jon Buller, Michael Denman, Reggie Holladay, Susan Hendron, Anne Kennedy, Kathy Marlin, Bob Masheris, Mark Mason, and Marybeth Rivera
Interior design by Quack & Company
Maps (pages 205–250) copyright © Linda Ward Beech

Photos ©: 252: scigelova/iStockphoto; 254: Romaoslo/iStockphoto; 257 top: anankkml/iStockphoto; 257 bottom: Minden Pictures/Masterfile; 260 left: Epkin/iStockphoto; 260 center: scanrail/iStockphoto; 260 right: Pairoj/iStockphoto; 260 bottom left: robynmac/iStockphoto; 266 top: Randi Scott/Shutterstock; 266 bottom: calebphoto/iStockphoto; 272: georgeclerk/iStockphoto; 275 left: David Clapp/Getty Images; 275 right: Peter Unger/Getty Images; 279: karandaev/iStockphoto; 284: Nazzu/Shutterstock; 287 top: NASA; 287 bottom: Science Source/NASA/Getty Images; 288: anilakkus/iStockphoto; 290: Roman Sakhno/Shutterstock; 292: SteveUnit4/Shutterstock; 295 top: cruphoto/iStockphoto; 295 bottom: alexsl/iStockphoto; 297 top, left and right: korionov/iStockphoto; 297 center: leonello/iStockphoto; 297 bottom: Pr3t3nd3r/iStockphoto; 299 top, left, right and bottom row: korionov/iStockphoto; 299 center: leonello/iStockphoto; 299 center bottom: Pr3t3nd3r/iStockphoto; 301: RichVintage/Getty Images; 305: paulvision/iStockphoto; 308: monticello/Shutterstock.

ISBN 978-1-338-30660-6

Table of Contents

READING COMPREHENSION

SQ3R (Understanding the reading process) 12

The Invention of the Telephone
(Understanding the reading process) 13

The Milky Way (Finding the main idea
and details) 14

Wagon Train (Finding the main idea
and details) 15

What a Nose! (Finding the main idea
and details) 16

The Math Contest (Identifying story
elements) 17

Best Friends (Identifying story elements) 18

The Tallest Trees (Developing vocabulary) 20

Let's Play Soccer! (Developing vocabulary) 21

Scrambled Eggs (Sequencing) 22

My Crazy Dream (Sequencing) 23

Berry Colorful Ink (Sequencing) 24

Simon Says (Following directions) 25

Sneaky Snakes (Following directions) 26

Fun With Words (Following directions) 27

Where Is Holly? (Drawing conclusions) 28

Who Invented Potato Chips?
(Drawing conclusions) 30

The Lake Cabin (Visualizing) 31

Monroe's Mighty Youth Tonic
(Using context clues) 32

Double It Up (Using context clues) 34

Where Am I? (Making inferences) 35

On the Border (Classifying) 36

Moving In (Classifying) 37

The Pyramid Game (Classifying) 38

News or Views? (Identifying fact or opinion) 39

TV Commercials (Identifying fact or opinion) 40

News Report (Identifying fact or opinion) 41

Homer's Big Adventure (Making predictions) 42

Mary's Mystery (Making predictions) 44

Special Charts (Comparing and contrasting) 46

Sports Chart (Comparing and contrasting) 47

Sharks (Comparing and contrasting) 48

Earthquake! (Identifying cause and effect) 50

Wacky Water Slides
(Identifying cause and effect) 51

Nonfiction: A Biography
(Appreciating literature) 52

Acrostic Poems (Appreciating literature) 54

CONTEMPORARY CURSIVE

Aa 56

Bb 57

Cc 58

Dd 59

Ee 60

Ff 61

Gg 62

Hh 63

Ii 64

Jj 65

Kk 66

Ll 67

Mm 68

Nn 69

Oo 70

Pp 71

Qq 72

Rr 73

Ss 74
Tt 75
Uu 76
Vv 77
Ww 78
Xx 79
Yy 80
Zz 81
A–Z 82
a–z 83
Numbers 0–9 84
Our Solar System 85
Ancient Astronomers 86
What Is a Year? 87
From Hot to Cold 88
How Many Moons? 89
Speedy Mercury 90
Beautiful Venus 91
Our Incredible Earth 92
Mysterious Mars 93
Sensational Saturn 94
King Jupiter 95
Understanding Uranus 96
Not Much About Neptune 97
What's Up With Pluto? 98
Flying Rocks 99
Stationery Lined Paper 100

GRAMMAR

Statements and Questions 102
Exclamations and Commands 104
Singular and Plural Nouns 108
Common and Proper Nouns 111
Singular and Plural Pronouns 114

Action Verbs 117
Present- and Past-Tense Verbs 120
The Verb Be 123
Main Verbs and Helping Verbs 126
Linking Verbs 129
Subjects and Predicates 132
Adjectives 135
Articles and Other Adjectives 138
Possessive Nouns 141
Subject and Object Pronouns 144
Possessive Pronouns 147
Compound Subjects and Predicates 150
Contractions 153
Using Punctuation 156
Irregular Verbs 159

WRITING

Dinnertime (Identifying sentences
and fragments) 162
A Real Meal (Changing fragments
to sentences) 163
Rock Your World (Capitalizing and
punctuating statements) 164
Rock and Roll (Writing statements) 165
Wacky World (Capitalizing and
punctuating questions) 166
The Real World (Writing questions) 167
The Dry Desert (Punctuating statements,
questions, and exclamations) 168
The Sunny Sahara (Punctuating statements,
questions, and exclamations) 169
A Snowy Scene (Writing statements
and questions) 170
A Snowy Story (Proofreading) 171
Sentences That Slither (Identifying the
subject of a sentence) 172

A Reptile Fact Sheet *(Identifying the verb in a sentence)*............................. 173

Stretching Sentences *(Expanding sentences)*.... 174

Stretch It! *(Expanding sentences)*.............. 175

Ketchup and Mustard *(Combining sentences)*... 176

Let's Eat Out! *(Combining sentences)* 177

Buckets of Fun *(Brainstorming descriptive words)*........................ 178

At the Beach *(Expanding sentences with descriptive words)* 179

The Great Outdoors *(Expanding sentences with descriptive words)* 180

Outdoor Excitement *(Expanding sentences with descriptive words)* 181

Crazy Cartoons *(Writing a dialogue)* 182

What Did She Say? *(Using quotation marks)*.... 183

Look Who's Talking! *(Using quotation marks and punctuation)* 184

Chitchat *(Proofreading sentences)* 185

Under the Big Top *(Completing a sequenced paragraph)* 186

A Circus Train *(Completing a sequenced paragraph)* 187

Terrific Topics *(Building a paragraph: Following a topic)* 188

It Just Doesn't Belong! *(Building a paragraph: Following a topic sentence)*....... 189

Missing Topics *(Building a paragraph: Writing a topic sentence)*.................. 190

Try These Topics *(Building a paragraph: Writing a topic sentence)*....................191

That Drives Me Crazy! *(Building a paragraph: Identifying supporting sentences)*............ 192

Do You Agree? *(Building a paragraph: Writing supporting sentences)*.............. 193

A Great Trick *(Building a paragraph: Sequencing supporting sentences)* 194

Good to Know *(Building a paragraph: Writing supporting sentences)*.............. 195

Closing Time! *(Building a paragraph: Identifying a closing sentence)* 196

That's All Folks! *(Building a paragraph: Writing a closing sentence)* 197

A Paragraph Plan *(Building a paragraph: Following a plan)*........................198

My Very Own Paragraph *(Planning and writing a paragraph)* 199

Do I Have a Story for You! *(Planning and writing a narrative paragraph)* 200

Map It Out *(Planning and writing a narrative paragraph)*..................... 201

I'm Sure You'll Agree! *(Planning and writing a persuasive paragraph)* 202

That's a Fact! *(Planning and writing an expository paragraph)* 203

Paragraph Pen Pals *(Writing a friendly letter)* 204

MAPS

Map Basics..................................206

Understanding Directions 208

The World on a Globe 210

Intermediate Directions.................... 212

Using a Map Grid 214

Understanding Distance.................... 216

Learning About Scale 218

Using a Map Scale 220

Comparing Maps 222

The United States 224

North America 226

South America 228

Landforms 230

Using a Landform Map 232
A Resource Map 234
A Rainfall Map 236
A History Map 238
A Tourist Map 240
A City Map. 242
A Transit Map 244
Map Review 1. 246
Map Review 2 247
Thinking About Maps 248
Glossary 249

SCIENCE

Fascinating Frogs (Amphibians) 252
Which Equine? (Comparing equines) 254
Animals of Africa (Animals of Africa) 256
Saving Moto (Needs of living things) 257
Animals Down Under (Animals of Australia) 262
Record Breakers (Science vocabulary). 263
Anatomy of a Whale (Anatomy of a whale) 264
A Prickly Idea (Scientific inventions) 266
What Is the Meaning of This?
    (Parts of a tree) 268
Stately Trees (Science vocabulary). 269
Let's Recycle! (Recycling) 270
Avalanche! (Avalanches) 272
An American Volcano (Volcanoes) 274
The Ice Hotel (Ice). 275
Words for the Weather-Wise
    (Weather) 280
Waiting Out Winter (Animal behavior) 281
Animal Weather Forecasters?
    (Animal senses) 284
Weather Watchers (Weather). 286
Hello, Sun (The sun) 287
Hello, Roy G. Biv! (Rainbows) 292

Our Solar System (Space) 294
Moon Shapes (The moon) 295
Life in Space (Gravity) 300
Let's Roll (Gravity). 301
As Fit as a Clown (Health and Fitness) 306
Food for Thought (Nutrition) 308
Healthy and Crispy (Nutrition). 310
Chocolate Lover's Experiment
    (Designing an experiment) 312

ADDITION & SUBTRACTION

On the Mayflower (Adding/Subtracting
    through 18) 314
Great States (Adding/Subtracting through 18) . . . 315
United We Stand (Adding/Subtracting
    2-digit numbers without regrouping) 316
Stars and Stripes Forever (Regrouping review—
    ones to tens) 317
The U.S. Capital (Adding 2-digit numbers
    with regrouping) 318
Mr. President (Adding 2-digit numbers
    with regrouping) 319
Travel the Nation (Regrouping review—
    tens to ones) 320
Great Vacations (Subtracting 2-digit
    numbers with regrouping) 321
America's Favorite Pastime (Adding/Subtracting
    2-digit numbers with regrouping) 322
High-Scoring Game (Adding/Subtracting
    2-digit numbers with regrouping) 323
More Fun Sports (Adding/Subtracting
    2-digit numbers with regrouping) 324
Skating Shapes (Adding/Subtracting 2-digit
    numbers with regrouping) 325
Great Math Inventions (Adding/Subtracting
    2-digit numbers with regrouping) 326
It All Adds Up! (Adding 3-digit numbers
    without regrouping) 327

It's Electrifying! (Regrouping review—
tens to hundreds) 328

Let the Light Shine (Regrouping review—
hundreds to tens) 329

A, B, C, . . . (Adding 3-digit numbers
with regrouping) 330

. . . X, Y, and Z (Adding 3-digit numbers
with regrouping) 331

Number Decoder (Subtracting 3-digit numbers
with regrouping) 332

Out of This World (Subtracting 3-digit
numbers with regrouping) 333

Your Part of the World (Adding/Subtracting
3-digit numbers with regrouping) 334

Home Sweet Home (Adding/Subtracting
3-digit numbers with regrouping) 335

What a Beautiful World! (Adding/Subtracting
3-digit numbers with regrouping) 336

Majestic Mountains (Adding 4-digit
numbers without regrouping) 337

Reach for the Top (Adding 4-digit numbers
without regrouping) 338

One in a Thousand (Adding money/
Regrouping review) 339

Great Beginnings (Adding 4-digit numbers
with regrouping) 340

Styles Change (Adding 4-digit numbers
with regrouping) 341

Dynamite Dominoes (Regrouping review—
thousands to hundreds) 342

Pictures in the Sky (Subtracting 4-digit
numbers with regrouping) 343

Fun With Numbers (Adding/Subtracting
4-digit numbers with regrouping) 344

MATH

Space Chase Place Value (Place value) 346

Newspaper Math (Number sense) 348

Place-Value Puzzler (Place value). 349

Bee Riddle (Rounding to the nearest
ten and hundred) 350

Discover Coordinates! (Ordered pairs
and coordinates) 351

Tropical Tree (Ordered pairs
and coordinates) 352

Animal Caller (Bar graphs). 353

Great Graphing (Bar graphs) 354

Graph Drafter (Line graphs) 355

Code Zero! Code One!
(Multiplication facts 0–1) 356

Two, Four, Six, Eight, Who Do We
Appreciate? (Multiplication facts—2s) 357

A Positive Answer (Multiplication facts—3s) 358

Puzzling Facts (Multiplication facts—4s) 359

How Many Can You Find?
(Multiplication facts—5s) 360

Mathematics Fireworks
(Multiplication facts—6s) 361

Flying Sevens (Multiplication facts—7s) 362

The Ultimate Eight Track
(Multiplication facts—8s) 363

Cross-Number Puzzle
(Multiplication facts—9s) 364

Around Town (Review 0–9s) 365

Cloud Ten (Multiplication facts—10s). 366

Eleven! Eleven! (Multiplication facts—11s) 367

Thinking Thoughts of Twelve
(Multiplication facts—12s) 368

There Are No Obstacles Too Big for You!
(Review 0–12s). 369

Friendship (Reviewing fact families). 370

Rainy Day *(Reviewing fact families)* 371

Space Traveler *(Multiplying 1-digit and 2-digit numbers)*. 372

Eager Seeker *(Introducing division with remainders)* 373

Exploding Star *(Division facts)* 374

Flying Carpet *(1-digit divisors)* 375

Who's Got the Button? *(Solving story problems)* 376

Problems and More *(Reasoning and logic)*. 377

More Problems and More *(Reasoning and logic)* 378

Brain Power! *(Reasoning and logic)* 379

Flag Wagger *(Identifying parts of a whole)*. 380

Goody for Fractions! *(Identifying parts of a whole)*. 381

Flower Shop Fractions *(Identifying parts of a group)* 382

Cooking With Fractions *(Using fractions)*. 383

Into Infinity *(Adding like fractions, reducing fractions)* 384

Put the Brakes on Math Mistakes! *(Counting money)* 385

Autumn Harvest *(Counting money)*. 386

Dollar Scholar *(Counting money)*. 388

Time for a Riddle! *(Telling time)*. 389

Curves Ahead! *(Measuring length)* 390

Measure With Me *(Measuring length)*. 391

Weight Watcher *(Comparing units of measure)* 392

Degree Overseer *(Comparing units of measure)* 393

Fact Finder *(Comparing units of measure)* 394

Amount Counter *(Properties of shapes, geometric patterns)* 395

Shape Gaper *(3-Dimensional shapes)* 396

Riddle Teller *(Properties of shapes)*. 397

Terrific Tessellations *(Tessellate patterns)* 398

Pattern Block Design *(Geometric patterns)*. 400

Answer Key 401

"Nothing succeeds like success."

Alexandre Dumas the Elder, 1854

Dear Parent,

Congratulations on choosing this excellent educational resource for your child. Scholastic has long been a leader in educational publishing—creating quality educational materials for use in school and at home for nearly a century.

As a partner in your child's academic success, you'll want to get the most out of the learning experience offered in this book. To help your child learn at home, try following these helpful hints:

★ Provide a comfortable place to work.

★ Have frequent work sessions, but keep them short.

★ Praise your child's successes and encourage his or her efforts. Offer positive help when your child makes a mistake.

★ Display your child's work and share his or her progress with family and friends.

In this workbook you'll find hundreds of practice pages that keep kids challenged and excited as they strengthen their skills across the classroom curriculum.

The workbook is divided into eight sections: Reading Comprehension; Contemporary Cursive; Grammar; Writing; Maps; Science; Addition & Subtraction; and Math. You and your child should feel free to move through the pages in any way you wish.

The table of contents lists the activities and the skills practiced. And a complete answer key in the back will help you gauge your child's progress.

Take the lead and help your child succeed with the *Scholastic Success With 3rd Grade Workbook!*

FOCUS SKILLS

The activities in this workbook reinforce age-appropriate skills and will help your child meet the following standards established as goals by leading educators.

Mathematics

* Uses a variety of strategies when problem-solving

* Understands and applies number concepts

* Uses basic and advanced procedures while performing computation

* Understands and applies concepts of measurement

* Understands and applies concepts of geometry

* Understands and applies properties of functions and algebra

Writing

* Understands and uses the writing process

* Uses grammatical and mechanical conventions in written compositions

Reading

* Understands and uses the general skills and strategies of the reading process

* Can read and understand a variety of literary texts

* Can understand and interpret a variety of informational texts

Geography

* Understands the characteristics and uses of maps and globes

* Knows the location of places, geographic features, and patterns of the environment

Science

* Plans and carries out investigations to answer questions or test solutions

* Understands basic details about animals and plants including what living things need to live

* Analyzes patterns of weather, natural hazards, and geological events and how these affect people and animals

* Recognizes basic details of our solar system including how Earth's orbit and rotation, and the orbit of the moon around Earth cause observable patterns

* Analyzes force and motion

Scholastic Success With

READING COMPREHENSION

SQ3R

Do you know about SQ3R? It is a formula to help you understand what you read. It can be useful for any reading assignment. SQ3R is especially helpful when you are reading a textbook, like your social studies or science book. Each letter of the formula tells you what to do.

S = Survey

Survey means to look over the assignment. Look at the pictures. Look at the title and the headings, if there are any. Read the first sentence or two.

Q = Question

Question means to ask yourself, "What is this assignment about? What is the author trying to tell me?" Once you get an idea of what you are going to read, then you can read with a better understanding.

3R = Read, Recite, Review

1. Read the assignment, looking for the answers to the questions you had. Concentrate. Picture in your mind what the words are saying.

2. Recite in your mind, or write on paper, the main ideas of what you have just read. Write the main ideas in your own words.

3. Review what you have learned. Make notes to help you review.

Now you have a valuable study tool. Use it to help study for a test. Use it to help remember what you read. Use it to help understand important information.

Let's practice. Read the assignment on page 13. Use the SQ3R formula step by step.

© Scholastic Inc.

The Invention of the Telephone

Alexander ~~Graham Bell~~ invented the telephone. He was a teacher of the deaf in Boston. At night, he worked on experiments using a telegraph. Once when the metal in the telegraph stuck, Bell's assistant plucked the metal to loosen it. Bell, who was in another room, heard the sound in his receiver. He understood that the vibrations of the metal had traveled down the electric current to the receiver. He continued to work on this idea.

March 10, 1876, was the first time Alexander Graham Bell successfully spoke words over a telephone line. He was about to test a new transmitter when he spilled some battery acid on his clothes. He cried out to his assistant who was in another room, "Mr. Watson, come here! I want to see you!" Watson heard every word clearly on the telephone and rushed into the room.

Bell demonstrated his invention to many people. Over time, more and more telephone lines were installed, and people began to use the invention in their homes and businesses.

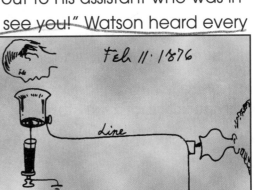

partial page from inventor's notebook

Did SQ3R help you? Let's find out.

1. **Who invented the telephone?** Graham Bell

2. **What was his regular job?** It was to make the telephone.

3. **What did Mr. Bell say to Mr. Watson during the first telephone conversation?** Mr. Watson come here. I need too see you!

4. **Who was Mr. Watson?** _____

5. **How did people first learn about the telephone?** Mr. Graham Bell told the town about it.

On another piece of paper, write a paragraph telling why you are glad the telephone was invented. Read your paragraph to a friend.

The Milky Way

*The **main idea** of a story tells what the story is mostly about. **Details** in a story tell more information about the main idea.*

What do you think of when you hear the words, "Milky Way"? Do you think of a candy bar? Well, there is another Milky Way, and you live in it! It is our galaxy. A galaxy is a grouping of stars. Scientists have learned that there are many galaxies in outer space. The Milky Way is a spiral-shaped galaxy with swirls of stars spinning out from the center of it. Some scientists believe there are hundreds of billions of stars in the Milky Way. One of those stars is the sun. Several planets orbit the sun. One of them is Earth. Even from Earth, on a clear night away from city lights, you can see part of the Milky Way. It is called that because so many stars close together look like a milky white stripe across the sky. However, if you looked at it with a telescope, you would see that it is made up of many, many stars.

Complete the main idea and each detail about the story.

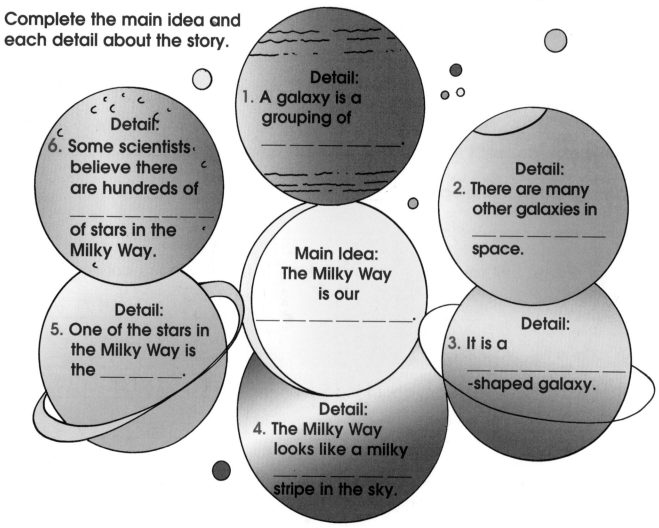

Detail:
1. A galaxy is a grouping of _ _ _ _ _ _.

Detail:
6. Some scientists believe there are hundreds of _ _ _ _ _ _ of stars in the Milky Way.

Detail:
5. One of the stars in the Milky Way is the _ _ _.

Main Idea:
The Milky Way is our _ _ _ _ _ _ _.

Detail:
2. There are many other galaxies in _ _ _ _ _ space.

Detail:
3. It is a _ _ _ _ _ _ -shaped galaxy.

Detail:
4. The Milky Way looks like a milky _ _ _ _ _ stripe in the sky.

Wagon Train

Will and Kate thought it would be a great adventure to travel west with the wagon train. In the spring of 1880, their family left their home in Pennsylvania and joined a wagon train headed for California. For months, their only home was the wagon. A large canvas was spread over metal hoops on top of the wagon to make a roof. Will helped his father oil the canvas so that the rain would slide off and keep them dry inside. Each day Kate and Will gathered wood as they walked beside the wagon. In the evening when the wagons stopped, Kate and her mother built a campfire for cooking supper. They hauled supplies with them so that they could cook beans and biscuits. Sometimes the men went hunting and brought back fresh deer meat or a rabbit for stew. When it rained for several days, the roads were so muddy that the wagons got stuck. There was always danger of snakes and bad weather. There were rivers and mountains to cross. There was no doctor to take care of those who got sick or injured. Will and Kate were right. Traveling with a wagon train was a great adventure, but it was a very hard life.

Unscramble the words to make a complete sentence that tells the main idea.

wagon dangerous. on a Life hard and was train _____

_____

Choose a word from the wagon to complete each detail.

1. __ __ __ __ __ __ the canvas

2. __ __ __ __ __ __ __ __ __
   wood

3. __ __ __ __ __ __ __ __ over a
   campfire

4. __ __ __ __ __ __ __ supplies

5. __ __ __ __ __ __ __ __ for meat

6. __ __ __ __ __ __ __ __ __ out
   for snakes

7. __ __ __ __ __ __ __ __ for
   the rain to stop

8. __ __ __ __ __ __ __ __ __ rivers
   and mountains

9. __ __ __ __ __ __ __ __ sick or
   hurt with no doctor to help

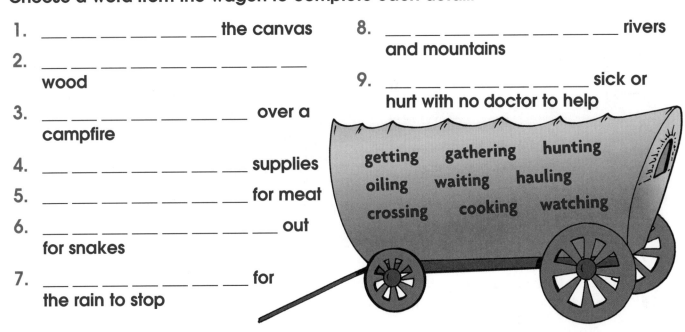

getting   gathering   hunting
oiling   waiting   hauling
crossing   cooking   watching

What a Nose!

An elephant's trunk is probably the most useful nose in the world. Of course, it is used for breathing and smelling, like most noses are. However, elephants also use their trunks like arms and hands to lift food to their mouths. They suck water into their trunks and pour it into their mouths to get a drink. Sometimes they spray the water on their backs to give themselves a cool shower. An adult elephant can hold up to four gallons of water in its trunk. Elephants can use their trunks to carry heavy things, such as logs that weigh up to 600 pounds! The tip of the trunk has a little knob on it that the elephant uses like a thumb. An elephant can use the "thumb" to pick up something as small as a coin. Trunks are also used for communication. Two elephants that meet each other touch their trunks to each other's mouth, kind of like a kiss. Sometimes a mother elephant will calm her baby by stroking it with her trunk. Can your nose do all those things?

Find the statement below that is the main idea of the story. Write *M.I.* in the elephant next to it. Then find the details of the story. Write *D* in the elephant next to each detail. Be careful! There are two sentences that do not belong in this story.

 Elephants use their trunks to greet each other, like giving a kiss.

 Elephants use their trunks to give themselves a shower.

 Some people like to ride on elephants.

 Elephants can carry heavy things with their trunks.

 Mother elephants calm their babies by stroking them with their trunks.

 Elephants use their trunks to eat and drink.

 Elephants use their noses for smelling and breathing.

 Elephants have very useful noses.

 Giraffes are the tallest animals in the world.

On another piece of paper, finish this story: When I was on safari, I looked up and saw a herd of elephants. Underline the main idea.

The Math Contest

Story elements *are the different parts of a story. The* characters *are the people, animals, or animated objects in the story. The* setting *is the place and time in which the story takes place. The* plot *of the story includes the events and often includes a* problem *and a* solution.

Every Friday, Mr. Jefferson, the math teacher, held a contest for his students. Sometimes they played math baseball. Sometimes they had math relays with flash cards. Other times, they were handed a sheet of paper with a hundred multiplication problems on it. The student who finished fastest with the most correct answers won the contest. One Friday, there was a math bee. It was similar to a spelling bee, except the students worked math problems in their heads. There was fierce competition, until finally, everyone was out of the game except Riley and Rhonda. Mr. Jefferson challenged them with problem after problem, but both students continued to answer correctly every time. It was almost time for class to end, so Mr. Jefferson gave them the same difficult problem. They had to work it in their heads. Riley thought hard and answered, "20." Rhonda answered, "18." Finally they had a winner!

To find out who won the game, work the problem below in your head. Write the answer on the blank.

$$6 + 4 + 6 - 4 - 4 + 6 + 6 = \underline{\qquad}$$

Now, to see if you are correct, circle only the 6's and 4's in the box. The answer will appear.

Answer each question below.

7	4	6	5	3	1	2	6	4	8	0
6	9	1	4	3	5	6	2	8	6	7
5	0	8	6	0	4	9	7	3	1	4
3	1	7	4	0	6	5	8	7	2	6
7	0	6	5	8	4	9	3	2	9	6
8	4	9	8	0	6	1	5	7	8	4
6	2	7	3	9	2	4	8	1	6	5
6	4	4	6	1	9	0	6	6	2	3

1. Name the three people in the story. _____, _____, and _____

2. Circle where the story takes place.
   a. in the gym   b. in the cafeteria   c. in Mr. Jefferson's classroom

3. Circle the problem in the story.
   a. Mr. Jefferson held the contest on Thursday.
   b. Class was almost over, and the contest was still tied.
   c. Riley and Rhonda both answered incorrectly.

4. Who answered the difficult question correctly? _____

Best Friends

Amy dreaded recess every day. She did not have any friends to play with. All the girls in her class were paired up with a best friend or in groups, and she always felt left out. So, instead of playing with anyone, Amy just walked around by herself. She wanted to seesaw, but that is something you need to do with a friend. She liked to swing, but she could not go very high. She wished someone would push her to get her started.

One day, the teacher, Mrs. Gibbs, walked up and put her arm around Amy. "What's the matter, Amy? Why don't you play with the other children?" she asked kindly.

Amy replied, "Everyone has a friend except me. I don't have anyone." Mrs. Gibbs smiled and said, "Amy, the way to get a friend is to be a friend." Amy asked, "How do I do that?"

Mrs. Gibbs answered, "Look around the playground. There are three classes of third-graders out here during this recess time. Find someone who is alone and needs a friend. Then go to that person and ask them to play." Amy said she would think about it, but she was afraid she would be too embarrassed. She wasn't sure she could do it.

The next day, Amy noticed a dark-haired girl all alone on the playground. She worked up her courage and walked over to the girl. "Hi! My name is Amy. Do you want to play with me?" she asked.

"Okay," the girl said shyly. As they took turns pushing each other on the swings, Amy found out that the girl's name was Ming. She and her family had just moved from Japan. She did not know anyone and could not speak much English yet. She needed a friend.

"Want to seesaw?" Amy asked. Ming looked puzzled. Amy pointed to the seesaw. Ming smiled and nodded. Amy was so happy. She finally had a friend!

On each blank, write the letter of the picture that correctly answers the question. One answer is used twice.

1. Where does this story take place? _____

2. Who is the main character in the story? _____

   Who are the other two characters in the story? _____ and _____

3. What is the problem in the story? _____

4. How does Amy solve her problem? _____

5. What is Ming's problem? _____

   How does Ming's problem get solved? _____

A. Mrs. Gibbs

B. playground

C. Ming needed a friend, too.

D. Ming

E. Amy

F. Amy asked Ming to play, and they became friends.

G. Amy needed a friend.

 Think about what you did during recess or another part of your day. On another piece of paper, list the characters, setting, problem, and solution. Use this list to write a story. Read the story to a friend.

The Tallest Trees

Redwood trees are the tallest trees in the world. Some grow over 300 feet high, which is taller than a 30-story building. Think of it this way: If a six-foot tall man stood at the base of a redwood tree, the tree would be 50 times taller than the man! These giant trees grow near the **coast** of California and Oregon. The **climate** is foggy and rainy there, which gives the redwoods a **constant** supply of water. Redwoods can grow for hundreds of years; in fact, some have lived for over 2,000 years! The **bark** is very thick, protecting the trees from insects, **disease**, and fires. The bark of redwood trees is a reddish-brown color. Redwood trees are very important to the lumber companies because the trees are so large that each one can be cut into lots of **lumber**. You may have seen lumber like this in redwood fences or redwood patio furniture. However, many of the trees are protected by law in the Redwood National Park. Lumber companies cannot cut trees that grow there. This is so the trees will not become **extinct**.

Put an *X* beside the correct definition of each bolded word in the story.

1. coast ____ land by the sea ____ a desert
2. climate ____ time ____ weather
3. constant ____ happens regularly ____ never happens
4. bark ____ leaves ____ outer covering of trees
5. disease ____ illness ____ high temperatures
6. lumber ____ plastic pipes ____ wood cut into boards
7. extinct ____ no longer existing ____ expensive

Read an article about another type of tree. On another piece of paper, list five new words from the article. Use a dictionary to learn the meaning of each word.

© Scholastic Inc.

Let's Play Soccer!

Soccer is the world's most popular sport. It is played in many countries all over the world. Every four years, an international competition is held. It is called the World Cup.

A **soccer field** is rectangular with a goal on each end. Each **goal** is made of a rectangular, frame-covered net. The game is played with a **soccer ball**. The ball is usually made of leather and is filled with air.

Two teams compete against each other. One point is awarded to a team when it scores a goal. Whichever team scores the most goals wins the game.

There are 11 players on each team. **Forwards** have the most responsibility to score goals. Sometimes forwards are called strikers. They are helped by teammates who play at midfield. These players are sometimes called **halfbacks**. Halfbacks help to score goals and try to keep the other team's ball away from the goal. Other teammates play farther back on the field to defend their goal. They try to keep the other team from getting close enough to score. They are sometimes called **fullbacks**. Each team has one **goalie** whose job is to keep the other team from scoring by blocking the ball or catching it before it goes into the goal. A goalie may catch or throw the ball, but no other players may use their hands. They may use their feet, legs, chest, or head to move the ball. A **referee** will penalize a team if any players other than the goalie use their hands. Soccer is definitely a team sport. All the positions are important in winning the game.

Label the diagram using the bolded words from the story.

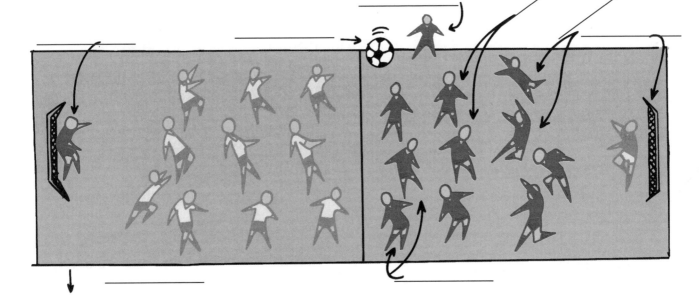

Scrambled Eggs

 Sequencing *means putting the events of a story in the order in which they happened.*

The sentences below are scrambled. Number them in the correct sequence.

A. ____ I took a shower.
   ____ I got out of bed.
   ____ I got dressed.

B. ____ She planted the seeds.
   ____ Big pink flowers bloomed.
   ____ Tiny green shoots came up.

C. ____ He ate the sandwich.
   ____ He spread some jelly on them.
   ____ He got out two pieces of bread.

D. ____ He slid down the slide.
   ____ He climbed up the ladder.
   ____ He landed on his feet.

E. ____ We built a snowman.
   ____ Low gray clouds drifted in.
   ____ It began to snow hard.

F. ____ Firefighters put out the fire.
   ____ Lightning struck the barn.
   ____ The barn caught on fire.

G. ____ The pepper spilled out of the jar.
   ____ I sneezed.
   ____ My nose began to itch.

H. ____ "My name is Emma."
   ____ "Hi, what is your name?"
   ____ "It's nice to meet you, Emma."

I. ____ I said, "Okay, do a trick first."
   ____ Rover whined for a treat.
   ____ I gave him a dog biscuit.
   ____ He danced on his hind legs.

J. ____ She built a nest.
   ____ Baby birds hatched from the eggs.
   ____ I saw a robin gathering straw.
   ____ She laid four blue eggs.

My Crazy Dream

I don't know why, but I went to school in my underwear. Everyone was laughing! I walked up and down the hall looking for my classroom, but I could never find it. Then I went to the Lost and Found box and put on some clothes. I heard my principal say, "Son, are you lost?" However, when I turned around, it was the President of the United States talking to me. He asked me to fly on his jet with him. As we were flying, I looked out the window and saw a pterodactyl flying next to us! How could that be? They are extinct! It smiled and waved good-bye. Then all of a sudden, the airplane turned into a roller coaster. It climbed upward a million miles, then down we went! For hours and hours we just kept going straight down! The roller coaster finally came to a stop, and I was on an island entirely made of chocolate. I ate a whole tree made of fudge! Then a chef sneaked up and captured me. He put me in a pot of boiling water to make soup out of me. I got hotter and hotter and hotter! Finally, I woke up and realized I had fallen asleep with my electric blanket on high.

Number the pictures in the order that they happened in the dream.

 On another piece of paper, draw a picture of a dream you once had. Then write a sentence about the beginning, middle, and end of the dream on separate strips of paper. Have a friend put the sentences in order.

Berry Colorful Ink

 When sequencing a story, look for key words such as first, then, next, *and* finally *to help you determine the correct sequence.*

In early American schools, students used a quill pen and ink to practice writing letters and numerals. Since these schools did not have many supplies, the students often had to make their own ink at home. There were many different ways to make ink. One of the most common ways was to use berries such as blackberries, blueberries, cherries, elderberries, or strawberries. The type of berry used depended on the color of ink a student wanted. First, the type of berry to be used had to gathered. Then a strainer was filled with the berries and held over a bowl. Next, using the back of a wooden spoon, the berries were crushed. This caused the juice to strain into the bowl. After all the berry juice was strained into the bowl, salt and vinegar were added to the juice and then stirred. Finally, the juice was stored in a small jar with a tight-fitting lid. Not only did the students make colorful inks to use, they also made invisible and glow-in-the dark inks.

Number the phrases below in the order given in the story.

_____ **The mixture was stirred.**

_____ **Using the back of a wooden spoon, the berries were crushed.**

_____ **The ink was stored in a small jar with a tight-fitting lid.**

_____ **Berries were gathered.**

_____ **All the berry juice was strained into the bowl.**

_____ **The strainer was held over a bowl.**

_____ **Salt and vinegar were added to the berry juice.**

_____ **A strainer was filled with berries.**

Look in a cookbook for a recipe you would like to try. Read all the steps. Have someone help you make the recipe. Be sure to follow each step in order.

Simon Says

 *When **following directions**, it is important to read the directions carefully and to follow them in the order they are listed.*

When you play Simon Says, you only follow the directions that Simon says. You do not follow any other directions. Play the game following the directions below.

1. Simon says draw a hand in the box below.

2. Simon says draw a ring on the ring finger.

3. Simon says draw fingernails on each finger.

4. Color each fingernail red.

5. Simon says write the names of five school days, one on each finger.

6. Circle your favorite day.

7. Write your teacher's name in the lower left-hand corner of the box.

8. Simon says write an addition problem on the hand, using the numbers 4, 5, and 9.

9. Now write a subtraction problem next to it.

10. Simon says draw a red scratch on the pinky finger.

11. Simon says draw a watch on the wrist.

12. Make the watch show 2:30.

13. Simon says outline the box with a yellow crayon.

14. Simon says write your name in the top right-hand corner of the box.

Sneaky Snakes

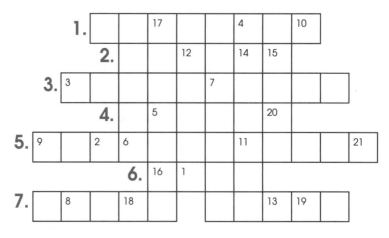

Snakes are very good at hiding. Most snakes can **camouflage** themselves into their environment. That means they have different colors and patterns on their bodies that allow them to blend in with the colors and patterns of things around them. Camouflage helps them hide from their enemies and helps them be **sneaky** when they are trying to capture something to eat. For example, the emerald tree boa lives in the **jungle**. Its green skin makes it nearly invisible among the green leaves of the trees. **Rattlesnakes** live in rocky, dry places. The patterns of black, tan, and brown on their backs help them blend in with their rocky environment. The horned viper lives in the desert. Its skin is the same color as **sand** where it burrows underground. It is hard to see unless it is moving. Also, some snakes that are harmless look very similar to **venomous** snakes. The harmless milk snake is colored orange, with yellow and black stripes, much like the poisonous **coral snake**. The enemies of the milk snake mistake it for a coral snake because they look so much alike.

Find the answers in the story. Write them in the puzzle.

1. Write the word that starts with a v and means "poisonous."

2. Write another word for "tricky."

3. Write what helps a snake blend in with its surroundings.

4. Write where emerald tree boas live.

5. Write what snakes live in rocky places and have black, tan, and brown patterned skin.

6. Write what is the same color as the horned viper.

7. Write the name of the snake that looks like a milk snake.

Write the letter from the numbered squares in the puzzle above to fill in each box.

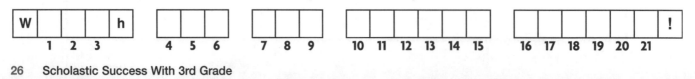

Fun With Words

Follow the directions to play each word game.

1. A palindrome is a word that is spelled the same forward or backward. Write each word backward. Circle each word that is a palindrome. Put an X on each word that is not.

   wow _____

   dad _____

   mom _____

   funny _____

   noon _____

   tall _____

   deed _____

2. Some words imitate the noise that they stand for. For example, when you say "pop," it sounds like a popping sound! That is called onomatopoeia. Unscramble each noise word. Write it correctly.

   seechrc _____

   owp _____

   plurs _____

   mobo _____

   lckic _____

   zzisel _____

   chnucr _____

3. Homophones are words that sound alike when you say them but are spelled differently and have different meanings. For example, see and sea are homophones. Draw a line to match each pair of homophones.

   knot   flew

   break   soar

   flu   not

   sore   write

   right   road

   rode   brake

4. Add or subtract letters from each word to change it into another word. Write the new word.

   peach – ch + r = _____

   shirt – irt + oe = _____

   sports – p – rts + ccer = _____

   love – ove + ike = _____

   stove – st + n = _____

   chicken – c – ick = _____

   brother – bro + nei = _____

Some names sound funny when you pronounce them backward. For example, Carol would be pronounced Lorac, and Jason would be pronounced Nosaj! Write your name and each of your friends' names backward. Then pronounce each name. Are any of the names palindromes?

© Scholastic Inc.

Where Is Holly?

Drawing conclusions *means to make reasonable conclusions about events in a story using the information given.*

One day, while Mom was washing dishes in the kitchen, she realized that she had not heard a peep out of three-year-old Holly in a long time. The last time she had seen her, she was playing in the living room with some building blocks. "She sure is being good," thought Mom.

Write an X next to the best answer.

1. **Why did Mom think Holly was being good?**

   _____ Holly was washing dishes for her.

   _____ Holly was playing with dolls.

   _____ Holly was being so quiet.

After rinsing the last dish, Mom went to the living room to see what Holly had built. But Holly was not there. "Holly! Where are you?" Mom asked. Mom heard a faraway voice say, "Mommy!" So Mom went outside to see if Holly was there.

2. **Why did Mom go outside to look for Holly?**

   _____ Holly's voice sounded so far away.

   _____ The last time Mom saw Holly, she was riding her tricycle.

   _____ Holly said, "I'm outside, Mommy."

Mom looked down the street, up in the tree, and in the backyard, but Holly was not outside. She called her again but did not hear her voice. So, she went back inside. "Holly! Where are you? Come out right now."

3. **Why did Mom say, "Come out right now."**

   _____ She was mean.

   _____ She heard Holly's voice coming from the closet.

   _____ She thought Holly might be hiding.

Once again, Mom heard a faraway sound. "Help me!" cried Holly. Mom ran to the bathroom, but Holly was not there. She ran to the garage, but Holly was not there either. Finally, she ran to Holly's room and saw Holly's feet sticking out of the toy box, kicking wildly in the air!

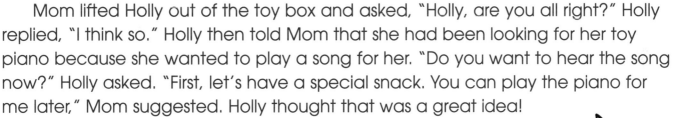

4. **What had happened to Holly?**

   _____ **She had fallen headfirst into the toy box and could not get out.**

   _____ **She was playing with the blocks again.**

   _____ **She was playing hide-and-seek with Mom.**

Mom lifted Holly out of the toy box and asked, "Holly, are you all right?" Holly replied, "I think so." Holly then told Mom that she had been looking for her toy piano because she wanted to play a song for her. "Do you want to hear the song now?" Holly asked. "First, let's have a special snack. You can play the piano for me later," Mom suggested. Holly thought that was a great idea!

5. **Where was Holly's toy piano?**

   _____ **The piano was under Holly's bed.**

   _____ **The piano was at the bottom of the toy box.**

   _____ **She was playing hide-and-seek with Mom.**

Mom and Holly walked to the kitchen. Mom made Holly a bowl of ice cream with chocolate sauce and a cherry on top. Holly told Mom that she wanted to go to the park. Mom really liked that idea.

5. **What will Mom and Holly do next?**

   _____ **Mom and Holly will go shopping.**

   _____ **Mom and Holly will go for a bike ride.**

   _____ **Mom and Holly will play on the swings in the park.**

Read a chapter from a book. On another piece of paper, write a sentence telling what you think will happen next. Read the next chapter. Were you correct?

Who Invented Potato Chips?

Have you ever wondered who invented potato chips? Some people say George Crum was the first person to make them . . . by accident! In 1853, he was a chef at an elegant restaurant in Saratoga Springs, New York, called Moon's Lake House. A regular item on the menu was fried potatoes, which was an idea that had started in France. At that time, French fried potatoes were cut into thick slices. One day, a dinner guest at Moon's Lake House sent his fried potatoes back to the chef because he did not like them so thick. So, Mr. Crum cut the potatoes a little thinner and fried them. The guest did not like those either. That made Mr. Crum angry, so he thought he would just show that guy. He sliced the potatoes paper-thin and fried them, thinking that would hush the complaining diner. However, his plan backfired on him! The diner loved the crispy, thin potatoes! Other diners tried them and also liked them. So, Mr. Crum's potato chips were added to the menu. They were called Saratoga Chips. Eventually, Mr. Crum opened his own restaurant to sell his famous chips. Now potato chips are packaged and sold in grocery stores worldwide!

Color each chip and its matching bag the same color.

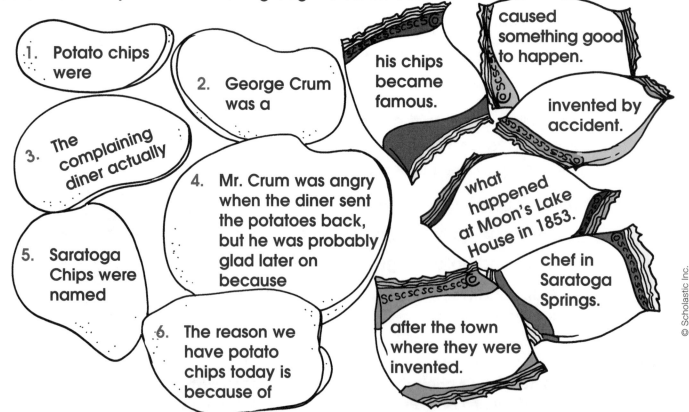

1. Potato chips were

2. George Crum was a

3. The complaining diner actually

4. Mr. Crum was angry when the diner sent the potatoes back, but he was probably glad later on because

5. Saratoga Chips were named

6. The reason we have potato chips today is because of

his chips became famous.

caused something good to happen.

invented by accident.

what happened at Moon's Lake House in 1853.

chef in Saratoga Springs.

after the town where they were invented.

The Lake Cabin

As you read the paragraph, imagine the scene that the words are describing. In the picture below, draw everything that has been left out. Color the picture.

My favorite thing to do in the summer is to go to Grandpa's lake cabin. In the evening after a full day of fishing, Grandpa and I sit on the back porch and enjoy the scenery. The sun setting behind the mountain fills the blue sky with streaks of orange and yellow. Colorful sailboats float by us in slow motion. Suddenly a fish jumps out of the water, making tiny waves in rings. A deer quietly walks to the edge of the water to get a drink. Red and yellow wildflowers grow near the big rock. On the shore across the lake, we see a couple of tents. Someone must be camping there. A flock of geese fly over the lake in the shape of a V. Every time we sit and look at the lake, Grandpa says, "This is the best place on Earth!"

On another piece of paper, write a paragraph describing the place that you think is "the best place on Earth." Read your paragraph to a friend.

Monroe's Mighty Youth Tonic

Way back yonder in 1853, a traveling salesman named "Shifty" Sam Monroe rode into our little town of Dry Gulch. I was there that day when Shifty stood on the steps of his **buckboard** selling Monroe's Mighty Youth Tonic. Shifty announced, "Ladies and gentlemen, **lend me your ears**. I, Sam Monroe, have invented a tonic that will give you back your youth. It will **put a spring in your step**. You'll feel years younger if you take a spoonful of this **heavenly elixir** once a day. It contains a **special blend of secret ingredients**. Why, it once made a 94-year-old cowboy feel so young, he went back to **bustin' broncs** again! An old settler that was over 100 felt so young he let out a **war whoop** that could be heard in Pike County! **It's a steal** at only one dollar a bottle. Step right up and get yours now." Well, I wondered what those secret ingredients were, so I bought a bottle and tasted it. It tasted like nothing but sugar water. So I hid behind Shifty Sam's wagon and waited for the crowd to **mosey** on home. When Shifty went inside to make some more tonic, I **kept my eye on him**. Sure enough, he mixed sugar and water and added a drop of vanilla. We'd been **hornswoggled**! I **hightailed it** right then over to the sheriff's office and had him arrest that no-good varmint. Old Shifty is now spending the rest of his "mighty youth" **behind bars**!

Howdy, partner! Read the bolded words in the story. What do they mean? Draw a rope to hitch up the words on the left with the correct meanings on the right.

1. way back yonder

2. buckboard

3. Lend me your ears.

4. Put a spring in your step.

5. heavenly elixir

6. special blend of secret ingredients

7. bustin' broncs

8. war whoop

9. It's a steal!

10. mosey

11. kept my eye on him

12. hornswoggled

13. hightailed it

14. no-good varmint

15. behind bars

walk slowly

cheated; tricked

watched him closely

making wild horses gentle

ran quickly

evil creature

Listen to me.

in jail

wagon

You are getting it for a low price.

I won't tell what's in it.

makes you feel peppy

many years ago

loud yell

wonderful tonic

Double It Up

Some words can share the same spelling but have completely different meanings. To figure out the correct meaning of each word, use context clues. Using **context clues** *means to look at the meaning of the whole sentence. One meaning for the word will make sense, and the other one will not. Read the following examples:*

The bat flew out of the dark cave. *(Would a baseball bat fly out of a cave? No. Then it must be the other kind of bat: a small flying animal.)*

He swung the bat so hard that the ball went over the fence. *(Would someone swing a small animal in order to hit a ball? Of course not!)*

Picture each of the following sentences in your mind to help you decide which meaning is correct for each italicized word. Then fill in the bubble next to the correct meaning.

1. I am sneezing because I have a *cold.*
   ○ opposite of hot
   ○ an illness

2. I rowed up to the *bank* and got out of the boat.
   ○ building where money is kept
   ○ shoreline of a river or creek

3. The garage is 15-*feet* wide.
   ○ a measurement
   ○ body parts used for walking

4. The *mouse* ran under the bushes.
   ○ a small, furry animal
   ○ hand control for a computer

5. I like to put butter on my *roll.*
   ○ hot bread
   ○ to turn over and over

6. Let's give the winner a big *hand*!
   ○ body part with fingers on it
   ○ applause

7. I *can* sing soprano.
   ○ a metal container
   ○ am able to

8. The wolf crept into the sheep *pen.*
   ○ writing instrument that uses ink
   ○ area that is fenced in

On another piece of paper, write two sentences showing a different meaning for the word "star" in each.

© Scholastic Inc.

Where Am I?

Making inferences *means to use information in a story to make judgments about information not given in the story.*

Read each riddle below. Look for clues to help you answer each question.

1. It is dark in here. I hear bats flying. With my flashlight, I see stalactites hanging above me. I hear water dripping. Where am I?

   _____

2. Let's sit in the front row! Ha ha ha! That's funny . . . a cartoon about a drink cup that is singing to a candy bar. That makes me hungry. I think I'll go get some popcorn before it starts. Where am I?

   _____

3. This thing keeps going faster and faster, up and down, and over and around. It tickles my tummy. The girls behind me are screaming. I hope I don't go flying out of my seat! Where am I?

   _____

4. I can see rivers and highways that look like tiny ribbons. I am glad I got to sit by the window. Wow, we are in a cloud! Yes, ma'am. I would like a drink. Thank you. Where am I?

   _____

5. I am all dressed up, sitting here quietly with my parents. The flowers are pretty. The music is starting. Here she comes down the aisle. I wish they would hurry so I can have some cake! Where am I?

   _____

6. Doctor, can you help my dog? His name is Champ. He was bitten by a snake, and his leg is swollen. I hope he will be all right. Where am I?

   _____

7. How will I ever decide? Look at all the different kinds. There are red hots, chocolates, candy corn, gummy worms, jawbreakers, and lollipops. Boy, this is my favorite place in the mall! Where am I?

   _____

8. This row has carrots growing, and this one has onions. The corn is getting tall. The soil feels dry. I better water the plants today. Don't you think so, Mr. Scarecrow? Where am I?

   _____

On another piece of paper, write two "Where Am I?" riddles of your own. Read your riddles to someone else and have them guess where you are.

On the Border

Classifying *means to put things into groups. One way to classify is to look for similarities, ways things are alike.*

Read the words around the border of the picture. Find the words that belong with each picture. Write the words inside the picture. There will be five words in each picture.

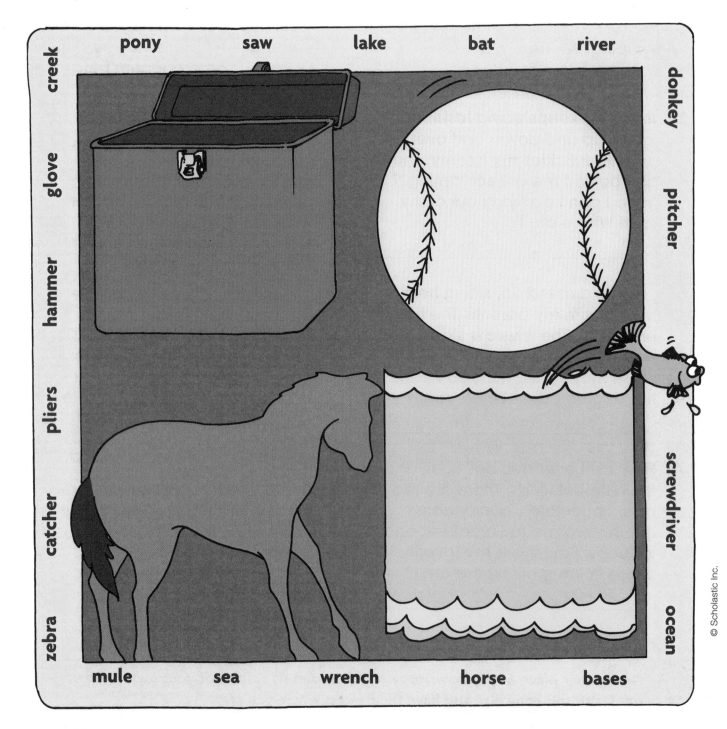

creek pony saw lake bat river donkey

glove

hammer pitcher

pliers

catcher screwdriver

zebra mule sea wrench horse bases ocean

Moving In

The day we moved to our new house, there was a lot of work to do. Mom gave me the job of organizing the cabinets and closets. I unpacked each box and put things in their proper places. I filled up the medicine chest in the bathroom and the linen closet in the hall. I organized the silverware drawer in the kitchen, as well as the food in the pantry. I lined up Dad's stuff on the garage shelves. Last of all, I filled the bookshelf.

Write each word from the box in the correct category.

Medicine Chest	Linen Closet
_____	_____
_____	_____
_____	_____
_____	_____

Silverware Drawer	Pantry
_____	_____
_____	_____
_____	_____
_____	_____

Garage Shelves	Bookshelf
_____	_____
_____	_____
_____	_____
_____	_____

encyclopedias

eyedrops   teaspoons

car wax   motor oil

quilts   dictionary

cake mix   forks

serving spoons

atlas   aspirin

bandages   blankets

fishing tackle

crackers   novels

pillowcases

cereal   knives

sheets   toolbox

cough syrup

canned soup

THIS END UP →

 On another piece of paper, make a list of eight things that people might store in an attic.

The Pyramid Game

Every morning before school, Mrs. Cavazos writes five words inside a pyramid on the chalkboard. When class begins, her students are to think of a title for the group of words. The title is to tell how the words are alike. The class then thinks of three words to add to the list.

Write a title for each pyramid of words.

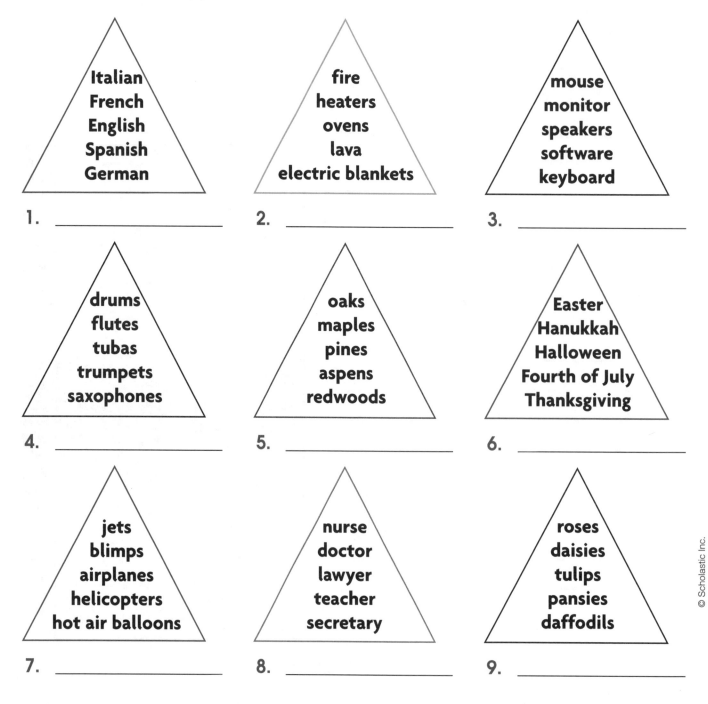

Italian
French
English
Spanish
German

1. _____

fire
heaters
ovens
lava
electric blankets

2. _____

mouse
monitor
speakers
software
keyboard

3. _____

drums
flutes
tubas
trumpets
saxophones

4. _____

oaks
maples
pines
aspens
redwoods

5. _____

Easter
Hanukkah
Halloween
Fourth of July
Thanksgiving

6. _____

jets
blimps
airplanes
helicopters
hot air balloons

7. _____

nurse
doctor
lawyer
teacher
secretary

8. _____

roses
daisies
tulips
pansies
daffodils

9. _____

© Scholastic Inc.

News or Views?

 Facts *are true statement and can be proven.* **Opinions** *are a person's own personal views or beliefs.*

When people talk about things, they often mix news with opinions. Read each cartoon. Write *News* in the box if it is a fact. Write *Views* in the box if it is a person's own personal opinion.

TV Commercials

When you watch TV, you see a lot of commercials advertising different products. The people making the commercial want you to buy their product, so they make it sound as good as possible. Some of the things they say are facts, which can be proven. Other things are just the advertiser's opinion about how good the product is or how it will make you feel. Read each advertisement below. Write an *F* in the box beside each fact and an *O* in the box beside each opinion. The first one is done for you.

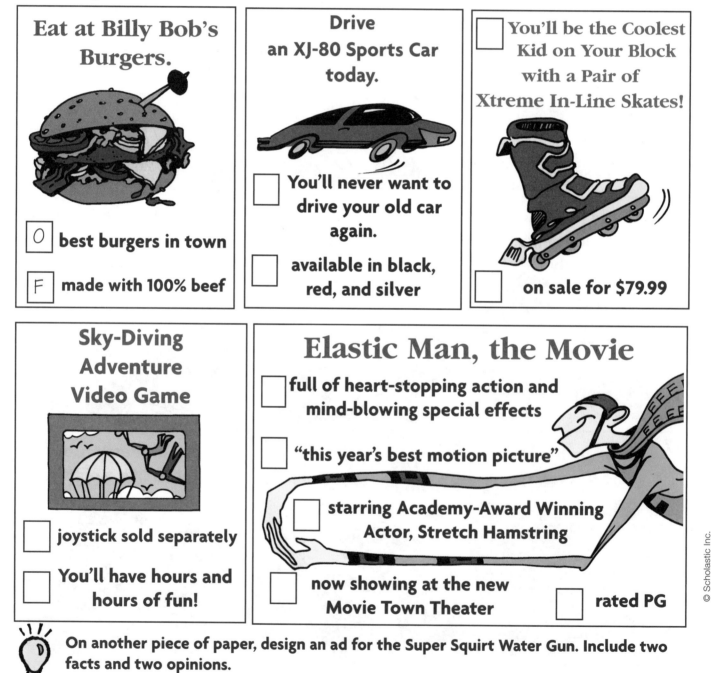

Eat at Billy Bob's Burgers.

[O] best burgers in town

[F] made with 100% beef

Drive an XJ-80 Sports Car today.

[ ] You'll never want to drive your old car again.

[ ] available in black, red, and silver

[ ] You'll be the Coolest Kid on Your Block with a Pair of Xtreme In-Line Skates!

[ ] on sale for $79.99

Sky-Diving Adventure Video Game

[ ] joystick sold separately

[ ] You'll have hours and hours of fun!

Elastic Man, the Movie

[ ] full of heart-stopping action and mind-blowing special effects

[ ] "this year's best motion picture"

[ ] starring Academy-Award Winning Actor, Stretch Hamstring

[ ] now showing at the new Movie Town Theater

[ ] rated PG

On another piece of paper, design an ad for the Super Squirt Water Gun. Include two facts and two opinions.

News Report

Read the following news report about a tornado that touched down in a small town in Oklahoma. If the sentence is a fact that can be proven, underline it in red. If the sentence is someone's opinion, highlight it in yellow.

1. At 10:35 A.M. today, a tornado touched down briefly in the small town of Parksville, Oklahoma.

2. The roofs of several buildings were torn off by the strong winds.

3. Many large trees were uprooted.

4. There were no injuries.

5. "It was so loud, I thought a freight train was coming right through my living room!" Mrs. Cox exclaimed.

6. The National Weather Service issued a warning ten minutes before the tornado hit.

7. "I was afraid my house was going to blow away!" Mr. Carey reported.

8. Officer Reeves commented, "This may have been the worst day in the history of Parksville."

9. Electrical power was out for over two hours.

10. The large scoreboard at the football field was blown down.

11. "It will take forever to clean up this mess!" remarked Mrs. McDonald.

12. "I'm sure I can count on the people of Parksville to work together to rebuild our town," Mayor Clark said.

13. Donations to the rebuilding fund can be left at the bank.

💡 Write a news report about a tiger that escaped from the zoo. Include three facts and three opinions.

Homer's Big Adventure

Use details from a story to help determine what will happen next. This is called **making predictions.**

Brian was in such a hurry to get to the school bus on time that he forgot to close the door on Homer's cage after he fed him. Homer T. Hamster knew this was his big chance. He crawled out of his cage and ran downstairs, careful to sneak past Brian's mother without being seen. He ducked through a hole in the screen door and stepped out into the great backyard.

"Yippeeee!" cried Homer, throwing his little arms into the air. "I'm free at last!" He zipped through the gate and down the alley. The first thing Homer saw was a huge, snarling German shepherd who thought it was fun to chase anything that could run. "R-r-ruff! R-r-ruff!"

Homer scurried here and there only inches ahead of the dog. He barely escaped by hiding under a flowerpot. "Whew, that was close!" he thought. He waited there awhile, shaking like a leaf.

Then he crept out into the alley again. He looked this way and that. The coast was clear, so he skipped happily along. He looked up just in time to see the big black tires of a pickup truck that was backing out of a driveway. He almost got squooshed! So, he darted quickly into someone's backyard where a boy was mowing the lawn. R-r-r-r-r! Homer had to jump out of the way again.

Back in the alley, he decided to rest somewhere that was safe. He crawled into a garbage dumpster and fell asleep. Later, he heard the sound of a big truck. He felt himself going high up into the air. The dumpster turned upside down, and the lid opened. Homer was falling. "Yikes!" screamed Homer. He had to think fast. He reached out and grabbed the side of the truck, holding on for dear life.

The truck rolled down the alley and into the street. As it turned the corner, Homer was flung off the truck and onto the hood of a school bus. He grabbed onto the windshield wipers as the bus drove to the corner and stopped.

The bus driver exclaimed, "Look, kids! There is a hamster riding on our bus!" All the kids rushed forward to see the funny sight. Homer looked through the windshield at all the surprised faces. All of a sudden, Homer saw Brian! Brian ran out of the bus and carefully picked up Homer. "Hey, buddy, how did you get out here? Are you okay?" Brian asked as he petted Homer's fur.

1. **What do you think happened next? Color the picture that seems to be the most likely ending to the story.**

2. **Underline the sentence that tells the main idea of the story.**

   Homer hid under a flowerpot to escape from a German shepherd.

   Homer had many exciting adventures after crawling out of his cage.

   Brian was surprised to see Homer riding the school bus.

3. **Do you think Homer will leave his cage again? Write a sentence to tell why or why not.** _____

_____

 On another piece of paper, write a paragraph telling about one more adventure Homer might have had while he was out of his cage. Read your paragraph to a friend.

Mary's Mystery

Monday afternoon, Mom called my sister, Mary, to the door. The florist had just delivered a dozen red roses to her. "For me?" asked Mary. "Who would be sending me flowers?" Mom told her to read the card. It said, "Mary, I'm sorry I hurt your feelings. Can you forgive me?" Mary looked puzzled. She could not think of anyone that had hurt her feelings.

On Wednesday, a delivery boy brought a package to the door. He said, "This is for Mary." It was a box of chocolate candy. Mary liked chocolate very much, but she could not figure out who was sending her gifts, or why.

On Friday, a teenage girl dressed in a sparkly costume rang the doorbell. Mary answered the door. The teenager asked, "Are you Mary?" She nodded her head and said yes, and the teenager told her that she was sent by someone to perform a singing

telegram. She sang, "Mary, I want you to be . . . the girl who will marry me . . ." Then she left. Mary looked at Mom. "I am only nine years old! I don't want to get married!" Mom laughed. "There must be some mistake."

That night, a handsome young man came to the door with a ring box in his hand. He rang the doorbell at Mary's apartment. Mary opened the door. When the man saw Mary, he looked surprised. He said, "Oh, I'm sorry. I was looking for Mary's apartment." Mary said, "Well, I am Mary." The man stood there frowning for a moment. Then he started to laugh.

"No wonder my girlfriend has not mentioned the gifts I sent her. I bet they have all been coming here." Then he told Mary to step outside and look at the metal numbers over her apartment door. Mary's apartment was #620, but the 6 had come loose and had turned upside down. That made it look like #920. The man said, "I am sorry about the mix-up. My girlfriend, Mary, just moved into apartment #920. I think all the delivery people saw your #920 and stopped here, just like I did. I guess when they found out your name was Mary, they thought they had the right place." Mary laughed. "Now I understand," she said. "Oh, I am sorry, but I already ate the chocolates." The man replied, "That's okay." Then as he turned to walk away he added, "You can also keep the flowers." "Thank you," Mary said grinning, "but I am not going to marry you!"

1. **Underline two sentences below that tell what might happen next. Mark an X on two sentences that tell about something that probably will not happen.**

    The man found the other Mary, his girlfriend, and gave her the ring.

    The man sent Mary a bill because she ate the chocolates.

    Nine-year-old Mary sent the man a dozen roses.

    Mary's mom turned the 9 over to make a 6 again and nailed it tight so their apartment number would be correct.

2. **Circle what the title of the song the singing telegram might have been.**

    "Love Me Always"

    "Crossing the Mississippi"

    "The Champion Cheer"

3. **What did the florist deliver to Mary?** _____

4. **Which gift do you think Mary liked the best? Why?** _____

    _____

5. **On what day did Mary receive the singing telegram?** _____

6. **Where is the setting of this story?** _____

Special Charts

Comparing *and* **contrasting** *means to show the similarities and differences of things. A Venn diagram is a chart made of overlapping circles that can be used to organize the similarities and differences. The overlapping parts of the circles show how things are similar. The other part of the circles show how things are different.*

Joe, Kim, and Rob each got a lunch tray, went through the lunch line, and sat together to eat. These students all had the same lunch menu, but each one only ate what he or she liked. Joe ate chicken nuggets, green beans, applesauce, and carrots. Rob ate chicken nuggets, green beans, a roll, and corn. Kim ate chicken nuggets, a roll, applesauce, and salad.

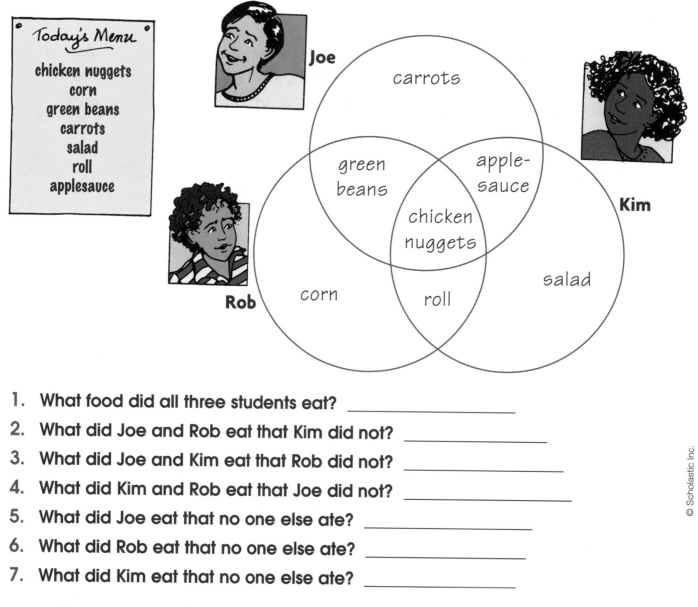

1. What food did all three students eat? _____
2. What did Joe and Rob eat that Kim did not? _____
3. What did Joe and Kim eat that Rob did not? _____
4. What did Kim and Rob eat that Joe did not? _____
5. What did Joe eat that no one else ate? _____
6. What did Rob eat that no one else ate? _____
7. What did Kim eat that no one else ate? _____

Sports Chart

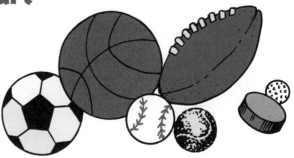

There are three brothers who love to play sports. Each one is good at several different sports. Jeff plays hockey, football, soccer, and baseball. Allen plays hockey, football, tennis, and golf. Seth plays hockey, tennis, soccer, and basketball.

1. **Complete the Venn diagram showing which sports each brother plays. Start with the sport all three brothers have in common. Write it in the shared space of all three circles.**

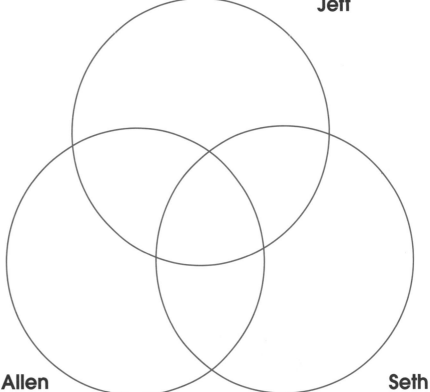

1. What sport do all three boys like to play? _____
2. What sport do Jeff and Allen like to play that Seth does not? _____
3. What sport do Jeff and Seth like to play that Allen does not? _____
4. What sport do Allen and Seth like to play that Jeff does not? _____
5. What sport does Jeff like to play that no one else does? _____
6. What sport does Allen like to play that no one else does? _____
7. What sport does Seth like to play that no one else does? _____

Sharks

There are over 400 different kinds of sharks. The whale shark is the largest. It is as big as a whale. The dwarf lantern is the smallest. It is less than seven inches long.

All sharks live in the ocean, which is salt water, but a few kinds can swim from salt water to fresh water. Bull sharks have been found in the Mississippi River!

Sharks do not have bones. They have skeletons made of cartilage, which is the same thing your ears and nose are made of. A shark's skin is made of spiky, hard scales. The jaws of a shark are very powerful. When a great white shark bites, it clamps down on its prey and thrashes its head from side to side. It is the deadliest shark.

Sharks eat fish, dolphins, and seals. The tiger shark will eat just about anything. Some fishermen have discovered unopened cans of food, clocks, boat cushions, and even a keg of nails inside tiger sharks. Sometimes sharks even eat other sharks. For example, a tiger shark might eat a bull shark. The bull shark might have eaten a blacktip shark. The blacktip shark might have eaten a dogfish shark. So a tiger shark could be found with three sharks in its stomach!

Some sharks look very unusual. The hammerhead shark has a head shaped somewhat like a hammer, with eyes set very far apart. A cookie cutter shark has a

circular set of teeth. When it bites a dolphin or whale, it leaves a perfectly round hole in its victim. The sawshark has a snout with sharp teeth on the outside, which makes it look like a saw. The goblin shark has a sharp-pointed spear coming out of its head, and its ragged teeth make it look scary!

The mako shark is the fastest swimmer. Sometimes makos have been known to leap out of the water, right into a boat! These are just a few of the many kinds of fascinating sharks.

© Scholastic Inc.

Complete the chart with the name of the correct shark. If the statement is about all sharks, write *all*.

1. the largest shark	whale shark
2. the smallest shark	
3. the deadliest shark	
4. the fastest swimmer	
5. live in the ocean	
6. have skeletons of cartilage	
7. has a sharp-pointed spear coming out of its head	
8. has a head shaped like a hammer	
9. skin of spiky, hard scales	
10. leaves a round bite mark	
11. looks like a saw	
12. has eaten unopened cans, clocks, and boat cushions	

 Read more about two different kinds of sharks. On another piece of paper, list two similarities and two differences.

Earthquake!

*The **cause** in a story is what made something happen. The **effect** is what happened.*

Earthquakes are one of the most powerful events on the earth. When large sections of underground rock break and move suddenly, an earthquake occurs. This causes the ground to shake back and forth. Small earthquakes do not cause much damage, but large ones do. Some earthquakes have caused buildings and bridges to fall. Others have caused rivers to change their paths. Earthquakes near mountains and cliffs can cause landslides that cover up the houses and roads below. If a large earthquake occurs under the ocean, it can cause giant waves which flood the seashore. When large earthquakes occur in a city, there is danger of fire from broken gas lines and electric lines. Broken telephone lines and damaged roads make it difficult for rescue workers to help people who are in need. Scientists are trying to find ways to predict when an earthquake will happen so that people can be warned ahead of time.

Draw a shaky line under each effect.

Earthquakes can cause . . .
1. landslides
2. tornadoes
3. fires from broken gas and electric lines
4. huge waves that flood the seashore
5. swarms of flies
6. buildings and bridges to fall
7. sunburns
8. rivers to change their paths
9. damaged roads
10. lightning

© Scholastic Inc.

Read about tornadoes. On another piece of paper, make a list of eight things a tornado might cause.

Wacky Water Slides

Have you ever gone to a water park in the summertime? Some of the most popular attractions are the water slides. How do they work? Construction crews put together sections of large plastic and fiberglass tubes to form the slides. They can make the tubes go straight down or around and around. Either way, the tubes must have a starting point that is high off the ground. This is because water slides work by gravity. Gravity is the natural pull of the earth. It is the force that makes things fall to the ground. So, when a swimmer begins to slide from up high, gravity pulls the swimmer down the slide into the pool below. There is another thing that water slides need in order to work. Water, of course! Water parks have huge pumps that pump the water to the top of the slides. The rushing water runs down the slides, making them slippery. Then the fun begins. Slip! Slide! Splash!

Fill in the blanks on each water slide to explain how they work. Find the answers in the pool below.

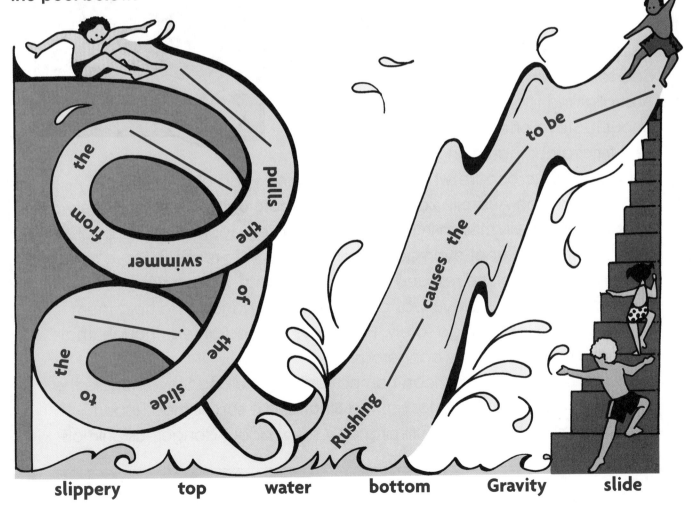

slippery   top   water   bottom   Gravity   slide

Nonfiction: A Biography

*A **biography** is the history of a person's life. You have probably read biographies of presidents or famous people in history. The following biography is about one of the most popular zookeepers of our time.*

Steve Irwin

Steve Irwin was a famous TV personality and **reptile** specialist from **Australia**. People knew him as the **Crocodile Hunter**.

Steve's parents, Bob and Lyn Irwin, owned a reptile park. Steve grew up learning about and handling reptiles, as well as many other kinds of **animals**. When Steve was six years old, his father gave him a snake called a scrub **python**. Steve named it **Fred**. Steve's dad taught him all about the **wildlife** of Australia and took him on field trips to study about it. Steve often begged to go on these field trips rather than going to school. He caught his first crocodile when he was only nine years old.

Steve ran the Australia **Zoo**. He was a **herpetologist**. That means he was a reptile **expert**. His mission in life was to educate people about animals, teaching them to treat even dangerous animals with **respect**. Steve never hurt animals. In fact, he rescued many animals that were in **danger**, especially crocodiles. Steve was an expert snake handler. He held them by the tail and let them go safely. He always warned others, though, that picking up a **snake** is very dangerous.

Steve married an American named **Terri**. She helped Steve handle the animals. They had a daughter named **Bindi** and a son named Robert. Steve Irwin died in 2006 while filming a TV show about dangerous animals.

Look at the bolded words in the story. Find each word in the puzzle and circle it. The words may go up, down, forward, backward, or diagonally.

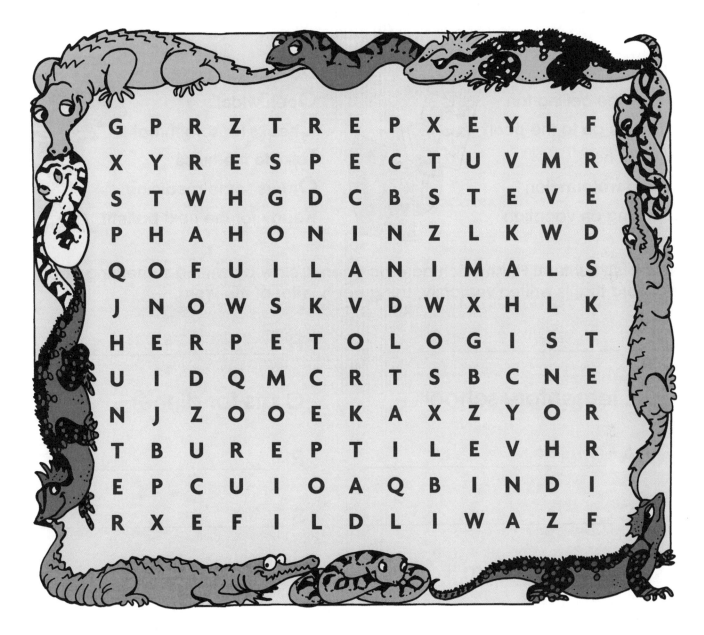

```
G P R Z T R E P X E Y L F
X Y R E S P E C T U V M R
S T W H G D C B S T E V E
P H A H O N I N Z L K W D
Q O F U I L A N I M A L S
J N O W S K V D W X H L K
H E R P E T O L O G I S T
U I D Q M C R T S B C N E
N J Z O O E K A X Z Y O R
T B U R E P T I L E V H R
E P C U I O A Q B I N D I
R X E F I L D L I W A Z F
```

List two facts about Steve Irwin.

1. _____

2. _____

💡 **Find the biography section in the library. Check out a biography about someone who had a career that interests you.**

Acrostic Poems

*Acrostic poetry is fun. An **acrostic poem** starts with a word that is the subject of the whole poem. The word is written vertically. Then words or phases about that subject are written using each letter. Look at the examples below.*

Sleeping late
Under the ceiling fan
May we go to the pool?
My, it's hot!
Eating watermelon
Relaxing on vacation

Do you have a fever?
Open wide!
Checks for sore throat
Talks to the nurse
Orders some medicine
Ready for the next patient

Now it is your turn! Finish each acrostic poem below by writing something about the word that is written vertically, using each letter of the word.

T _____

E lementary school

A _____

C _____

H elps me learn

E _____

R _____

H _____

O ats for dinner

R _____

S _____

E _____

S addle them up!

On another piece of paper, make an acrostic poem about yourself. Start by writing your name vertically.

© Scholastic Inc.

Scholastic Success With

CONTEMPORARY CURSIVE

Aa

Trace and write.

a a

a a

Aa

Atlantic

ape   apple

Active ants awaken

angry Asian aardvarks.

Bb

Trace and write.

B B

b b

Bb

Baltimore

baby   boy

Beautiful baboons blow

bubbles in a bathtub.

© Scholastic Inc.

Scholastic Success With 3rd Grade   57

Cc

C c

Trace and write.

C C

c c

C c

Cincinnati

candy   case

Confident camels carry

cute, cuddly cats.

58   Scholastic Success With 3rd Grade

Dd

Trace and write.

D D

d d

Dd

Detroit

dandy   dirt

Daring dogs decide

to drive to Dallas.

Ee

Trace and write.

E E

e e

Ee

Erie

ever   eye

Elderly, elegant elephants

eagerly eat eggs.

Ff

Trace and write.

$\mathcal{F}$ $\mathcal{F}$

f f

$\mathcal{F}f$

Fenton

five   fast

Frisky foxes frequently

fumble footballs.

Gg

Trace and write.

G G

g g

Gg

Green Bay

gauge   grate

Giggling geese gobble

giant green gumballs.

Hh

Trace and write.

H H H

h h

Hh

Hanover

honor   halt

Happy hamsters have

huge, hilarious hats.

Ii

Trace and write.

I I

i i

Ii

Inglewood

ink   ill

Idle inchworms ignore

irate insects in Iowa.

Jj

Trace and write.

J J

j j

J j

Joliet

jump   jet

Jaguars   juggle   jars   of

jelly beans   in   January.

Kk

Trace and write.

K K

k k

Kk

Kenosha

kite   kick

Kind kangaroos knit

knickers for kids.

Ll

Trace and write.

L L

l l

Ll

Littleton

lock   little

Large, lazy lobsters

lounge leisurely.

Mm

Trace and write.

M M

m m

M m

Missoula

miss   movie

Many merry mice

make mushy meatballs.

$\mathcal{N}n$

Trace and write.

$\mathcal{N}\ \mathcal{N}$

$n\ n$

$\mathcal{N}n$

$\mathcal{N}ewton$

$navy$ $next$

$\mathcal{N}ine\ nocturnal\ newts$

$navigate\ north\ nightly.$

Oo

Trace and write.

O O

o o

Oo

Omaha

over   oblong

Odorous otters order

olive oil over oysters.

Pp

Trace and write.

P P

p p

Pp

Princeton

pipe   parrot

Pretty pigs pop popcorn

perfectly in Pittsburgh.

$\mathcal{Qq}$

Trace and write.

$\mathcal{Q}$ $\mathcal{Q}$

q q

$\mathcal{Qq}$

$\mathcal{Q}uincy$

$quick$ $quit$

$\mathcal{Q}uaint$ $queens$ $quilt$

$quickly$ and $quietly.$

Tt

Trace and write.

𝒯𝒯 𝒯

𝓉 𝓉

𝒯𝓉

Texarkana

total   tea

Talented, toothy toads

teach talkative turtles.

Uu

Trace and write.

U U

u u

Uu

Urbana

utter   use

Uniformed umpires

usher upset unicorns.

Vv

Trace and write.

V V

v v

Vv

Vancouver

vivid   vase

Vain vultures

vacuum vigorously.

Ww

Trace and write.

W W

w w

Ww

Westover

women   wow

Wiggly worms wander

westward with whistles.

Xx

Trace and write.

X X

x x

Xx

Xenia

axis   exit

Xavier Ox x-rayed

six extra xylophones.

Y y

Trace and write.

Y Y

y y

Y y

Yorktown

yacht   yet

Youthful yaks yell,

"Yeah, yellow yo-yos!"

Zz

Trace and write.

Zz

Zz

Zz

Zanesville

zipper   zero

Zany zebras zigzag

zestfully to Zimbabwe.

ZIMBABWE

A-Z

A B C D E F G

H I J K L M

N O P Q R S T

U V W X Y Z

Write.

_____
- -
_____
_____
- -
_____
_____
- -
_____
_____
- -
_____

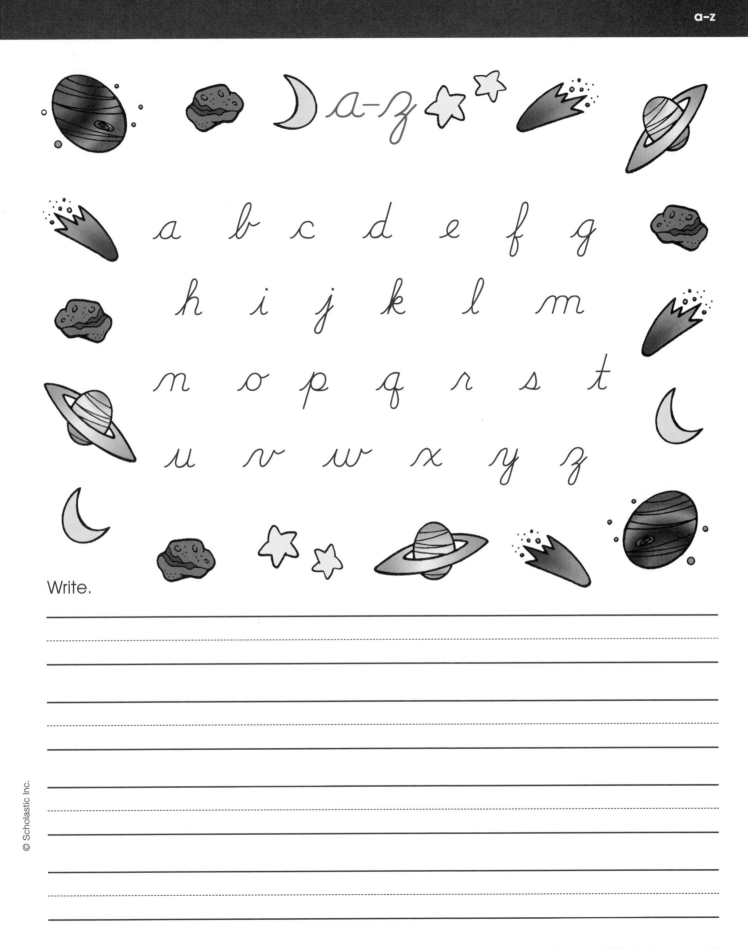

a b c d e f g

h i j k l m

n o p q r s t

u v w x y z

Write.

Numbers 0-9

Trace and write.

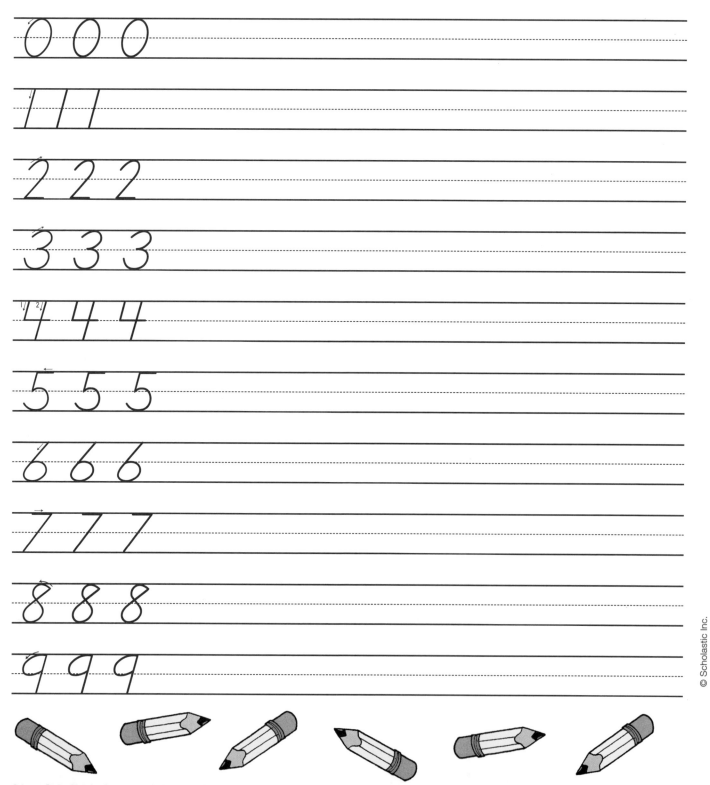

0 0 0

1 1 1

2 2 2

3 3 3

4 4 4

5 5 5

6 6 6

7 7 7

8 8 8

9 9 9

Our Solar System

The sun is the center of our solar system. It is the only star in our solar system. The planets and their moons all orbit the sun. The sun provides heat and light to the planets and their moons.

Write.

_____
- - - - - - - - - - - - - - - - -
_____

_____
- - - - - - - - - - - - - - - - -
_____

_____
- - - - - - - - - - - - - - - - -
_____

_____
- - - - - - - - - - - - - - - - -
_____

_____
- - - - - - - - - - - - - - - - -
_____

_____
- - - - - - - - - - - - - - - - -
_____

Ancient Astronomers

People who study the sun, moon, planets, and stars are called astronomers. Cave people were some of the first astronomers. They drew the different shapes of the moon on walls of their caves. Long ago, sailors studied the stars to help them travel. The ancient Greeks discovered many of the planets.

Write.

_____

_____

_____

_____

_____

_____

_____

_____

_____

_____

_____

_____

_____

© Scholastic Inc.

What Is a Year?

A year is the time it takes for a planet to orbit the sun. A year on Earth is 365 days. It only takes Mercury 88 days to make a trip around the sun. However, it takes Uranus 84 Earth years and Neptune 165 Earth years to orbit the sun one time.

Write.

From Hot to Cold

Some planets are so hot or so cold that people cannot live on them. Some days it is 750°F on Mercury. On Venus, the temperature is nearly 900°F! The temperature on Uranus and Neptune is about -350°F. Earth's highest recorded temperature is 134°F and the lowest is -136°F.

Write.

_____

_____

_____

_____

_____

_____

_____

_____

_____

_____

How Many Moons?

In our solar system, scientists have found over 146 moons. Saturn has 53 known moons. Jupiter has 50 known moons, and Earth has only one. New moons are being discovered all the time.

Write.

_____

- -

_____

- -

_____

- -

_____

- -

_____

- -

_____

- -

_____

- -

_____

- -

_____

- -

_____

- -

_____

Speedy Mercury

Mercury is the planet that is closest to the sun. It spins slowly, but it moves around the sun very quickly. Mercury was named after the speedy Roman messenger for the gods.

Write.

Beautiful Venus

Venus is the easiest planet to see in the sky because it is the closest to Earth. It is sometimes called the Evening Star. The Romans named Venus after their goddess of love and beauty. Venus is so hot, it could melt lead. It has an orange sky.

Write.

Our Incredible Earth

Earth is the only planet known to have life. It is the right distance from the sun to give it the perfect temperature to have water in all three forms—liquid, vapor, and ice. Although 70 percent of Earth's surface is water, its name means "soil."

Write.

_____

_____

_____

_____

_____

_____

_____

_____

_____

_____

_____

_____

_____

_____

Mysterious Mars

Has there ever been life on Mars? That remains a mystery. Scientists are studying the possibility of past, present, or future life there. Mars is often called the Red Planet because the rocks on its surface look like rust. Mars was named after the Roman god of war.

Write.

_____

_____

_____

_____

_____

_____

_____

_____

Sensational Saturn

Saturn is the second largest planet in our solar system. It is most famous for its seven rings made of glittering pieces of ice. Saturn was named after the Roman god of agriculture.

Write.

_____
- -
_____
- -
_____
- -
_____
- -
_____
- -
_____
- -
_____
- -
_____
- -
_____
- -
_____

King Jupiter

Jupiter is the largest planet. It is so big that 1,300 Earths could fit inside of it! That is why the Romans named it after the king of the Roman gods. Jupiter spins faster than all the other planets.

Write.

_____

_____

_____

_____

_____

_____

_____

_____

_____

_____

_____

Understanding Uranus

How can anyone understand very much about a planet nearly two billion miles away? Uranus was the first planet to be discovered through a telescope. It was named after the Roman god who was Saturn's father.

Write.

_____
_____
_____
_____
_____
_____
_____
_____
_____
_____
_____
_____
_____

Not Much About Neptune

Neptune is difficult to see even if you have a telescope. It is nearly three billion miles from the sun. Neptune takes 165 Earth years to orbit the sun once. Neptune was named after the Roman god of the sea.

Write.

What's Up With Pluto?

Scientists used to think that Pluto was a planet. Now we know it is too small to be a planet. It is a dwarf planet. Pluto is far, far away from the sun—3,666,200,000 miles!

Write.

_____

- -

_____

- -

_____

- -

_____

- -

_____

- -

_____

- -

_____

- -

_____

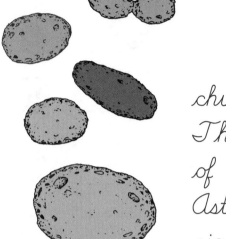

Flying Rocks

Between Mars and Jupiter are chunks of rock that circle the sun. There are thousands and thousands of these flying rocks called asteroids. Asteroids come in many shapes and sizes. Some even look like potatoes!

Write.

_____
_____
_____
_____
_____
_____
_____
_____
_____
_____
_____
_____

Scholastic Success With

GRAMMAR

Statements and Questions

A **statement** is a sentence that tells something. It ends with a period. A **question** is a sentence that asks something. It ends with a question mark.

A. Read each sentence. Write Q on the line if the sentence is a question. Write S if the sentence is a statement.

1. Where did the ant live? _____

2. The ant had many cousins _____

3. She found the crumb under a leaf. _____

4. How will she carry it? _____

5. Who came along first? _____

6. The lizard wouldn't help. _____

7. He said he was too cold. _____

8. Why did the rooster fly away? _____

B. The sentences below do not make sense. Rewrite the words in the correct order.

1. How crumb did carry the ant the? _____

_____

2. She herself it carried.

_____

_____

Statements and Questions

 *A **statement** is a sentence that tells something. It ends with a period. A **question** is a sentence that asks something. It ends with a question mark.*

A. Rewrite each sentence correctly. Begin each sentence with a capital letter. Use periods and question marks correctly.

1. can we take a taxi downtown

_____

2. where does the bus go

_____

3. the people on the bus waved to us

_____

4. we got on the elevator

_____

5. should I push the elevator button

_____

B. Write a question. Then write an answer that is a statement.

1. Question: _____

_____

2. Statement: _____

_____

Statements and Questions

Look at the underlined part of each sentence. Decide if it is correct. Fill in the bubble next to the correct answer.

1. <u>The ant found</u> a big crumb.
   - ⬭ Found the ant
   - ⬭ Ant the found
   - ⬭ correct as is

2. The ant needs <u>help?</u>
   - ⬭ help
   - ⬭ help.
   - ⬭ correct as is

3. The coyote <u>not help would</u>.
   - ⬭ help not would
   - ⬭ would not help
   - ⬭ correct as is

4. <u>the ants</u> live in an anthill.
   - ⬭ The ants
   - ⬭ the Ants
   - ⬭ correct as is

5. She has many <u>cousins?</u>
   - ⬭ cousins
   - ⬭ cousins.
   - ⬭ correct as is

6. <u>the man</u> didn't see the ant.
   - ⬭ The Man
   - ⬭ The man
   - ⬭ correct as is

7. Did he lose his <u>hat?</u>
   - ⬭ hat
   - ⬭ hat.
   - ⬭ correct as is

8. He ran <u>the ant from.</u>
   - ⬭ from the ant.
   - ⬭ ant from the.
   - ⬭ correct as is

9. I am the <u>strongest?</u>
   - ⬭ strongest.
   - ⬭ strongest
   - ⬭ correct as is

10. <u>do you</u> think you can?
   - ⬭ Do you
   - ⬭ Do You
   - ⬭ correct as is

Exclamations and Commands

An **exclamation** is a sentence that shows strong feeling. It ends with an exclamation point. A **command** is a sentence that gives an order. It ends with a period.

A. Read each sentence. Write *E* on the line if the sentence is an exclamation. Write *C* if the sentence is a command.

1. They chase buffaloes! —————

2. You have to go, too. —————

3. Wait at the airport. —————

4. It snows all the time! —————

5. Alligators live in the sewers! —————

6. Look at the horse. —————

7. That's a great-looking horse! —————

8. Write a letter to Seymour. —————

B. Complete each exclamation and command. The punctuation mark at the end of each line is a clue.

1. I feel ————————————————————!

2. Help your ————————————————————.

3. That's a ————————————————————!

4. I lost ————————————————————!

5. Turn the ————————————————————.

6. Come watch the ————————————————————.

7. Please let me ————————————————————.

Exclamations and Commands

*A **sentence** tells a complete thought. It tells who or what, and it tells what happens.*

A. Draw a line between the words in Column A and Column B to form complete sentences. Then write the complete sentences on the lines below. Remember to add an exclamation mark or a period.

Column A
There's a
Look at
Pack

Column B
the buffaloes
your toys and games
Gila monster at the airport

1._____

2._____

3._____

B. Write sentence after each complete thought. Write not a sentence after each incomplete thought. Then make each incomplete thought into a sentence.

1. I ate a salami sandwich. _____

2. I like to ride horses. _____

3. Subway driver. _____

4. There are horned toads. _____

5. Kids on our street _____

6. We are moving tomorrow. _____

Exclamations and Commands

Look at the underlined part of each sentence. Decide if it is correct. Fill in the bubble next to the correct answer.

1. <u>I'm going to Texas!</u>
   - ○ I'm going to Texas?
   - ○ I'm to Texas!
   - ○ correct as is

2. I am so <u>excited</u>
   - ○ excited!
   - ○ excited?
   - ○ correct as is

3. Please help me <u>pack!</u>
   - ○ pack?
   - ○ pack.
   - ○ correct as is

4. Her baby brother is <u>adorable</u>
   - ○ adorable?
   - ○ adorable!
   - ○ correct as is

5. I can't <u>wait!</u>
   - ○ wait.
   - ○ wait
   - ○ correct as is

6. <u>Help me find.</u>
   - ○ Help me find a game.
   - ○ Help find game.
   - ○ correct as is

7. We'll have such <u>fun!</u>
   - ○ fun
   - ○ fun?
   - ○ correct as is

8. <u>It be!</u>
   - ○ It will be great!
   - ○ It great!
   - ○ correct as is

9. Remember <u>to write to me</u>
   - ○ to write to
   - ○ to write to me.
   - ○ correct as is

10. My <u>team the game!</u>
    - ○ team won the game!
    - ○ team won game!
    - ○ correct as is

Singular and Plural Nouns

A **singular noun** names one person, place, or thing. A **plural noun** names more than one person, place, or thing. Add **-s** to form the plural of most nouns.

A. Each sentence has an underlined noun. On the line, write S if it is a singular noun. Write P if it is a plural noun.

1. She has a new <u>baby</u>.   ———

2. <u>It</u> is very cute.   ———

3. She has small <u>fingers</u>.   ———

4. She drinks from a <u>bottle</u>.   ———

5. I can tell my <u>friends</u> all about it.   ———

B. Read each sentence. Underline the singular noun. Circle the plural noun.

1. The baby has two sisters.

2. The nightgown has pockets.

3. Her hand has tiny fingers.

4. My parents have a baby.

5. The family has three girls.

C. Complete the chart. Write the singular or plural of each noun.

Singular	Plural
fence	
	trains
gate	
	cows

Singular and Plural Nouns

*A **singular noun** names one person, place, or thing. A **plural noun** names more than one person, place, or thing. Add **-s** to form the plural of most nouns. Add **-es** to form the plural of nouns that end in **ss**, **x**, **ch**, or **sh**. Some nouns change their spelling to form the plural.*

A. Finish the chart. Write singular nouns in each column.

Nouns that end in *ch, sh, ss, x*	Nouns that end in *y*	Nouns that end in *f*
bench	party	loaf

B. Complete each sentence with the plural form of the noun in ( ).

1. Mia picks _____ from the trees in her backyard. (cherry)

2. There are also many _____ with tiny berries. (bush)

3. Fresh _____ are her favorite snack. (peach)

4. She loads _____ with these different fruits. (box)

5. The kitchen _____ are filled with delicious jams. (shelf)

6. Mia shares the fruit with the third-grade _____. (class)

C. Use the words *story* and *stories* in one sentence. Use *fox* and *foxes* in another sentence.

1. _____

   _____

2. _____

   _____

Singular and Plural Nouns

Read each riddle. Decide if the underlined noun is correct. Fill in the bubble next to the correct answer.

1. We are square and made from cardboard. We are <u>boxs</u>.
   - ○ boxes
   - ○ box
   - ○ correct as is

2. We help you chew your food. We are <u>tooth</u>.
   - ○ tooths
   - ○ teeth
   - ○ correct as is

3. You can find us on a farm. We are <u>geese</u>.
   - ○ goose
   - ○ gooses
   - ○ correct as is

4. Be sure not to drop us when you take a drink. We are <u>glassess</u>.
   - ○ glass
   - ○ glasses
   - ○ correct as is

5. We are animals in the forest. We are <u>fox</u>.
   - ○ foxs
   - ○ foxes
   - ○ correct as is

6. You can use us to comb your hair. We are <u>brush</u>.
   - ○ brushes
   - ○ brushs
   - ○ correct as is

7. You can buy us in a food store. We are <u>grocerys</u>.
   - ○ grocery
   - ○ groceries
   - ○ correct as is

8. We are places trains can stop. We are <u>stations</u>.
   - ○ station
   - ○ stationes
   - ○ correct as is

9. We like to eat cheese. We are <u>mouse</u>.
   - ○ mice
   - ○ mices
   - ○ correct as is

10. We are tales to read. We are <u>story</u>.
    - ○ stories
    - ○ storys
    - ○ correct as is

Common and Proper Nouns

 A **common noun** *names any person, place, or thing. A* **proper noun** *names a particular person, place, or thing. A proper noun begins with a capital letter.*

A. Is the underlined word a common noun or a proper noun? Write *common* or *proper*.

1. The <u>girl</u> likes to learn. ————————

2. She goes to two <u>schools</u>. ————————

3. She lives in <u>America</u>. ————————

B. Underline the common nouns. Circle the proper nouns.

1. April has a brother and a sister.

2. Their names are Julius and May.

3. Their parents were born in Taiwan.

4. April goes to school on Saturday.

5. She is learning a language called Mandarin.

6. May read a book about the Middle Ages.

C. Underline the common nouns. Circle the proper nouns. Then write them on the chart in the correct category.

1. Last August David went to camp.

2. Many children go to a picnic on the Fourth of July.

Common Nouns	Proper Nouns
————————	————————
————————	————————
————————	————————

Common and Proper Nouns

*A **common noun** names any person, place, or thing. A **proper noun** names a particular person, place, or thing. A proper noun begins with a capital letter.*

A. Read each word in the box. Write it where it belongs on the chart.

doctor   park   football   Tangram   Pat   Atlanta

Category	Common Nouns	Proper Nouns
1. Person		
2. Place		
3. Thing		

B. Complete each sentence with a common noun or proper noun. In the box, write *C* if you wrote a common noun. Write *P* if you wrote a proper noun.

1. I threw the ball to _____. (person)

2. I have visited _____. (place)

3. My favorite food is _____. (thing)

4. My family lives in _____. (place)

5. My favorite author is _____. (person)

6. I wish I had a _____. (thing)

7. I like to read about _____. (historical event)

8. My favorite holiday is _____. (holiday)

Common and Proper Nouns

Is the underlined part of each sentence correct? Fill in the bubble next to the right answer.

1. The <u>fourth of July</u> is my favorite holiday.
   - ○ Fourth of July
   - ○ fourth of july
   - ○ correct as is

2. In Australia, winter begins in the <u>month of June</u>.
   - ○ Month of June
   - ○ month of june
   - ○ correct as is

3. I love <u>tom's apple pie</u>.
   - ○ Tom's apple pie
   - ○ tom's Apple Pie
   - ○ correct as is

4. Our <u>teacher, Dr. ruffin</u>, is from Louisiana.
   - ○ teacher, dr. Ruffin
   - ○ teacher, Dr. Ruffin
   - ○ correct as is

5. He speaks <u>Spanish and Japanese</u>.
   - ○ spanish and japanese
   - ○ Spanish and japanese
   - ○ correct as is

6. Susan's family is from <u>Kansas City, missouri</u>.
   - ○ Kansas City, Missouri
   - ○ kansas city, Missouri
   - ○ correct as is

7. Let's have a <u>new year's day</u> party!
   - ○ new year's Day
   - ○ New Year's Day
   - ○ correct as is

8. There will be no <u>school on monday</u>.
   - ○ School on Monday
   - ○ school on Monday
   - ○ correct as is

9. Dogs are the most popular <u>pets in north america</u>.
   - ○ pets in North America
   - ○ pets in North america
   - ○ correct as is

10. Do you want to go to <u>the Movies on Saturday</u>?
   - ○ the movies on Saturday
   - ○ the Movies on saturday
   - ○ correct as is

Singular and Plural Pronouns

 A **singular pronoun** *takes the place of a noun that names one person, place, or thing.* A **plural pronoun** *takes the place of a noun that names more than one person, place, or thing.*

A. Underline the pronoun in each sentence. On the line, write *S* if it is singular or *P* if it is plural.

1. He is called Spider. _____

2. I can see Spider has eight long legs. _____

3. They asked Spider a question. _____

4. We want to know what's in the pot. _____

5. It contains all the wisdom in the world. _____

B. Read each pair of sentences. Circle the pronoun in the second sentence. Then underline the word or words in the first sentence that it replaces. Write the pronoun under *Singular* or *Plural*.

	Singular	Plural
1. This story is funny. It is about wisdom.	_____	_____
2. The author retold the story.		
She is a good writer.	_____	_____
3. My friends and I read the story aloud.		
We enjoyed the ending.	_____	_____
4. Two boys acted out a scene.		
They each took a different role.	_____	_____

C. For each noun write a subject pronoun that could take its place.

1. Spider _____

2. the pot _____

3. Tortoise and Hare _____

4. Spider's mother _____

Singular and Plural Pronouns

 A **subject pronoun** *takes the place of a noun or nouns as the subject of a sentence. A subject pronoun can be singular or plural.* **I, you, she, he, it, we,** *and* **they** *are subject pronouns. An* **object pronoun** *takes the place of a noun or nouns in the predicate. An object pronoun can be singular or plural.* **Me, you, him, her, it, us,** *and* **them** *are object pronouns.*

A. Underline the object pronoun in each sentence. Circle *S* if it is singular or *P* if it is plural.

1. Darren and Tracy were
   playing soccer with us.   S or P
2. Tracy passed the ball to him.   S or P
3. He kicked the ball back to her.   S or P
4. She stopped it in front of the net. S or P
5. Tracy kicked the ball toward me. S or P
6. I kept them from scoring a goal. S or P

B. Complete each sentence. Write the correct pronoun in ( ) on the line.

1. Ms. Stone gave _____ a funny assignment. (we, us)
2. She asked _____ to tell a funny story. (I, me)
3. Ray and Pete brought _____ a book of jokes. (she, her)
4. She thanked _____. (them, they)
5. Dina acted out a story with _____. (him, he)

C. Write one sentence using *it* as a subject pronoun. Write another sentence using *it* as an object pronoun.

_____

_____

Singular and Plural Pronouns

Is the underlined pronoun correct? Fill in the bubble next to the right answer.

1. My parents took the three of <u>we</u> to a garage sale.
- ○ us
- ○ I
- ○ her
- ○ correct as is

2. Mom and Dad really wanted <u>I</u> to go.
- ○ She
- ○ me
- ○ They
- ○ correct as is

3. Mom wouldn't take "no" for an answer. <u>She</u> said that I might find something good.
- ○ Her
- ○ Me
- ○ Them
- ○ correct as is

4. The drive was boring. <u>He</u> was the longest trip I'd ever taken.
- ○ She
- ○ It
- ○ They
- ○ correct as is

5. My two sisters were sleepy. I let <u>they</u> lean on me.
- ○ them
- ○ she
- ○ us
- ○ correct as is

6. Dad found some golf clubs. <u>Him</u> was so excited.
- ○ You
- ○ Me
- ○ He
- ○ correct as is

7. Mom liked a vase. Dad bought it for <u>her</u>.
- ○ she
- ○ they
- ○ I
- ○ correct as is

8. Sonya and Kara both found mysteries. <u>They</u> began to read right away.
- ○ Her
- ○ Them
- ○ It
- ○ correct as is

9. There was a dusty box in the corner. <u>Him</u> was covered in cobwebs.
- ○ Them
- ○ It
- ○ Her
- ○ correct as is

10. I pulled out an old baseball mitt. <u>Me</u> was so surprised!
- ○ I
- ○ Them
- ○ Him
- ○ correct as is

Action Verbs

➡️ **Action verbs** *are words that tell what the subject of the sentence does.*

A. Underline the action verb in each sentence.

1. The villagers cheered loudly.
2. They added flavor to the cheese.
3. Please give them the milk.
4. He serves the cheese.
5. He emptied the buckets.

B. Circle the action verb in ( ) that paints a more vivid picture of what the subject is doing.

1. The villagers (walked, paraded) across the floor.
2. Father (whispered, talked) to the baby.
3. The puppy (ate, gobbled) down his food.
4. The girl (skipped, went) to her chair.
5. The ball (fell, bounced) down the stairs.

C. Write an action verb from the box to complete each sentence.

| whispered | laughed | sighed |

1. We ———————— at the playful kittens.
2. She ———————— deeply and fell asleep.
3. Megan ———————— to her friend in the library.

Action Verbs

Action verbs *are words that tell what the subject of the sentence does. Some action verbs help to paint a clearer picture in the reader's mind.*

A. On the line, write the action verb in ( ) that paints a clearer picture.

1. A squirrel _____ an acorn. (took, snatched)

2. It _____ the acorn open. (cracked, broke)

3. The squirrel _____ the nut. (nibbled, ate)

4. Then it _____ up the tree. (went, scrambled)

B. Circle each verb. Then write the verb from the box that gives a livelier picture of the action.

shouted	honked	ran	bounced	grabbed

1. The bus driver blew the horn. _____

2. The girl got her books. _____

3. She said, "Good-bye," to her family. _____

4. She went to the bus. _____

5. The bus moved down the bumpy road. _____

C. Write two sentences that show action. Use the verb *dashed* in the first sentence. Use the word *tiptoed* in the second sentence. Underline the verbs.

1. _____

2. _____

Action Verbs

A. Fill in the bubble next to the action verb in each sentence.

1. Crystal's whole family arrived for dinner.
   - ◯ dinner
   - ◯ family
   - ◯ arrived

2. Her grandmother hugged everyone.
   - ◯ grandmother
   - ◯ hugged
   - ◯ everyone

3. Her aunt and uncle roasted a huge turkey.
   - ◯ roasted
   - ◯ turkey
   - ◯ huge

4. Everyone ate the delicious meal.
   - ◯ ate
   - ◯ Everyone
   - ◯ meal

5. They cheered for the cooks!
   - ◯ cooks
   - ◯ They
   - ◯ cheered

B. Read each sentence. Fill in the bubble next to the more vivid verb.

1. The puppy —— after the ball.
   - ◯ went
   - ◯ chased

2. She —— all around the house and yard.
   - ◯ dashed
   - ◯ went

3. A yellow cat —— through the wooden fence.
   - ◯ looked
   - ◯ peeked

4. Then the puppy —— high into the air.
   - ◯ leaped
   - ◯ moved

5. She —— the ball.
   - ◯ got
   - ◯ grabbed

Present- and Past-Tense Verbs

Present-tense verbs *show action that is happening now. They agree in number with who or what is doing the action.* **Past-tense verbs** *show action that took place in the past. Most past-tense verbs end in* **-ed**.

A. Read each sentence. If the underlined verb is in the present tense, write *present* on the line. If it is in the past tense, write *past*.

1. We <u>worked</u> together on a

    jigsaw puzzle. _____

2. Mom <u>helped</u> us. _____

3. She <u>enjoys</u> puzzles, too. _____

4. Tom <u>picked</u> out the border pieces. _____

5. He <u>dropped</u> a puzzle piece on the floor. _____

6. I <u>looked</u> for the flower pieces. _____

7. Dad <u>likes</u> crossword puzzles better. _____

8. My little sister <u>watches</u> us. _____

9. Mom <u>hurries</u> us before dinner. _____

10. We <u>rushed</u> to finish quickly. _____

B. Underline the verb in each sentence. Then rewrite the sentence. Change the present-tense verb to the past. Change the past-tense verb to the present.

1. The man crosses the river.

    _____

2. He rowed his boat.

    _____

Practice

Present- and Past-Tense Verbs

Present-tense verbs *must agree in number with the subject. The letters* **-s** *or* **-es** *are usually added to a present-tense verb when the subject of the sentence is a singular noun or* **he**, **she**, *or* **it**.

A. Read each sentence. On the line, write the correct form of the present-tense verb in ( ).

1. The crow _____ the pitcher with pebbles. (fill, fills)

2. The man _____ the crow. (watch, watches)

3. Then he _____ the cabbage across the river. (take, takes)

4. The man and the goat _____ the wolf behind. (leave, leaves)

5. They _____ back on the last trip. (go, goes)

B. Write the correct past-tense form of the verb in ( ).

1. J.J. _____ for the hidden picture. (look)

2. He _____ at it for a long time. (stare)

3. Ana _____ by. (walk)

4. Then she _____ solve the puzzle. (help)

C. Write three sentences. Use the verb in ( ) in your sentence.

1. (play) _____

    _____

2. (plays) _____

    _____

3. (played) _____

    _____

© Scholastic Inc.

Present- and Past-Tense Verbs

Is the underlined verb in each sentence correct? Fill in the bubble next to the right answer.

1. Mr. Henry <u>bakes</u> delicious apple pies.
   - ⬭ bake
   - ⬭ baking
   - ⬭ correct as is

2. He <u>wash and peel</u> each apple carefully.
   - ⬭ washes and peels
   - ⬭ wash and peeled
   - ⬭ correct as is

3. He <u>slices</u> each apple into eight pieces.
   - ⬭ slicing
   - ⬭ slice
   - ⬭ correct as is

4. Mr. Henry's children <u>enjoys</u> the pies very much.
   - ⬭ enjoy
   - ⬭ enjoying
   - ⬭ correct as is

5. Last summer, Mr. Henry <u>enter</u> a pie-baking contest.
   - ⬭ enters
   - ⬭ entered
   - ⬭ correct as is

6. His whole family <u>travel</u> to the competition.
   - ⬭ traveling
   - ⬭ traveled
   - ⬭ correct as is

7. They <u>arrives</u> just in time.
   - ⬭ arriving
   - ⬭ arrived
   - ⬭ correct as is

8. The judges <u>awards</u> Mr. Henry's pie a blue ribbon.
   - ⬭ awarded
   - ⬭ awarding
   - ⬭ correct as is

9. They <u>tasted</u> Mr. Henry's pie and said it was wonderful.
   - ⬭ tastes
   - ⬭ taste
   - ⬭ correct as is

10. All the people <u>enjoys</u> the day!
    - ⬭ enjoying
    - ⬭ enjoyed
    - ⬭ correct as is

The Verb *Be*

*The verb **be** tells what the subject of a sentence is or was. **Am**, **is**, and **are** tell about someone or something in the present. **Was** and **were** tell about someone or something in the past.*

A. Read each sentence. Circle the word that is a form of the verb *be*.

1. Captain Fossy was Mr. Anning's good friend.

2. Mary Anning said, "The dragon is gigantic!"

3. "Its eyes are as big as saucers!" she told her mother.

4. "I am inside the cave!" she shouted to her brother.

5. The scientists were amazed by the remarkable fossil.

B. Read each sentence. If the underlined verb is in the past tense, write *past* on the line. If it is in the present tense, write *present*.

1. Mary Anning <u>was</u> a real person. _____

2. I <u>am</u> interested in fossils, too. _____

3. There <u>are</u> many dinosaurs in the museum. _____

4. The exhibits <u>were</u> closed yesterday. _____

5. This <u>is</u> a map of the first floor. _____

C. Write the form of *be* that completes each sentence.

am   is   are

1. I _____ on the bus with my mother and father.

2. Buses _____ fun to ride.

3. The bus driver _____ a friendly woman.

The Verb *Be*

Some verbs show action. Others, such as the verb **be***, show being, or what something is or was. The form of* **be** *must agree with the subject of the sentence.*

A. Circle each verb. If the verb shows action, write *action* on the line. If the verb shows being, write *being*.

1.   The sunshine is bright and hot.   _____

2.   We carried our umbrellas.   _____

3.   The sailboats were still.   _____

4.   There are no rocks on the beach.   _____

B. Circle the verb that best completes the sentence. Remember that the form of the verb *be* must agree with the subject.

1.   I (is, am) a third grader.

2.   Pat and I (is, are) partners in class.

3.   Jimmy (was, were) my partner last month.

4.   Mrs. Boynton (is, are) the science teacher.

5.   The students (was, were) interested in the experiment.

C. Write two sentences that tell about someone or something. Use *is* in one sentence. Use *was* in the other.

1.   _____

      _____

2.   _____

      _____

The Verb *Be*

Is the underlined verb in each sentence correct? Fill in the bubble next to the right answer.

1. All dinosaurs <u>is</u> extinct.
- ⬯ am
- ⬯ are
- ⬯ correct as is

2. A brontosaurus <u>is</u> a kind of dinosaur.
- ⬯ am
- ⬯ are
- ⬯ correct as is

3. Many people <u>are</u> puzzled about what happened to dinosaurs.
- ⬯ am
- ⬯ was
- ⬯ correct as is

4. Dinosaurs <u>was</u> plant-eaters or meat-eaters.
- ⬯ is
- ⬯ were
- ⬯ correct as is

5. I <u>are</u> interested in Tyrannosaurus rex.
- ⬯ am
- ⬯ were
- ⬯ correct as is

6. It <u>were</u> a fierce meat-eater.
- ⬯ are
- ⬯ was
- ⬯ correct as is

7. Dinosaurs <u>was</u> like some reptiles that live today.
- ⬯ is
- ⬯ were
- ⬯ correct as is

8. Their teeth, bones, and skin <u>was</u> like those of crocodiles.
- ⬯ were
- ⬯ is
- ⬯ correct as is

9 Large dinosaurs <u>were</u> the largest land animals that ever lived.
- ⬯ am
- ⬯ was
- ⬯ correct as is

10. I <u>are</u> amazed by their extraordinary size!
- ⬯ am
- ⬯ were
- ⬯ correct as is

Main Verbs and Helping Verbs

*A **main verb** is the most important verb in a sentence. It shows the action. A **helping verb** works with the main verb. Forms of **be** and **have** are helping verbs. The helping verb **will** shows future tense.*

A. Read each sentence. Write *M* if a main verb is underlined. Write *H* if a helping verb is underlined. Circle the main and helping verbs that show future tense.

1. We will <u>learn</u> about new buildings. _____

2. The backhoe <u>is</u> digging the foundation. _____

3. It <u>had</u> filled several dump trucks. _____

4. The dump trucks are <u>removing</u> the dirt. _____

5. Workers <u>are</u> building the outer wall. _____

6. A cement truck is <u>pouring</u> the concrete. _____

7. It <u>will</u> need several days to dry. _____

8. At noon the workers will <u>eat</u> their lunch. _____

B. Choose the correct main and helping verb from the box to complete each sentence. Write it on the line. Circle the main and helping verbs that show future tense.

had climbed	have lifted	will watch	are reading	is going

1. We _____ a movie about skyscrapers.

2. A building _____ up.

3. The workers _____ the plans.

4. Cranes _____ the heavy beams.

5. A worker _____ a tall ladder.

Main Verbs and Helping Verbs

 *A **main verb** is the most important verb in a sentence. It shows the action. A **helping verb** works with the main verb. Forms of **be** and **have** are helping verbs.*

A. Read each sentence. Circle the helping verb. Draw a line under the main verb.

1. Jamal had built his first model rocket last year.
2. He has painted it red, white, and blue.
3. Now Jamal is building another rocket.
4. It will fly many feet into the air.
5. A parachute will bring the rocket back to Jamal.
6. I am buying a model rocket, too.

B. Complete each sentence with the correct main verb or helping verb in ( ). Write the word on the line.

1. Kim _____ making a clay vase. (is, has)

2. The clay _____ arrived yesterday. (was, had)

3. I am _____ to watch her work. (go, going)

4. She is _____ a potter's wheel. (used, using)

5. The sculpture _____ go above the fireplace. (will, is)

6. People _____ admired Kim's beautiful vases. (are, have)

C. Write two sentences about something you will do later in the week. Use the future tense helping verb. Be sure to use a main verb and helping verb in each sentence.

1. _____

2. _____

Main Verbs and Helping Verbs

A. Read each sentence. Fill in the bubble next to the main verb.

1. Ed is reading a book in the park.
   - ◯ Ed
   - ◯ is
   - ◯ reading

2. The children are playing baseball nearby.
   - ◯ are
   - ◯ playing
   - ◯ baseball

3. I have walked to the park, too.
   - ◯ walked
   - ◯ have
   - ◯ park

4. Tomorrow, my sister will come along.
   - ◯ Tomorrow
   - ◯ come
   - ◯ will

5. She will share her lunch with me.
   - ◯ share
   - ◯ will
   - ◯ lunch

B. Read each sentence. Fill in the bubble next to the helping verb.

1. Jill has visited her grandparents many times this year.
   - ◯ Jill
   - ◯ has
   - ◯ visited

2. She is sending them an E-mail now.
   - ◯ E-mail
   - ◯ is
   - ◯ sending

3. In June, they will drive to Washington, D.C.
   - ◯ they
   - ◯ driving
   - ◯ will

4. Jill and her brother will go with them.
   - ◯ will
   - ◯ go
   - ◯ them

5. They have waited for this trip for a long time.
   - ◯ waited
   - ◯ this
   - ◯ have

© Scholastic Inc.

Linking Verbs

 A **linking verb** tells what someone or something is, was, or will be. The linking verb most often used is a form of the verb be, such as **am**, **is**, **are**, **was**, **were**, and **will be**.

A. Find the linking verb in each sentence. Write it on the line.

1. This book is a biography about Thomas Edison. _____

2. I am interested in books about inventors. _____

3. Thomas Edison was a hard worker. _____

4. His inventions were wonderful. _____

5. They are still important for us today. _____

6. You will be amazed by this book. _____

B. Read each sentence and underline the linking verb. Then circle the word that tells if it is past or present.

1. I am a fan of Thomas Edison.   Past or Present

2. Thomas Edison was a famous inventor.   Past or Present

3. Many of his inventions are well-known.   Past or Present

4. His parents were friendly.   Past or Present

5. Jared is Edison's great-great-grandson.   Past or Present

C. Finish each sentence correctly. Write *are*, *am*, or *was* on the line.

1. I _____ excited.

2. This book _____ great!

3. Inventors _____ interesting people.

Linking Verbs

A **linking verb** tells what someone or something is, was, or will be. **Am**, **is**, and **was** are used when the subject of the sentence is singular. **Are** and **were** are used when the subject is plural. **Are** and **were** are also used with **you**.

A. Underline the linking verb in each sentence. Circle *S* if the subject is singular. Circle *P* if the subject is plural.

1. I was very bored. S or P
2. Now I am so happy. S or P
3. Stacey and Leda are my new neighbors. S or P
4. They were surprised by my visit. S or P
5. Stacey is very funny. S or P

B. Complete each sentence with the correct linking verb in ( ). Write the word on the line.

1. Roberto Clemente _____ a great baseball player. (was, were)
2. All baseball fans _____ amazed by his talents. (were, was)
3. I _____ one of his biggest fans. (is, am)
4. He _____ a true hero to me. (are, is)
5. Derek Jeter and Henry Aaron _____ my other favorite players. (is, are)

C. Think of a favorite animal. Write two sentences to describe it. Use one of these linking verbs in each sentence: *am, is, are, was, were, will be*.

_____

_____

© Scholastic Inc.

Linking Verbs

A. Read each sentence. Fill in the bubble next to the linking verb.

1. My new computer is fast.
- ○ new
- ○ is
- ○ fast

2. I am excited about it.
- ○ am
- ○ I
- ○ excited

3. The two mouse pads are colorful.
- ○ two
- ○ pads
- ○ are

4. The speakers were heavy.
- ○ were
- ○ heavy
- ○ speakers

5. All of the software was free.
- ○ software
- ○ was
- ○ free

B. Read each sentence. Fill in the bubble next to the correct linking verb.

1. My mom ——— a rafting teacher.
- ○ is
- ○ are
- ○ were

2. The trip last week ——— so much fun.
- ○ will be
- ○ were
- ○ was

3. The rafts ——— very soft and bouncy.
- ○ are
- ○ is
- ○ was

4. Yesterday, the docks ——— crowded.
- ○ will be
- ○ was
- ○ were

5. I ——— a raft instructor in the future.
- ○ will be
- ○ am
- ○ is

Subjects and Predicates

The **complete subject** *tells whom or what the sentence is about. The* **complete predicate** *tells who or what the subject is or does. The* **simple subject** *is the main word in the complete subject. The* **simple predicate** *is the verb in the complete predicate.*

A. Draw a line between the complete subject and the complete predicate.

1. All of the families traveled to California.
2. Baby Betsy, Billy, Joe, and Ted stayed in the cabin.
3. My father told us stories.
4. I baked a pie.

B. Draw a circle around the simple subject in each sentence. Then write it on the line.

1. Betsy learned how to walk. _____
2. The miners ate it up. _____
3. The new baby looks like me. _____
4. My feet are tired. _____
5. The man started a laundry. _____

C. Draw a circle around the simple predicate in each sentence. Then write it on the line.

1. We made a pie together. _____
2. First we rolled the crust. _____
3. Then we added the berries. _____
4. It bakes for one hour. _____
5. Everybody loves our pie! _____

Subjects and Predicates

 *The **simple subject** is the main word in the complete subject. The **simple predicate** is the main word in the complete predicate.*

A. Read each sentence. Draw a line between the complete subject and the complete predicate. Then write the simple subject and the simple predicate.

		Simple Subject	Simple Predicate
1.	Mrs. Perez's class took a trip to the museum.	_____	_____
2.	Many large paintings hung on the walls.	_____	_____
3.	Maria saw a painting of an animal alphabet.	_____	_____
4.	All the children looked at the painting.	_____	_____
5.	Paul pointed to a cat on a leash.	_____	_____
6.	His friend liked the dancing zebra.	_____	_____
7.	Everyone laughed at the purple cow.	_____	_____
8.	Many people visited the museum that day.	_____	_____
9.	The bus took us to school.	_____	_____

B. Finish the sentences. Add a complete subject to sentence 1. Add a complete predicate to sentence 2.

1. _____ was funny.

2. My class _____.

Subjects and Predicates

A. Is the underlined part of the sentence the complete subject or a complete predicate? Fill in the bubble next to the correct answer.

1. <u>My little brother</u> carried his backpack.
   - ◯ complete subject
   - ◯ complete predicate

2. I <u>found my old fishing rod</u>.
   - ◯ complete subject
   - ◯ complete predicate

3. <u>My dad</u> put air in our bicycle tires.
   - ◯ complete subject
   - ◯ complete predicate

4. Our whole family <u>rode to the big lake</u>.
   - ◯ complete subject
   - ◯ complete predicate

5. <u>Many pink flowers</u> bloomed on the trees.
   - ◯ complete subject
   - ◯ complete predicate

B. Fill in the bubble that tells if the underlined word is the simple subject or the simple predicate.

1. A man <u>rowed</u> a boat on the lake.
   - ◯ simple subject
   - ◯ simple predicate

2. My <u>brother</u> played ball in the field.
   - ◯ simple subject
   - ◯ simple predicate

3. Some other <u>children</u> joined in the game.
   - ◯ simple subject
   - ◯ simple predicate

4. Our large <u>basket</u> sat unopened on the picnic table.
   - ◯ simple subject
   - ◯ simple predicate

5. We <u>ate</u> cheese sandwiches and fruit.
   - ◯ simple subject
   - ◯ simple predicate

Adjectives

Adjectives *describe nouns. They can tell what color, size, and shape something is. They can also tell how something sounds, feels, or tastes.*

A. Look at each underlined noun. Circle the adjective or adjectives that describe it. Then write the adjectives on the lines.

1. My big <u>brother</u> likes to eat sweet <u>fruits</u>.   _____ _____

2. He eats them on many hot <u>days</u>.   _____ _____

3. He cuts the red <u>apple</u> into four <u>pieces</u>.   _____ _____

4. The ripe <u>bananas</u> and juicy <u>peaches</u> are his favorites.   _____ _____

5. Mom bought him a large, round <u>watermelon</u>.   _____ _____

6. He made a delicious, colorful <u>salad</u> for all of us!   _____ _____

B. Write two adjectives to describe each noun. Use words that describe color, size, shape, sound, or how something tastes or feels.

1. the _____, _____ balloon

2. a _____, _____ apple

3. a _____, _____ day

C. Write a sentence about a pet. Use two adjectives to describe the pet.

_____

_____

Adjectives

An **adjective** *is a word that describes a person, place, or thing.*

A. Read each sentence. Write the adjective that describes the underlined noun on the line.

1. We live near a sparkling <u>brook.</u> _____

2. It has clear <u>water</u>. _____

3. Large <u>fish</u> swim in the brook. _____

4. Busy <u>squirrels</u> play near the brook. _____

5. You can enjoy breathing in the fresh <u>air</u> near the brook. _____

B. Complete each sentence by adding an adjective.

1. I love _____ apples.

2. I see a _____ ball.

3. I smell _____ flowers.

4. I hear _____ music.

5. I like the _____ taste of pickles.

 Write three sentences that tell about the foods you like the best. Use adjectives in your description.

© Scholastic Inc.

Adjectives

A. Read each sentence. Fill in the bubble next to the word that is an adjective.

1. Several relatives from Mexico visited us.
   - ○ Several
   - ○ relatives
   - ○ visited

2. The trip took six hours.
   - ○ trip
   - ○ six
   - ○ hours

3. They took many pictures of my family.
   - ○ took
   - ○ many
   - ○ pictures

4. My uncle wore a blue hat.
   - ○ uncle
   - ○ blue
   - ○ hat

5. My aunt wore a colorful serape.
   - ○ aunt
   - ○ wore
   - ○ colorful

B. Fill in the bubble next to the adjective that best completes the sentence.

1. We ate the —— food.
   - ○ loud
   - ○ fuzzy
   - ○ delicious

2. There were —— people in the restaurant.
   - ○ one
   - ○ many
   - ○ green

3. My dad ordered —— tortillas.
   - ○ sharp
   - ○ loud
   - ○ some

4. My cousin José ate —— tamales!
   - ○ noisy
   - ○ five
   - ○ curly

5. Everyone had a —— time!
   - ○ cold
   - ○ wonderful
   - ○ purple

Articles and Other Adjectives

The words a, an, and the are special adjectives called **articles**. **A** is used before words that begin with a consonant. **An** is used before words that begin with a vowel. **The** is used before either.

A. Circle the articles in each sentence.

1. The elk, moose, and bears grazed in the forest.

2. There was an abundant supply of grass and plants.

3. A bolt of lightning struck a tree and started a fire.

4. Fires have always been an important part of forest ecology.

5. The heat of the summer left the forest very dry.

6. The fires spread over a thousand acres.

7. The helicopters and an airplane spread chemicals on the fire.

8. Firefighters made an attempt to stop the flames.

B. Circle the article in ( ) that completes each sentence correctly. Then write it on the line.

1. Last summer I visited _____ National Park. (a, an)

2. We took a bus through _____ forests. (an, the)

3. The bus carried us up _____ narrow roads. (a, the)

4. I saw _____ elk grazing on some grass. (a, an)

5. We stayed in _____ old log cabin. (a, an)

6. Deer came up to _____ cabin window. (an, the)

7. We made _____ new friend. (a, an)

8. I wrote my friend _____ letter. (a, an)

© Scholastic Inc.

Articles and Other Adjectives

 The article **A** *is used before words that begin with a consonant.* **An** *is used before words that begin with a vowel.* **The** *is used before either.*

A. Circle the article that correctly completes the sentence.

1. I saw (a, an) octopus at the aquarium.

2. A trainer was feeding fish to (a, an) dolphin.

3. We took (a, an) elevator to the main floor.

4. We had (a, an) up-to-date listing of exhibits.

5. There was (a, an) exhibit about the ocean floor.

6. It was (a, an) day to remember!

B. Write a noun on each line to complete the sentences.

1. We read a _____ about a _____.

2. The _____ in a funny story had an _____ for a pet.

3. We went to the _____ to get an _____.

4. Angela saw a _____ on the _____.

5. A _____ was curled up on the _____.

C. Complete the sentence with three singular nouns. Use the article *a* or *an*.

Molly drew a picture of _____

_____

Articles and Other Adjectives

A. Fill in the bubble next to the article that correctly completes the sentence.

1. I want to be _____ firefighter in our class play.
   ○ the
   ○ an

2. My friend plans to play one of _____ astronauts.
   ○ an
   ○ the

3. Sue read an exciting story about _____ acrobat.
   ○ an
   ○ a

4. We wrote letters to _____ authors of the book.
   ○ a
   ○ the

5. _____ illustrations were done in bright colors.
   ○ The
   ○ An

B. Fill in the bubble next to the word that best completes the sentence.

1. A few days ago, we went on an _____ ride!
   ○ train
   ○ elephant
   ○ boat

2. John visited an _____ outside the city.
   ○ airport
   ○ zoo
   ○ museum

3. Bill and Michelle shared an _____.
   ○ seat
   ○ umbrella
   ○ peach

4. At the edge of the water, Keesha saw a _____.
   ○ oyster
   ○ eel
   ○ crab

5. Rachel drew pictures of a _____.
   ○ octopus
   ○ lobster
   ○ egg

Possessive Nouns

A **possessive noun** shows ownership. Add **'s** to make a singular noun show ownership. Add an apostrophe (') after the **s** of a plural noun to show ownership.

A. Underline the possessive noun in each sentence.

1. The king's palace is beautiful.

2. The palace's garden has many flowers.

3. The flowers' sweet smell fills the air.

4. The trees' branches shade the garden paths.

5. The gardener's tools are well-oiled and sharp.

6. People listen to the birds' songs.

7. The singers' voices are very beautiful.

8. The diamond reflects the sun's rays.

9. The diamond's light fills the palace.

10. Visitors' eyes open wide when they see all the colors.

B. Write each singular possessive noun from Part A.

1. _____ 2. _____ 3. _____

4. _____ 5. _____

C. Write each plural possessive noun from Part A.

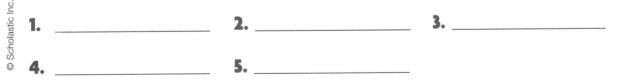

1. _____ 2. _____ 3. _____

4. _____ 5. _____

Possessive Nouns

A **possessive noun** *shows ownership. Add* **'s** *to make a singular noun show ownership. Add an apostrophe (') after the* **s** *of a plural noun to show ownership.*

A. Underline the possessive noun in each sentence. Write *S* on the line if the possessive noun is singular. Write *P* if the possessive noun is plural.

1. Anna's family took a walk in the woods. _____

2. They saw two birds' nests high up in a tree. _____

3. A yellow butterfly landed on Brad's backpack. _____

4. Anna liked the pattern of the butterfly's wings. _____

5. A turtle's shell had many spots. _____

6. Anna took pictures of two chipmunks' homes. _____

7. The animals' tails had dark stripes. _____

B. Complete each sentence with the singular possessive form of the noun in ( ).

1. Jim was going to play basketball at _____ house. (Carol)

2. One of _____ new sneakers was missing. (Jim)

3. He looked under his _____ desk. (sister)

4. He crawled under his _____ bed to look. (brother)

5. It was outside in his _____ flower garden. (dad)

6. The _____ lace had been chewed. (sneaker)

7. Jim saw his _____ footprints in the dirt. (dog)

Possessive Nouns

A. Choose the singular possessive noun to complete each sentence.

1. Joan _____ backpack was stuffed with library books.
   - ○ Kramer
   - ○ Kramers'
   - ○ Kramer's

2. She should have borrowed her _____ large book bag.
   - ○ mothers'
   - ○ mother's
   - ○ mothers

3. Her little _____ book was due back by five o'clock.
   - ○ brother's
   - ○ brothers'
   - ○ brothers

4. A sign on a _____ desk warned of fines for late books.
   - ○ librarians'
   - ○ librarians
   - ○ librarian's

5. _____ heart raced as she got there just in time.
   - ○ Joan's
   - ○ Joan
   - ○ Joans'

B. Choose the plural possessive noun to complete each sentence.

1. All the _____ telescopes were loaded onto the space shuttle
   - ○ astronomers'
   - ○ astronomers
   - ○ astronomer's

2. At take-off both _____ trails were long and straight.
   - ○ engine's
   - ○ engines'
   - ○ engines

3. The _____ loud cheers filled the air.
   - ○ spectators
   - ○ spectator's
   - ○ spectators'

4. Everyone applauded for the many _____ good work.
   - ○ scientists'
   - ○ scientist's
   - ○ scientists

5. The four _____ pictures appeared on the news.
   - ○ astronauts
   - ○ astronaut's
   - ○ astronauts'

Subject and Object Pronouns

A **pronoun** takes the place of a noun or nouns in a sentence. The words **I**, **you**, **she**, **he**, **it**, **we**, and **they** are subject pronouns. Use one of these pronouns to take the place of a subject in a sentence.

A. Underline the subject pronoun in each sentence.

1. We are going to the dentist.

2. It won't take long.

3. I went in first.

4. She asked the assistant for help.

5. He gave the dentist some pink toothpaste.

6. They said the toothpaste would taste like strawberries.

7. You will like the taste, too.

B. Decide which pronoun in the box can replace the underlined subject. Write the pronoun on the line. Remember to capitalize.

she	he	it	we	they

1. Dr. De Soto is a popular dentist. _____

2. Mrs. De Soto is his assistant. _____

3. The fox and the rabbit are waiting to be seen. _____

4. The fox has a bad toothache. _____

5. The chair is ready for the next patient. _____

6. Dr. and Mrs. De Soto do not trust the fox. _____

7. Roger and I enjoy reading this story. _____

Subject and Object Pronouns

 A **pronoun** *takes the place of a noun or nouns in a sentence. The words* **me**, **you**, **him**, **her**, **it**, **us**, *and* **them** *are object pronouns. Use these object pronouns in the predicates of sentences.*

A. Underline the object pronoun in each sentence.

1. Aunt Cindy gave us a football.

2. Our dog Rex found it.

3. He thinks the ball is for him.

4. I said, "Rex, that's not for you!"

5. Aunt Cindy gave me another ball for Rex.

6. Now Rex always wants to play with her.

7. I like to watch them.

B. Decide which object pronoun below can replace the underlined word or words. Write the object pronoun on the line.

1. I went to the movies with <u>Rachel and Kevin</u>. _____

2. Kevin asked <u>Rachel</u> for some popcorn. _____

3. Rachel was happy to share <u>the popcorn</u>. _____

4. I accidentally bumped <u>Kevin</u>. _____

5. The popcorn spilled all over <u>Rachel, Kevin, and me</u>. _____

C. Write two sentences. In one sentence use a subject pronoun. In the other sentence use an object pronoun.

1. _____

2. _____

Subject and Object Pronouns

Decide which pronoun can replace the underlined words.
Fill in the bubble next to the correct answer.

1. Uncle Sean is taking <u>Melina and me</u> ice skating at the pond.
   - ⬭ they
   - ⬭ us
   - ⬭ her

2. <u>The pond</u> freezes by late December.
   - ⬭ He
   - ⬭ You
   - ⬭ It

3. <u>Melina</u> knows how to skate.
   - ⬭ She
   - ⬭ Her
   - ⬭ I

4. Uncle Sean shows <u>Melina</u> how to skate backwards.
   - ⬭ her
   - ⬭ she
   - ⬭ them

5. I spot <u>skaters</u> nearby.
   - ⬭ us
   - ⬭ we
   - ⬭ them

6. <u>Pablo and Kim</u> are my friends.
   - ⬭ Us
   - ⬭ They
   - ⬭ Them

7. <u>Uncle Sean</u> skates over to say hello.
   - ⬭ It
   - ⬭ He
   - ⬭ Us

8. <u>Pablo, Kim, and I</u> listen to Uncle Sean's jokes.
   - ⬭ We
   - ⬭ Them
   - ⬭ Us

9. Everyone likes <u>Uncle Sean</u>.
   - ⬭ me
   - ⬭ he
   - ⬭ him

10. They will join <u>Uncle Sean, Melina, and me</u> for hot apple cider.
    - ⬭ it
    - ⬭ we
    - ⬭ us

Possessive Pronouns

*A **possessive pronoun** shows ownership or belonging. It takes the place of a noun that shows ownership. **My**, **your**, **his**, **her**, **its**, **our**, and **their** are possessive pronouns.*

A. Circle the subject pronoun in each sentence. Then underline the possessive pronoun. Use these answers to fill in the chart.

1. I am planning a trip with my family.

2. Will you wear your sunglasses?

3. He will bring his camera.

4. She will take her dog along.

5. It will eat all its food.

6. We will enjoy our vacation.

7. They will show their pictures.

Subject Pronouns	Possessive Pronouns
I	my

B. Underline the possessive pronoun in each sentence.

1. The desert is their home.

2. Her umbrella blocks out the sun.

3. That javelina likes to play his guitar.

4. His address is 1 Tumbleweed Avenue.

5. Coyote said, "My stomach is growling."

6. "I'll blow your house down," Coyote shouted.

7. Its walls are made of tumbleweeds.

8. "Our house is strong," the third javelina said.

Possessive Pronouns

A **possessive pronoun** *shows ownership or belonging. It takes the place of a noun that shows ownership.* **My**, **your**, **his**, **her**, **its**, **our**, *and* **their** *are possessive pronouns.*

A. Complete each sentence. Write the correct pronoun in ( ) on the line.

1. Nicole likes to pick apples at _____ farm. (we, our)

2. Autumn is _____ favorite season. (her, she)

3. Dad says, "Please use _____ special basket." (I, my)

4. It was _____ birthday present from Grandpa. (he, his)

5. Dad said that _____ handle was carved by a famous artist. (their, its)

6. I tell Dad, "We will not forget to take _____ basket." (your, you)

7. Later, my mom and dad enjoyed _____ apple pie. (their, they)

B. Read each sentence. Write the possessive pronoun that can replace the underlined word or words.

1. The art project was due soon, but <u>Zach's</u> computer

    was broken. _____

2. My brother was using <u>my family's</u> computer.   _____

3. Zach borrowed <u>Angela's</u> computer instead.   _____

4. He loaded a picture into <u>the computer's</u> scanner.   _____

5. <u>Zach's</u> idea was to stretch the picture into a funny shape. _____

6. <u>Tim's and Ming's</u> projects were exactly the same!   _____

C. Write a sentence using the possessive pronouns *my* and *her*.

_____

Possessive Pronouns

A. Read each sentence. Fill in the bubble next to the possessive pronoun.

1. She is fixing her tree fort.
   - ◯ She
   - ◯ is
   - ◯ her

2. Its roof started leaking after a storm.
   - ◯ Its
   - ◯ a
   - ◯ after

3. Now we can eat our lunch without getting wet.
   - ◯ we
   - ◯ our
   - ◯ without

4. I will share my favorite snack with a friend.
   - ◯ I
   - ◯ my
   - ◯ will

5. He will bring his brother.
   - ◯ his
   - ◯ He
   - ◯ will

B. Choose the possessive pronoun that can replace the underlined word or words.

1. Erika's tire-patch kit is very helpful.
   - ◯ My
   - ◯ Our
   - ◯ Her

2. She will use it to fix Brad's flat tire.
   - ◯ he
   - ◯ his
   - ◯ their

3. The tire's inner tube has a slow leak.
   - ◯ Its
   - ◯ Our
   - ◯ Their

4. Joel's and Diane's bike chains need to be oiled.
   - ◯ Our
   - ◯ Their
   - ◯ Her

5. Now everyone can bike to my family's picnic.
   - ◯ its
   - ◯ our
   - ◯ your

Compound Subjects and Predicates

A **compound subject** *is two or more nouns connected by and. A* **compound predicate** *is two or more verbs connected by* **and**.

A. Underline the nouns that form each compound subject. Then circle the word that connects the nouns.

1. Laura and Ramona are popular story characters.

2. In one story, Pa, Ma, and Laura traveled far.

3. The dog and horses trotted along.

4. Ma and Pa drove the wagon all day.

5. Grass and trees grow on the prairie.

B. Underline the verbs that form each compound predicate. Then circle the word that connects the verbs.

1. The wagon swayed and creaked.

2. Laura hummed and sang.

3. The road twisted and turned.

4. Pet and Patty neighed and snorted.

5. The deer stopped and stared.

C. Complete sentence 1 with two nouns joined by *and*. Complete sentence 2 with two verbs joined by *and*.

1. The _____ sang all day.

2. The dog _____ all the way home.

© Scholastic Inc.

Using Punctuation

Quotation marks *show the exact words of a speaker.* **Commas** *appear between the day and year in a date, between the city and state in a location, between the lines of an address, and after all but the last item in a series.* **Underlining** *shows book titles.*

A. Read each sentence. Add any missing commas.

1. Mrs. Wu's bank is located at 92 Maple Avenue Inwood Texas 75209.

2. She opened an account there on September 8 2001.

3. She also uses the branch office in Lakewood Texas.

4. That branch is open weekdays Saturdays and some evenings.

5. The main office is closed Saturdays Sundays and all holidays.

6. Mrs. Wu saw Ms. Ames Mr. Pacheco and Mrs. Jefferson at the bank on Saturday.

7. They carried checks bills and deposits.

8. Mr. Pacheco has had an account at that bank since May 2 1974.

B. Read the sentences below. Add any missing quotation marks, commas, or underlining.

1. My favorite author is Jerry Spinelli said Rick.

2. Spinelli was born on February 1 1941.

3. His home town is Norristown Pennsylvania.

4. What are your favorite books by him? asked Teresa.

5. I like Maniac Magee Dump Days and Fourth Grade Rats   replied Rick.

**Write a sentence that tells your own mailing address.
Then name three things you enjoy receiving in the mail,
such as letters from friends, magazines, or catalogs.**

Using Punctuation

A. Each sentence is missing one type of punctuation: quotation marks, commas, or underlining. Fill in the bubble next to the type of punctuation that needs to be added to the sentence to make it correct.

1. We read a book called At the Zoo.
- ○ quotation mark
- ○ commas
- ○ underlining

2. ! had pictures of a lion monkeys and bears.
- ○ quotation mark
- ○ commas
- ○ underlining

3. "Can we go to the wild animal show? asked Brent.
- ○ quotation mark
- ○ comma
- ○ underlining

4. The show will be in town on June 8 2002.
- ○ quotation mark
- ○ comma
- ○ underlining

B. Look at the underlined part of each sentence. Fill in the bubble that shows the correct answer.

1. <u>I have a new baby sister!</u> shouted Liz.
- ○ "I have a new baby sister"!
- ○ "I have a new baby sister!"
- ○ correct as is

2. She was born on <u>April 3 2002.</u>
- ○ April 3, 2002
- ○ April, 3 2002
- ○ correct as is

3. She was born at <u>1800 River Road, Centerville, North Carolina.</u>
- ○ 1800 River Road Centerville, North Carolina
- ○ 1800 River Road Centerville North Carolina
- ○ correct as is

4. <u>She has tiny fingers tiny toes and a big scream</u>
- ○ tiny fingers, tiny toes and a big scream.
- ○ tiny fingers, tiny toes, and a big scream
- ○ correct as is

Irregular Verbs

Irregular verbs *do not form the past tense by adding* **-ed**. *They change their form.*

A. In each sentence, underline the past tense of the verb in ( ). Then write the past-tense verb on the line.

1. Jessi told Jackie to be ready early. (tell) _____

2. He was nervous about his science fair project. (is) _____

3. Jackie's friends came to the table. (come) _____

4. They saw the volcano there. (see) _____

5. Jackie knew his speech by heart. (know) _____

6. The sign on the exhibit fell over. (fall) _____

7. The teacher lit the match for Jackie. (light) _____

8. Jackie threw his hands into the air. (throw) _____

B. Complete each sentence. Write the correct verb on the line.

fell   threw   saw   knew

1. Jackie _____ all about volcanoes.

2. He once _____ a real volcano.

3. It _____ ashes and fire into the air.

4. The ashes _____ all over the ground.

C. Complete each sentence. Use the past form of *know* in one and the past form of *tell* in the other. Sample answers are given.

1. When I was five, I _____

2. My brother _____

Irregular Verbs

Irregular verbs *do not form the past tense by adding* **-ed**. *They change their form.*

A. Complete each sentence. Write the past form of the verb in ( ).

1. Erin —————— dry lima beans at the store. (buy)

2. Her family —————— lima beans for dinner. (eat)

3. Erin —————— six lima bean plants for the science fair. (grow)

4. She —————— her project on Saturday. (begin)

5. Erin —————— three plants water and light. (give)

6. The other plants —————— all day in a dark closet. (sit)

B. Circle the past-tense form of the verb in ( ) to complete each sentence.

1. The judges (come, came) to Erin's table.

2. She (won, win) a blue ribbon.

3. Erin's family (went, go) to the fair.

4. One lima bean plant (is, was) 6 inches tall.

5. Two plants (fall, fell) over in the pot.

6. Erin (said, say), "I learned a lot."

C. Write a sentence about growing something. Use a past-tense irregular verb in your sentence.

————————————————————

————————————————————

© Scholastic Inc.

Scholastic Success With

WRITING

Dinnertime

 *A **sentence** is a group of words that expresses a complete thought.
A **fragment** is an incomplete thought.*

Write *S* for sentence or *F* for fragment.

_____ 1. Insects eat many different things.

_____ 2. Some of these things.

_____ 3. The praying mantis eats other insects.

_____ 4. Water bugs eat tadpoles and small frogs.

_____ 5. Flower nectar makes good.

_____ 6. Build nests to store their food.

_____ 7. The cockroach will eat almost anything.

_____ 8. Termites.

_____ 9. A butterfly caterpillar.

_____ 10. Bite animals and people.

_____ 11. Some insects will even eat paper.

_____ 12. Insects have different mouth parts to help

them eat.

On another piece of paper, write about three things you did during the day using only
sentence fragments. Have someone read it. Did they understand it? Why or why not?

© Scholastic Inc.

A Real Meal

*A **sentence** is a group of words that expresses a complete thought.*

Change each fragment from the previous page to a sentence by adding words from the Bug Box. Remember to use a capital letter at the beginning and a period at the end of each sentence.

1. _____

2. _____

3. _____

4. _____

5. _____

6. _____

BUG BOX

are wood eaters.

Mosquitoes

are wood, plants, and nectar.

eats leaves.

food for bees.

Wasps

On another piece of paper, write a fragment about your favorite dinner. Then change it into a sentence.

Rock Your World

 A telling sentence is called a **statement**.
A statement begins with a capital letter and ends with a period.

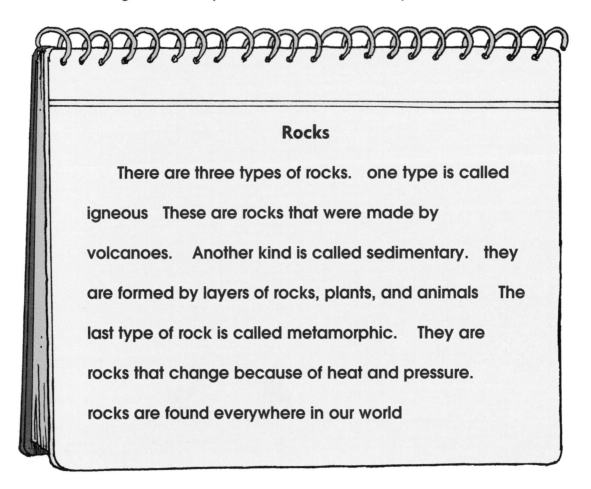

Rocks

There are three types of rocks.   one type is called

igneous   These are rocks that were made by

volcanoes.   Another kind is called sedimentary.   they

are formed by layers of rocks, plants, and animals   The

last type of rock is called metamorphic.   They are

rocks that change because of heat and pressure.

rocks are found everywhere in our world

Find the three statements that are missing a capital letter and a period. Rewrite
the three statements correctly.

1. _____

2. _____

3. _____

Rock and Roll

 A statement is used to answer a question.

Use a complete sentence to write the answer
to each question.

1. **How many types of rocks are on our planet? (three)**

   <u>There are three types of rocks on our planet.</u>

2. **How hot is the melted rock inside the earth? (more than 2000°F)**

   _____

3. **Where are most igneous rocks formed? (inside the earth)**

   _____

4. **What type of rock is marble? (metamorphic)**

   _____

5. **In what type of rock are fossils found? (sedimentary)**

   _____

Wacky World

An asking sentence is called a **question**. It begins with a capital letter and ends with a question mark (?).

Write each question correctly.

1. why is that car in a tree

_____

2. should that monkey be driving a bus

_____

3. did you see feathers on that crocodile

_____

4. can elephants really lay eggs

_____

5. is that my mother covered in spots

_____

On another piece of paper, draw your own picture of a wacky world. Write two questions about your picture.

© Scholastic Inc.

The Real World

 A question begins with a capital letter and ends with a question mark (?). It often begins with one of the words listed below.

Who	*When*
Will	*Can*
What	*Why*
Would	*Did*
Where	*How*
Should	*Is*

Imagine that you are interviewing your favorite famous person (for example, an actor, a president, or a rock star). Write five questions you would ask this person. Use a different beginning word for each question.

I am interviewing _____.

1. _____

2. _____

3. _____

4. _____

5. _____

On another piece of paper, write an answer to each question.

The Dry Desert

A sentence that shows strong feeling or excitement is called an **exclamation**. *It ends with an exclamation point (!).*

Finish each sentence with a period, a question mark, or an exclamation point.

1. It is hard for plants and animals to get water in the desert

2. Can a cactus live without enough water

3. Some deserts are hot, and others are cool

4. A lizard is running toward us

5. Does a camel really store water in its hump

6. Some deserts are cold and covered with ice

7. How often does it rain in the desert

8. The largest hot desert is the Sahara

9. Are there any deserts in the United States

10. There is a long snake slithering across the sand

11. People who live in the desert travel to find water

12. I see water up ahead

© Scholastic Inc.

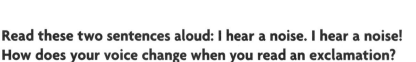

Read these two sentences aloud: I hear a noise. I hear a noise!
How does your voice change when you read an exclamation?

The Sunny Sahara

Every sentence begins with a capital letter.
A statement ends with a period.
A question ends with a question mark.
An exclamation ends with an exclamation point.

Write each sentence correctly.

1. the Sahara Desert is in Africa

_____

2. do people live in the Sahara Desert

_____

3. the Sahara Desert is about the same size as the United States

_____

4. how high is the temperature in the Sahara Desert

_____

5. the Sahara Desert is too hot for me

_____

**On another piece of paper, write a sentence with two mistakes. Ask a friend to circle
the mistakes.**

© Scholastic Inc.

A Snowy Scene

Complete:

Every sentence begins with a _____ .

A statement ends with a _____ .

A question ends with a _____ .

An exclamation ends with an _____ .

Write two statements, questions, and exclamations about the picture.

Statements:

1. _____

2. _____

Questions:

1. _____

2. _____

Exclamations:

1. _____

2. _____

**On another piece of paper, turn this statement into a question and an exclamation:
It snowed ten inches last night.**

A Snowy Story

 *After you write a sentence, go back and look for mistakes. This is called **proofreading** your work.*

Use these proofreading marks to correct 11 mistakes in the story.

mars = **Make a capital letter.**   (?) = **Add a question mark.**

(.) = **Add a period.**   (!) = **Add an exclamation point.**

Snow Day

the kids at Elm School had been waiting for a

snowstorm? they knew school would be

canceled if the storm brought a lot of snow last

week their wish came true it snowed 12 inches

school was canceled, and the kids spent the day

sledding, building snowmen, and drinking hot

chocolate. it was a great snow day

Find two sentences that had two mistakes and write them correctly.

1. _____

2. _____

 On another piece of paper, write a sentence with two mistakes. Ask a friend to find the mistakes.

Sentences That Slither

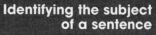

A sentence tells about someone or something.
This is called the **subject**.

Write the letter to show the subject of each sentence.

- **A.** The short blind snake
- **B.** Tree snakes
- **C.** The flowerpot snake
- **D.** Bird snakes
- **E.** A pit viper snake
- **F.** All snakes

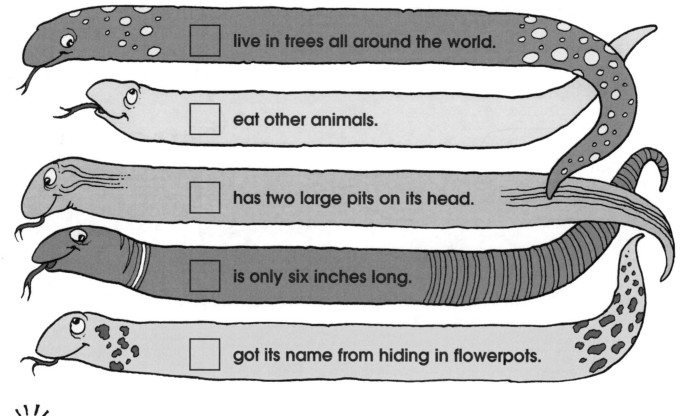

☐ feed on birds.

☐ live in trees all around the world.

☐ eat other animals.

☐ has two large pits on its head.

☐ is only six inches long.

☐ got its name from hiding in flowerpots.

**Confuse someone at home! Leave out the subject part of two sentences at dinner.
Can they understand?**

© Scholastic Inc.

A Reptile Fact Sheet

A sentence tells what the subject does or is. This part of the sentence is called the **verb***.*

Use the list of subjects as the beginning for eight sentences. Then add a verb to tell what the subject is doing.

Snakes

Lizards

Crocodiles

Turtles

Dinosaurs

Iguanas

Alligators

Pythons

1. _____

2. _____

3. _____

4. _____

5. _____

6. _____

7. _____

8. _____

On another piece of paper, write three sentences about your favorite things to do after school. Circle the verb in each sentence.

Stretching Sentences

A sentence is more interesting when it includes more than just a subject and a verb. It may tell where or when the sentence is happening. It may also tell why something is happening.

Write a sentence describing each set of pictures. Include a part that tells where, why, or how something is happening.

1. _____

2. _____

3. _____

4. _____

Find a cartoon in the newspaper. Use the pictures to write a sentence on another piece of paper that includes a subject, a verb, and a part that tells where, when, or why.

© Scholastic Inc.

Stretch It!

A sentence includes a subject and a verb. A sentence is more interesting when it also includes a part that tells where, when, or why.

Add more information to each sentence by telling where, when, or why. Write the complete new sentence.

1. **Mom is taking us shopping.** Where?

_____

2. **The stores are closing.** When?

_____

3. **We need to find a gift for Dad.** Why?

_____

4. **I will buy new jeans.** Where?

_____

5. **We may eat lunch.** When?

_____

 Find two sentences in your favorite book that include a subject, verb, and a part that tells where, when, or why. Write the sentences on another piece of paper.

Ketchup and Mustard

Sometimes two sentences can be combined to make one sentence.

Sentences that share the same subject seem to go together like ketchup and mustard. Rewrite the sentences by combining their endings with the word *and*.

1. I ordered a hamburger.
I ordered a milkshake.

I ordered a hamburger and a milkshake.

2. I like salt on my French fries.
I like ketchup on my French fries.

_____

3. My mom makes great pork chops.
My mom makes great applesauce.

_____

4. My dad eats two huge helpings of meat loaf!
My dad eats two huge helpings of potatoes!

_____

5. My brother helps set the table.
My brother helps clean the dishes.

_____

6. We have cookies for dessert.
We have ice cream for dessert.

_____

Let's Eat Out!

 Two sentences can be combined to make one sentence by using the words **although,** **after, because, until,** *and* **while.**

Choose a word from the menu to combine the two sentences into one sentence.

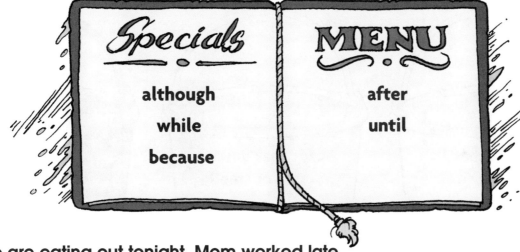

Specials

although

while

because

MENU

after

until

1. We are eating out tonight. Mom worked late.

_____

2. We are going to Joe's Fish Shack. I do not like fish.

_____

3. Dad said I can play outside. It's time to leave.

_____

4. We can play video games. We are waiting for our food.

_____

5. We may stop by Ida's Ice Cream Shop. We leave the restaurant.

_____

 Read the back of a cereal box. Find two sentences that could be combined.

Buckets of Fun

A **describing word** *helps you imagine how something looks, feels, smells, sounds, or tastes.*

Write a list of describing words on each bucket to fit the bucket's category.

words that
describe size

_____

_____

_____

words that describe
taste or smell

_____

_____

words that
describe sounds

_____

_____

words that describe
how something feels

_____

_____

_____

words that describe
weather

_____

_____

words that describe
feelings

_____

_____

Make a "mystery bag" by putting a secret object inside. Tell someone at home about the object inside using describing words!

At the Beach

A **describing word** *makes a sentence more interesting.*

Read the describing words found in the beach balls. Add the describing words to make each sentence more interesting. Write each new sentence.

1. The snow cone sat in the sun.

_____

2. Many children ran toward the ocean waves.

_____

3. My friends built a sandcastle.

_____

4. My brother grabbed his beach toys.

_____

5. Our dog tried to catch beach balls.

_____

On another piece of paper, draw a beach ball. Fill it with words that describe a day at the beach.

The Great Outdoors

A **describing word** *can tell more about a subject or a verb.*

Add describing words to make each sentence more interesting.

1. The _____ hikers walked back to camp _____.

2. The _____ bird sang _____.

3. The _____ tree grew _____.

4. _____ children played _____.

5. My _____ sister swam _____.

6. The _____ crickets chirped _____.

7. The _____ flowers bloomed _____.

8. The _____ swing set creaked _____.

9. The _____ ice cream melted _____.

10. The _____ trees shook _____ in the storm.

Where do you like to spend time outside? On another piece of paper, write the name of your favorite outdoor place. Then write three words that describe it.

Outdoor Excitement

A **describing word** can be added to a sentence.

☐ = Add a describing word.   She wore a ∧ dress.   ┌─────┐
                                              │ red │
                                              └─────┘

Read the sentences about each picture. Then use proofreading marks to add a describing word to each sentence.

1. The girl picked flowers.

2. The girl swatted the bees.

3. A bee stung the girl.

1. The boy played a game.

2. The boy won a trophy.

3. The boy held his trophy.

Add two describing words to this sentence: The campers heard a sound in the night.

Crazy Cartoons

A story is more interesting when the characters talk with one another.

Use the speech bubbles to show what each character is saying.

💡 **Cut a comic strip from the newspaper. Glue it to another piece of paper and make large speech bubbles. Rewrite the cartoon with your own words.**

What Did She Say?

Quotation marks (" ") *are used to show a character is talking in a story. They surround only the character's words.*

Fill in the speech bubbles to match the paragraph below each picture.

1. Daisy put on her rain boots, coat, and hat. "I think it's fun to splash in the puddles," she said.

2. As the rain continued, the puddles turned to streams. "Rain, rain, don't go away!" Daisy sang.

3. "Wow! I should have worn my bathing suit!" Daisy shouted as the water rose higher.

4. Then Daisy had an idea. She turned her umbrella upside down and climbed in. "It's a perfect day to go sailing," she said.

Ask someone at home for an old photograph of yourself and someone else. Glue it to another piece of paper and make speech bubbles to show what you may have been saying when the picture was taken.

Look Who's Talking!

Quotation marks surround a character's exact words. In a statement, use a comma to separate the character's exact words from the rest of the sentence. In a question and an exclamation, use the correct ending punctuation after the character's exact words.

Statement: **"I have to go now," said my friend.**
Question: **"Where are you?" asked my mom**.
Exclamation: **"Wow!" the boy exclaimed.**

Write a sentence to match each speech bubble. Use the examples above to help you.

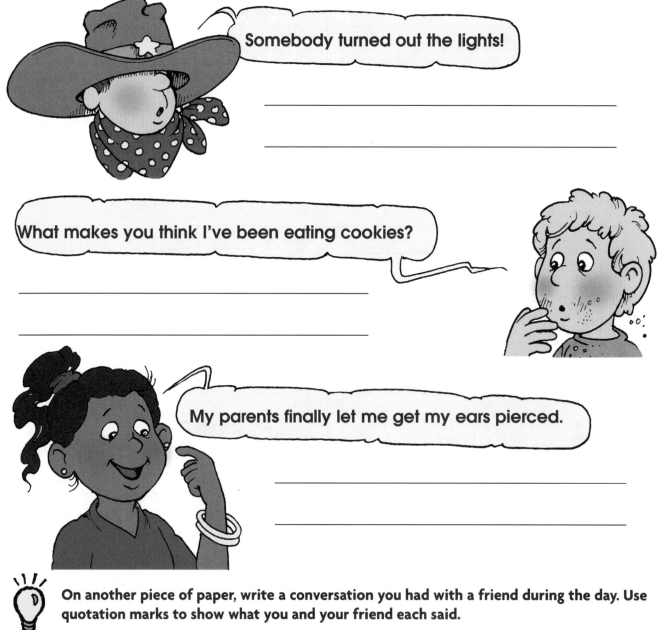

Somebody turned out the lights!

_____

_____

What makes you think I've been eating cookies?

_____

_____

My parents finally let me get my ears pierced.

_____

_____

On another piece of paper, write a conversation you had with a friend during the day. Use quotation marks to show what you and your friend each said.

Chitchat

 Quotation marks can be added to a story using these proofreading marks.

<u>m</u>ars = **Make a capital letter.**   (?) = **Add a question mark.**   (!) = **Add an exclamation point.**

(.) = **Add a period.**   (,) = **Add a comma.**   (") (") = **Add quotation marks.**

Find 16 mistakes in the story. Use proofreading marks to correct them.

Lucky Day

Drew woke up early on Saturday. No school today, he said He found his mom working in the garden What are you doing ” he asked.

"I am planting these flowers, she answered.

Drew looked down He couldn't believe it. A four-leaf clover” he shouted "This should help us win our big game today he said.

Drew's entire day was perfect. his sister shared her toys, the ice-cream truck brought his favorite flavor, and his team won the big game "What a day! he whispered to himself as he fell asleep that night.

On another piece of paper, write about your luckiest day. Include at least two sets of quotation marks.

Under the Big Top

*Sentences can be written in order of beginning (B), middle (M), and ending (E) to make
a paragraph.*

Write a middle and ending sentence to complete each paragraph.

B   The circus started with a roll of drums and flashing lights.

M   Next, _____

E   Last, _____

B   The tightrope walker stepped into the spotlight.

M   Next, _____

E   Last, _____

B   The lion tamer came on stage.

M   Next, _____

E   Last, _____

B   The dancing ponies appeared in the center ring.

M   Next, _____

E   Last, _____

© Scholastic Inc.

A Circus Train

 Sometimes a paragraph tells a story.

Write three sentences about the set of pictures to make a short story paragraph.

_____

_____

_____

_____

_____

_____

_____

_____

_____

Terrific Topics

A **paragraph** *is a group of sentences that tells about one idea, called the* **topic***.*

Imagine that you are planning to write a paragraph about each topic below. Write three ideas for each topic.

gardening	fish	homework
1. flowers	1.	1.
2. vegetables	2.	2.
3. pesky insects	3.	3.
summer sports	**friends**	**favorite books**
1.	1.	1.
2.	2.	2.
3.	3.	3.
favorite movies	**American history**	**healthy foods**
1.	1.	1.
2.	2.	2.
3.	3.	3.

It Just Doesn't Belong!

The sentence that tells the topic of a paragraph is called the **topic sentence**.

Draw a line through the sentence that does not belong with the topic.

Topic: Dogs make great family pets.

Dogs have great hearing, which helps them protect a family from danger.

Most dogs welcome their owners with wagging tails.

My favorite kind of dog is a boxer.

Many dogs are willing to play with children in a safe manner.

Topic: The history of the American flag is quite interesting.

The first American flag had 13 stars.

Not much is known about the history of Chinese flags.

Historians cannot prove that Betsy Ross really made the first American flag.

The American flag has changed 27 times.

Topic: Hurricanes are called by different names depending on where they occur.

Hurricanes have strong, powerful winds.

In the Philippines, hurricanes are called baguios.

Hurricanes are called typhoons in the Far East.

Australian people use the name willy-willies to describe hurricanes.

Read a paragraph from a favorite chapter book. Read the topic sentence to someone at home.

© Scholastic Inc.

Missing Topics

➤ *A topic sentence is sometimes called the* **main idea**.

Read the groups of sentences. Then write a topic sentence that tells the main idea of the paragraph.

_____

_____

One reason is that guinea pigs do not usually bite. Second, guinea pigs don't make as much noise as other rodents might during the night. Last, they are large enough that they can be found if they ever get lost in a house.

_____

_____

First, spread peanut butter on two pieces of bread. Next, cut a banana into slices and lay them on top of the peanut butter. Then close the two pieces of bread into a sandwich. Last, eat up!

_____

_____

Frogs usually have longer legs and wetter skin than toads do. Many frogs live near a water source of some kind while toads prefer a damp, muddy environment. Frog eggs and toad eggs are different in shape.

On another piece of paper, make a list of three subjects you know a lot about. Write a possible topic sentence for each of the subjects.

© Scholastic Inc.

Try These Topics

*Writing a topic sentence takes thought because your
entire paragraph must follow the main idea.*

Write a topic sentence for each subject.

1. My Chores

_____

2. The Best Book Ever

_____

3. My Favorite After-School Activity

_____

4. Appropriate TV Shows for Kids

_____

5. Types of Coins

_____

6. Our Greatest Presidents

_____

That Drives Me Crazy!

The sentences that follow the topic sentence tell more about the topic. They are called **supporting sentences**.

Read the paragraph below. Cross out the three sentences that do not support the topic.

My Pet Peeves

I am a pretty agreeable person, but there are a few things around my house that drive me crazy. One such thing is when my younger brothers go into my bedroom and destroy my building creations. My three-year-old brothers both have blonde hair. I also get upset when my sister sings at the dinner table. Her favorite sport is gymnastics. My greatest pet peeve is when my older brother taps his pencil on the kitchen table while I am studying spelling words. I wish I had a fish tank in my room. My brothers and sister are really great, but there are moments when they make me crazy!

Rewrite the paragraph above skipping the sentences that you crossed out. The new paragraph should have one topic sentence followed by the supporting sentences.

_____

_____

_____

_____

_____

_____

Do You Agree?

➡️ *The supporting sentences in a paragraph tell more about the topic.*

Write three supporting sentences to complete each paragraph.

Shorter Weeks

I think the school week should be shortened to four days for three reasons. The first reason is _____

_____

_____ Another reason is _____

_____

_____ The last reason is _____

_____

_____ I think four-day

weeks just make more sense!

Looking Back:
Now proofread your paragraph for:
     capital letters and periods
     complete sentences
     describing words
     sentences that support the topic

 **On another piece of paper, write a paragraph that begins with this topic sentence:
I think I should be able to stay up later for three reasons.**

A Great Trick

The supporting sentences should be in an order that makes sense.

Read the topic sentence, then number the supporting ideas first (1) to last (4).

Last week I played a great trick on my mom.

_____ won a huge rubber snake

_____ went to a carnival

_____ called my mom outside

_____ put snake in my mom's flower garden

Now use the topic sentence and ideas in the correct order to write a paragraph telling the story. Be sure to use complete sentences.

_____

_____

_____

_____

_____

_____

_____

 Think of a trick you have played on someone. On another piece of paper, write a topic sentence and three supporting sentences about the trick.

© Scholastic Inc.

Good to Know

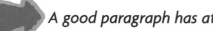 *A good paragraph has at least three supporting sentences.*

Finish the paragraphs below by writing three sentences that support each topic sentence.

Airplanes are useful in many ways. First, _____

_____

Second, _____

_____

Third, _____

_____

Life as a child today is quite different from the way it was when my

parents were young. First, _____

_____

Second, _____

_____

Third, _____

_____

Clip a topic sentence from a magazine or newspaper article. Glue it to another piece of paper and write three supporting sentences.

Closing Time!

*The last sentence in a paragraph is called the **closing sentence**.*
It retells the topic sentence in a new way.

Find a closing sentence to match each topic
sentence. Write the closing sentence.

Closing Sentences

Some gardeners in Florida and Texas can enjoy their
flowers all year long.

Of all the seasons, autumn is the best.

Life would never be the same without computers.

There are many subjects in school, but math is the
most difficult.

Though dangerous, the job of an astronaut is

1. **Fall is my favorite season in the year.**

   _____

2. **Astronauts have one of the most exciting and dangerous jobs.**

   _____

3. **Math is the toughest part of our school curriculum.**

   _____

4. **Many types of flowers grow year-round in the southern states.**

   _____

5. **Computer technology has changed many aspects of our lives.**

   _____

© Scholastic Inc.

That's All Folks!

The **closing sentence** *retells the topic sentence or main idea of a paragraph.*

Write a closing sentence for each paragraph.

All cyclists should wear helmets while riding their bikes. Many injuries occur to the head in biking accidents. Helmets could help prevent the injuries. Helmets also make cyclists more easily noticed by car drivers. _____

_____

_____

There are many things to do on a rainy day. If you like to write, you could send a letter to a friend or make a book. If you prefer craft projects, you could make a bookmark or a collage. If you really enjoy games, you could play cards or build a puzzle. _____

_____

The wheel must be one of the world's most important inventions. First, we would have no means of transportation if it were not for wheels. Second, we would not be able to enjoy many of our favorite pastimes, like in-line skating and riding a bike. Last, it would be very difficult to move heavy objects around without wheels. _____

_____

A Paragraph Plan

Follow these steps in planning a paragraph.
  1. Choose a topic (main idea).
  2. Brainstorm ideas about the topic. (You will need at least three.)
  3. Write a topic sentence.
  4. Write a closing sentence by retelling the topic sentence.

Follow this plan to write a paragraph about Ben Franklin.

1. **Ben Franklin**

2. a) **inventor of bifocal eyeglasses and Franklin stove**
   b) **scientist who proved that lightning is electricity**
   c) **involved in writing the Declaration of Independence**

3. **Ben Franklin was a man of many talents.**

4. **Ben Franklin displayed his talents in many ways.**

_____

_____

_____

_____

_____

_____

_____

_____

_____

Read your paragraph to yourself. Then add a describing word to each supporting sentence.

© Scholastic Inc.

My Very Own Paragraph

 Use a paragraph plan before you begin writing.

It is time to plan and write your own paragraph. You may want to use your own topic or one of the following topics: My Favorite Vacation, Collecting Coins, Our Pet Snake.

1. **Choose a topic.** _____

2. **Brainstorm three supporting ideas.**

    a) _____

    b) _____

    c) _____

3. **Write a topic sentence.** _____

4. **Write a closing sentence.** _____

Use the plan to write your own paragraph.

_____

_____

_____

_____

_____

_____

_____

_____

Do I Have a Story for You!

*A paragraph that tells a story is called a **narrative paragraph**. Its supporting sentences tell what happen at the beginning, middle, and end. A **story map** helps you plan the story's setting, characters, problem, and solution.*

Write a sentence about each part of the map. Then complete the plan for a narrative paragraph using the story map.

Beginning	**Middle**	**End**
setting and characters	problem	solution

_____

_____

_____

1. Write a topic sentence. _____

_____

2. Write a supporting sentence for the beginning, middle, and end.

B) _____

M) _____

E) _____

3. Write a closing sentence. _____

_____

On another piece of paper, use the plan to write a narrative paragraph.

Map It Out

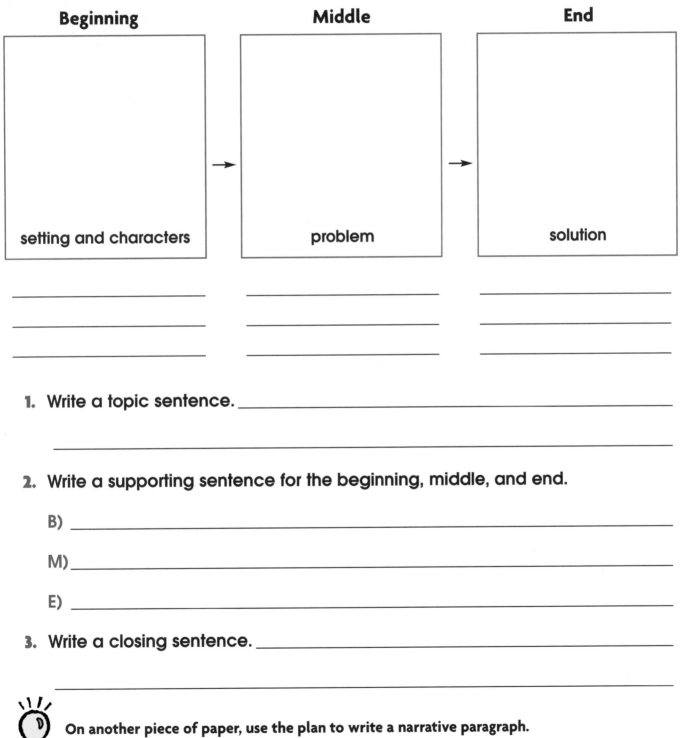

Use a story map to help plan a narrative paragraph before you begin writing.

Draw pictures to complete the map. Then use it to write a narrative paragraph.

Beginning	**Middle**	**End**
setting and characters	problem	solution

_____
_____
_____

1. Write a topic sentence. _____

_____

2. Write a supporting sentence for the beginning, middle, and end.

B) _____

M) _____

E) _____

3. Write a closing sentence. _____

_____

On another piece of paper, use the plan to write a narrative paragraph.

I'm Sure You'll Agree!

A **persuasive paragraph** *gives your opinion and tries to convince the reader to agree. Its supporting ideas are reasons that back up your opinion.*

Topic sentence
Reason 1

→ Our family should have a dog for three reasons.

First, pets teach responsibility. If we get a dog, I will

feed him and take him for walks after school. The

second reason for having a pet is that he would ← *Reason 2*

make a good companion for me when everyone else is busy. I won't

drive Dad crazy always asking him to play catch with me. The third ← *Reason 3*

reason we need a dog is for safety. He would warn us of danger and

keep our house safe. For all of these reasons, I'm sure you'll agree that

we should jump in the car and head toward the adoption agency right

away. I don't know how we have made it this long without a dog! ← *closing sentence*

Plan and write a persuasive paragraph asking your parents for something (such as a family trip, expensive new shoes, or an in-ground pool).

1. Choose a topic. _____

2. Write a topic sentence. _____

3. Brainstorm three supporting reasons.

Reason 1 _____

Reason 2 _____

Reason 3 _____

© Scholastic Inc.

On another piece of paper, use your plan to write a persuasive paragraph.

That's a Fact!

 An **expository paragraph** *provides facts or explains ideas. The supporting sentences give more details about the topic.*

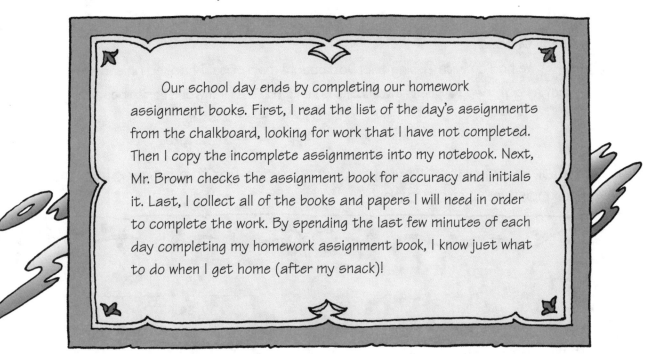

Our school day ends by completing our homework assignment books. First, I read the list of the day's assignments from the chalkboard, looking for work that I have not completed. Then I copy the incomplete assignments into my notebook. Next, Mr. Brown checks the assignment book for accuracy and initials it. Last, I collect all of the books and papers I will need in order to complete the work. By spending the last few minutes of each day completing my homework assignment book, I know just what to do when I get home (after my snack)!

Plan an expository paragraph explaining one part of your school day.

Write the topic sentence. _____

_____

List the four supporting ideas.

1) _____

2) _____

3) _____

4) _____

Write the closing sentence. _____

_____

On another piece of paper, use your plan to write an expository paragraph.

Paragraph Pen Pals

*The five parts of a **personal letter** include the date, greeting, body, closing, and signature. Notice the punctuation marks that are used in each part.*

greeting
August 13, 2003 ← *date*

→ Dear Gramps,

body → We had a great fishing trip! Dad caught two bass. I hooked an enormous catfish, but he got away. I guess Swan Lake is lucky for us. I'll always remember this trip.

Love, ← *closing*

John ← *signature*

Write a letter to an out-of-town family member. For the body of your letter, write an expository paragraph.

_____
(today's date)

_____

_____

_____

_____

_____

_____

_____

_____,

_____
(your name)

MAPS

Map Basics

A map is a drawing of a place from above. A map can show all of Earth or just a small part of it. The map on this page shows a community.

Helpful Hint

Sometimes a map key is called a legend.

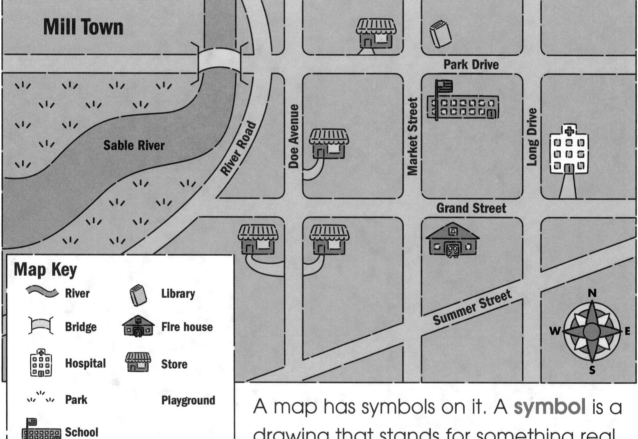

A map has symbols on it. A **symbol** is a drawing that stands for something real. A symbol can also be a color or a pattern. To learn what a map's symbols stand for, check the **map key**. The map key tells what each symbol means.

Use the map and map key to answer these questions.

1. What is the name of this community? _____

2. What does the symbol  stand for? _____

3. What is the symbol for a park? _____

4. What body of water runs through the park? _____

5. How do you get across the river? _____

6. On what street are most of the stores? _____

7. Name three buildings you would see if
   you walked along Market Street. _____

   _____

   _____

8. On what street is the hospital? _____

9. Mill Town needs a new
   playground.
   Create your own symbol in the
   space at right and then draw it
   on the map and in the key.

Understanding Directions

This picture shows a **globe**.
A globe is a model of Earth.
A globe is the same shape as
Earth but much smaller.

Read the labels on the globe.
The North and South poles help
you tell directions. North is toward
the North Pole. South is toward the
South Pole. When you face north,
east is to your right. West is to your left.

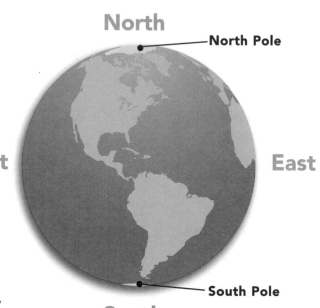

A compass rose is a symbol that
shows the four main directions on a map.
On a compass rose the letters **N**, **S**, **E**,
and **W** stand for the four directions.

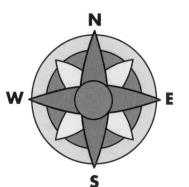

Complete these sentences.

1. The most northern place on the globe is the _____.

2. The _____ is the most southern place on a globe.

3. On a compass rose, the letter W stands for _____.

4. The direction East is sometimes written as _____ on a
    compass rose.

Helpful Hint

The four main directions are known as "cardinal" directions.

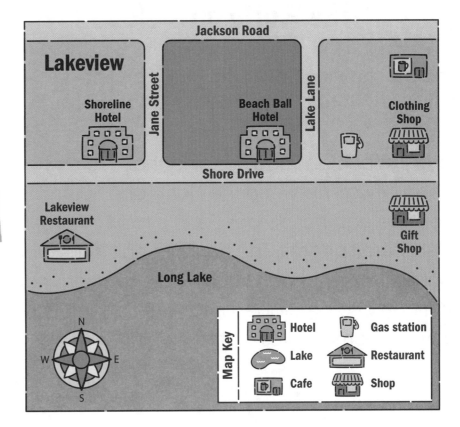

This map shows Lakeview. Use the compass rose to help answer these questions.

1. Is the lake on the north or south side of Lakeview?

_____

2. In which direction are the hotels from the lake?

_____

3. In which direction is the gift shop from the restaurant?

_____

4. Can you go north on Jackson Road? _____

5. What building is east of the gas station? _____

Word Search

Find and circle the four main directions.

R	E	A	S	T
H	T	R	O	N
L	S	Q	U	Z
O	E	N	T	Y
P	W	Y	H	L

© Scholastic Inc.

The World on a Globe

A globe shows all of Earth. You can see Earth's continents and oceans on a globe.

The **equator** is an imaginary line that circles the globe halfway between the North and South poles. The equator divides Earth into two halves called **hemispheres**. The northern half is the Northern Hemisphere. What do you think the southern half is called? Earth can also be divided into Western and Eastern Hemispheres. Study the hemispheres on the globes.

Helpful Hint

"Hemi" means half. A "hemisphere" is half of a sphere.

1. Does the equator run through North America? _____

2. What are the seven continents? _____

3. What are the five oceans? _____

4. In what hemispheres is most of South America? _____

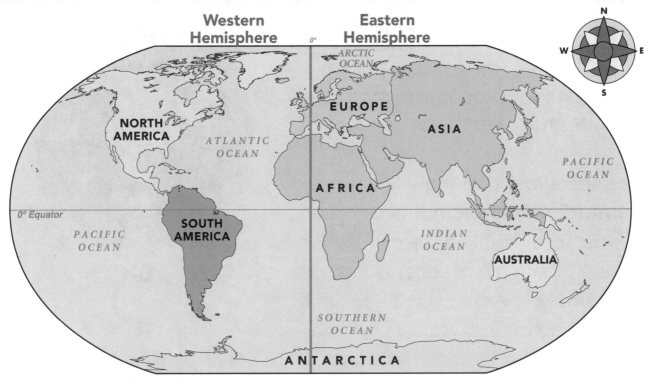

A globe is the best way to show what Earth looks like. However, globes are not so easy to carry around. So people use flat maps to represent Earth, too. Study the globes and map, then answer the questions.

1. Is Asia in the Eastern or Western Hemisphere? _____

2. What ocean is entirely north of the equator? _____

3. On the map, is east to the right or to the left? _____

4. The North Pole is at the _____ of the globe.

5. The area south of the
   equator is called the Southern _____ .

Code Word Fill in the blanks with the first letter of the answers for questions 1-5 to figure out the secret code word.

_____ _____ _____ _____ _____
1.   2.   3.   4.   5.

Intermediate Directions

You know that a compass rose has four main directions.

A compass rose can show **intermediate directions**, too. Intermediate directions are between the main directions. For example, the direction between north and west is northwest. Letters sometimes stand for the intermediate directions on a compass rose. For example, NE stands for northeast.

Answer these questions.

1. What direction is between south and east?_____

2. What direction is between north and east?_____

3. What direction is opposite of northwest? _____

4. What do the letters NW stand for on a compass rose? _____

5. What letters stand for southwest? _____

This map shows an **intersection**.

An intersection is where two roads cross.

Find the bank on the map. It is east of Water Street and north of Central Avenue. So the bank is on the northeast corner of the intersection.

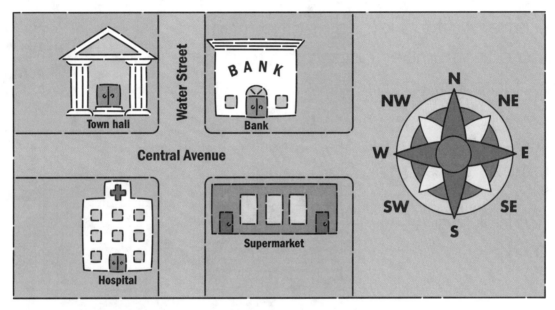

Color each compass rose to show the correct direction.

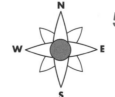

1. In what direction is the town hall from the hospital?

2. On which corner is the supermarket?

3. On which corner is the hospital?

4. You ran out of money at the supermarket. In which direction do you go to get more?

5. In which direction would you go from the supermarket to the town hall?

Using a Map Grid

Some maps have a **grid** on them.

A grid is a pattern of lines that cross to form squares.
Each square on a grid has a letter and a number.
Find the letter A at the left side of the map.
Then locate the number 1 along the top of the map.
The first square in the top row is A1. Now find A2.

Helpful Hint
A grid makes it easier to pinpoint places on a map.

Use the map to
answer these questions.

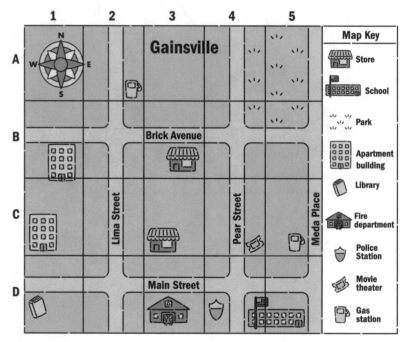

1. What building is in D1?

   _____

2. In which square is the police station?

   _____

3. Name all the squares that Lima Street runs through.

   _____

4. In which squares is the school located? _____

5. Can you buy gas in C5? _____

Sometimes a map has letters and numbers along the side and top, but no grid lines. Then you must imagine where the lines go. For example, look in B1 and C1 to find the apartment buildings in Gainsville.

Use the map to answer these questions.

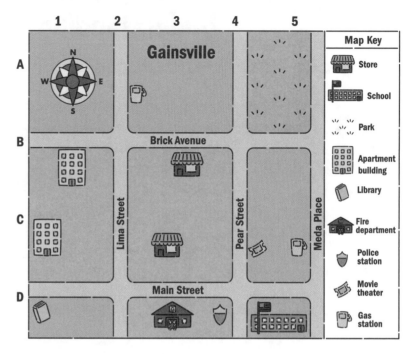

1. What building is in D3? _____

2. Find the park in A4. In what other square is the park? _____

3. What squares does Meda Place run through? _____

4. What is in C3? _____

5. Find C4. What can you do there? _____

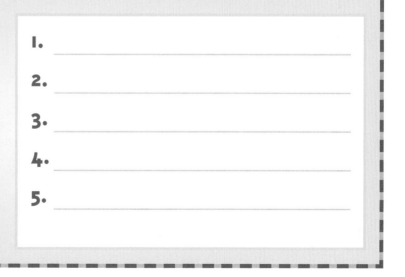

My Tour of Gainsville

Pretend you are giving a new friend a tour of Gainsville. You visit the squares in this order: C1, D1, C3, A4, C4. Write a list describing the places you will visit.

1. _____

2. _____

3. _____

4. _____

5. _____

Understanding Distance

A map can show where places are in relation to one another.

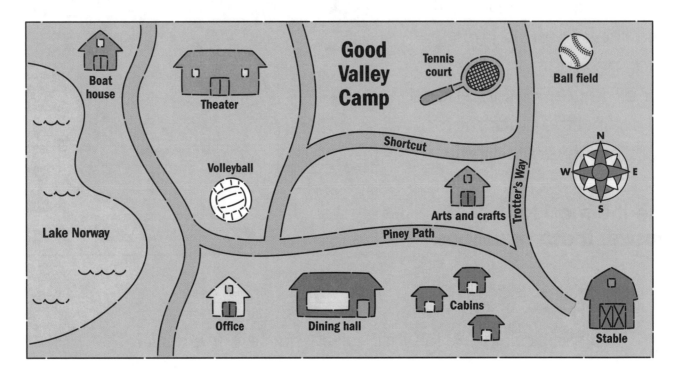

Use the map to answer these questions.

1. What is the nearest building to the lake? _____

2. What building is farthest from the theater? _____

3. What is the nearest building to
    the west of the dining hall? _____

4. What is the nearest building to
    the north of the cabins? _____

5. Is the volleyball court nearer
    the ball field or the tennis court? _____

A map can show **distance**, or how far it is from one place to another. This map has lines between the towns. The number on each line tells how many miles it is from one town to another. For example, it is 20 miles from Dover to Clark City.

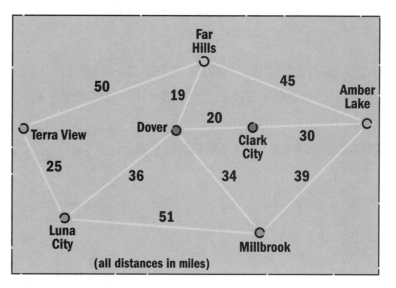

(all distances in miles)

1. How far is it from Terra View to Luna City? _____

2. How many miles is Amber Lake from Far Hills? _____

3. Will it take longer to drive from Millbrook to Luna City or from Millbrook to Dover? _____

4. What is the shortest way from Clark City to Terra View? _____

    How many miles would it be? _____

5. What is the closest town to Dover? _____

Distance is one thing that you need to know when you plan a trip. Other things make a difference, too. For example, it takes longer to drive over a mountain than it does to cross a plain. Draw a picture of something else that could make a car trip take longer.

Learning About Scale

A map is not the same size as the place it shows. It is much smaller. Places on a map are inches or less apart. To show distance on a map, mapmakers use a **scale**.

A scale is a kind of ruler that helps you measure distance on a map. Look at the scale on this map. It shows that one inch equals ten feet. That means one inch on the map stands for ten feet of the real place.

Room 310

0   5   10
scale: 1 inch = 10 feet

printer

hamsters

desk   desk

fish   desk   desk   computer

desk   book-case   desk

plants   desk   desk

N
W   E
S

teacher's desk   lockers

Use a ruler to measure the distances on the map.

1. How many feet is the classroom from the east side to the west side? _____

2. How far is the bookcase from the door? _____

3. How far is the teacher's desk from the lockers? _____

4. How far are the fish from the computer? _____

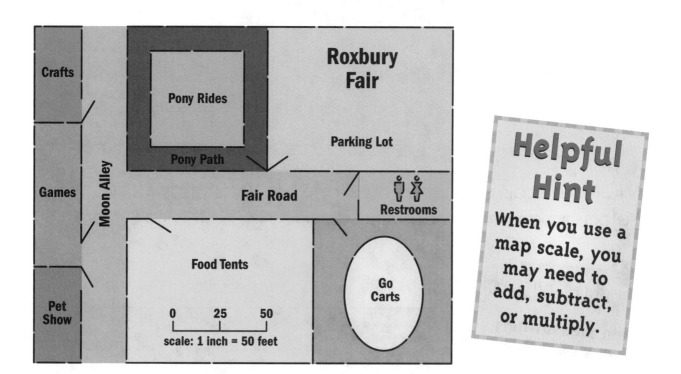

Always check the map scale to find the distance it represents. Use a ruler to help you answer these questions.

1. How long is Fair Road? _____

2. How wide is the parking lot? _____

3. About how many feet is it from
    the games entrance to the crafts entrance? _____

4. How far is it from the pet show
    entrance to the gate of the go carts? _____

5. If a pony goes once around the
    pony path, how far does it go? _____

Using a Map Scale

A map scale often looks like this:

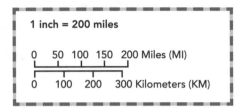

1 inch = 200 miles

0   50 100 150   200 Miles (MI)

0   100   200   300 Kilometers (KM)

The MI on the scale stands for miles, and the KM stands for kilometers. Kilometers are a way of measuring distance in the Metric System.

Helpful Hint

When measuring distance on a map, always line up the end of the ruler with the "zero" on the map scale.

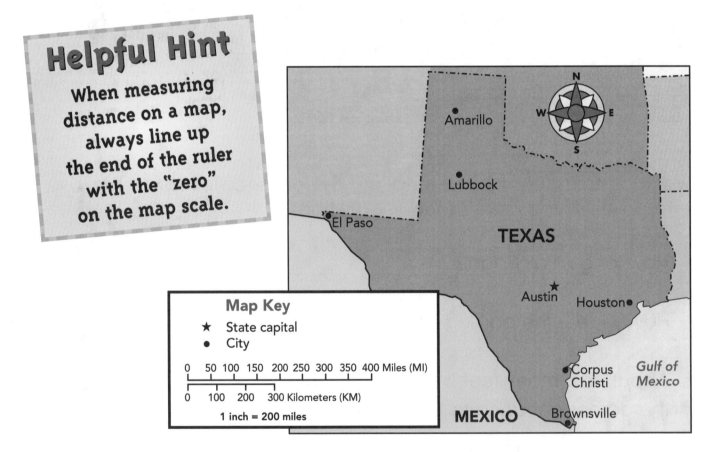

Map Key

★ State capital
● City

0   50 100 150 200 250 300 350 400 Miles (MI)

0   100   200   300 Kilometers (KM)

1 inch = 200 miles

Use the map scale to answer these questions.

1. From Houston to Austin it is about _____ miles.

2. Corpus Christi is about _____ miles from Houston.

3. Lubbock is about _____ miles from El Paso.

4. Is a kilometer longer or shorter than a mile? _____

5. It is a little less than 450 miles from Austin to _____ .

6. Are Brownsville and Corpus Christi more or less than 150 miles apart? _____

7. Corpus Christi and Austin are about 300 _____ apart.

8. From the capital of Texas to El Paso it is about _____ miles.

9. From its most northern part to its most southern part, Texas is about _____ miles long.

10. The widest part of Texas is about 1,200 _____ across.

Helpful Hint

If you don't have a ruler, lay the edge of a piece of paper along the map scale. Mark the paper, then use it to measure distances on the map.

Word Search

Find and circle four Texas cities.

N	O	R	A	O	Z	X	L	Y
A	S	L	U	B	B	O	C	K
M	A	V	S	K	Y	E	G	J
S	P	T	T	L	P	S	U	W
O	L	L	I	R	A	M	A	O
T	E	Q	N	H	O	X	F	B

Comparing Maps

Maps can show places of different sizes.

Look at the maps on these pages. One map shows a state. One map shows a country, and the third map shows a continent.

Helpful Hint

Even on maps with different scales, the distance between two places is always the same.

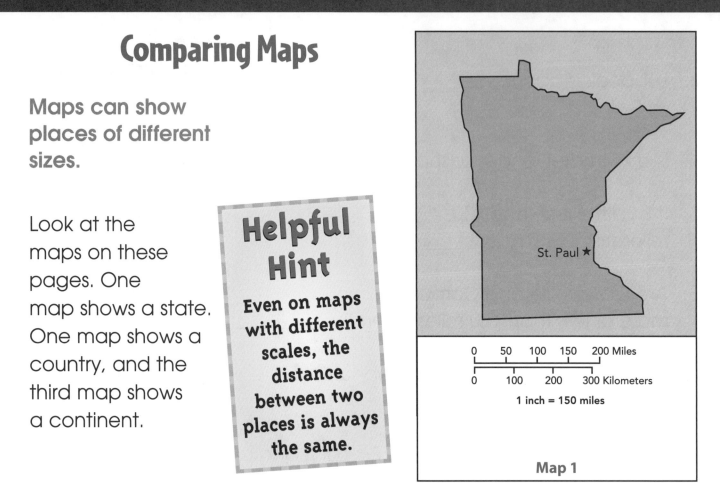

0   50   100   150   200 Miles
0   100   200   300 Kilometers
1 inch = 150 miles

Map 1

Use the maps to answer these questions.

1. What state does Map 1 show? _____

2. What does one inch stand for on the scale for Map 1? _____

3. The abbreviation for this state is MN. Find it on Map 2. Does Map 1 or Map 2 cover a larger area? _____

4. What does one inch stand for on Map 2? _____

5. About how many miles is it from the coast of California (CA) to the coast of Virginia (VA)? _____

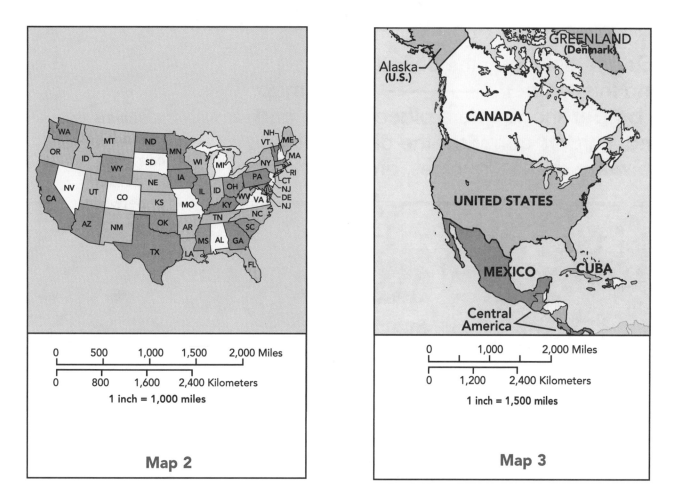

0   500   1,000 1,500   2,000 Miles

0   800   1,600   2,400 Kilometers
1 inch = 1,000 miles

Map 2

0   1,000   2,000 Miles

0   1,200   2,400 Kilometers
1 inch = 1,500 miles

Map 3

6. What does one inch stand for on Map 3?_____

7. What does Map 3 show?_____

8. Which of the maps shows the largest area? _____

9. Which of the maps shows the smallest area? _____

10. On Map 3, draw a box that shows the area shown on Map 2.
    Then draw another box on the map to show the area on Map 1.

The United States

You are looking at the United States.
Find this symbol ——————— on the map.
A **border** shows where places begin and
end. Borders can show the dividing lines
between states, countries, and other places.

Rivers
and lakes
can also form
borders
between
places.

Read the map, then answer these questions.

1. Find Alabama. What state shares
   a border with it on the west? _____

2. Find Colorado. What states share
   a border with it on the east? _____

3. What lake forms part of the
   northwest border of Pennsylvania?

   _____

4. What river forms the western
   border of Tennessee?

   _____

Helpful Hint

Two states do not touch any other states. Both of these states are far from the rest of the country. These states are shown in small boxes called inset maps.

5. Which states are shown
   in the inset maps? _____

6. What is the capital of Alaska? _____

7. Hawaii is in the Pacific Ocean.
   In which direction is it from California? _____

"Speedy Map Planner"

Imagine that you are taking a trip from the Atlantic Ocean to the Pacific Ocean. Plan a route that passes through the fewest number of states possible. Can you do it in less than eight states? Write the states on the chart.

1. _____   5. _____

2. _____   6. _____

3. _____   7. _____

4. _____   8. _____

© Scholastic Inc.

North America

The United States is on the continent of North America.

Two countries, Canada and Mexico, share borders with the United States. North America also includes Greenland, the countries of Central America, and many islands.

Helpful Hint

One state, Hawaii, is not part of North America.

Use the map to answer these questions about North America.

1. In which direction is Mexico from the United States? _____

2. Name two other countries that share a border with Mexico. _____

3. What country shares a border on the north with the United States? _____

4. What state is on the northwest part of North America? _____

5. What oceans border the east and west coasts of North America? _____

6. What ocean is north of this continent? _____

7. What is the capital of Canada? _____

8. What river forms part of the border between the U.S. and Mexico? _____

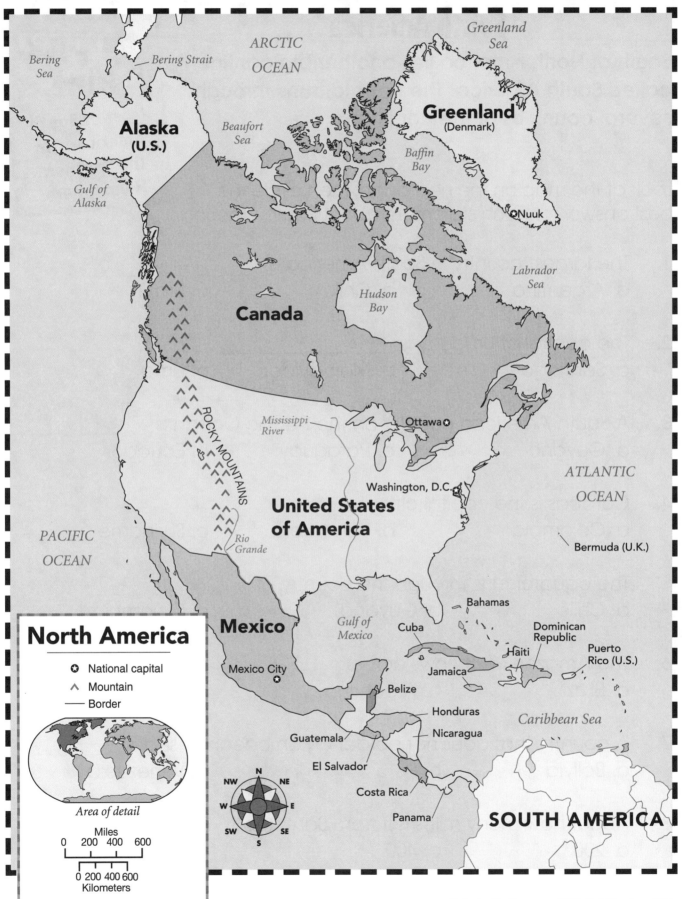

ARCTIC OCEAN

Greenland Sea

Bering Sea

Bering Strait

Alaska (U.S.)

Beaufort Sea

Greenland (Denmark)

Baffin Bay

Gulf of Alaska

Nuuk

Labrador Sea

Hudson Bay

Canada

ROCKY MOUNTAINS

Mississippi River

Ottawa

ATLANTIC OCEAN

United States of America

Washington, D.C.

PACIFIC OCEAN

Rio Grande

Bermuda (U.K.)

Bahamas

Mexico

Gulf of Mexico

Cuba

Dominican Republic

Mexico City

Haiti

Puerto Rico (U.S.)

Jamaica

Belize

Honduras

Guatemala

Nicaragua

Caribbean Sea

El Salvador

Costa Rica

Panama

SOUTH AMERICA

North America

- ✪ National capital
- ⋀ Mountain
- — Border

Area of detail

Miles
0 200 400 600

0 200 400 600
Kilometers

N
NW NE
W E
SW SE
S

South America

South of North America lies another big continent called South America. The equator runs through several countries of this continent.

Helpful Hint

Most of South America is in the Southern Hemisphere.

Look at the map on the next page. Then circle the best answer for each statement about South America.

1. The largest country in South America is _____.
   a. Argentina   b. Chile   c. Brazil

2. The capital of Uruguay is _____.
   a. Santiago   b. Montevideo   c. Lima

3. A South American country on the Pacific Ocean is _____.
   a. Guyana   b. Paraguay   c. Ecuador

4. Caracas is the capital city of _____.
   a. Colombia   b. Venezuela   c. Suriname

5. The equator runs through the country of _____.
   a. Chile   b. Guyana   c. Colombia

6. The Amazon River flows across _____.
   a. Brazil   b. Argentina   c. Paraguay

7. A country that does not border on an ocean or sea is _____.
   a. Bolivia   b. Peru   c. Venezuela

8. About how many miles is it from Santiago to Montevideo? _____.
   a. 200   b. 400   c. 900

Caribbean Sea

Dominica

Trinidad and Tobago

ATLANTIC
OCEAN

Caracas

Venezuela

Guyana

Georgetown

Paramaribo

Orinoco River

Suriname   Cayenne

Bogota

French Guiana

Colombia

Equator

Quito

Ecuador

Amazon River

Galapagos Islands
(Ecuador)

Peru

Brazil

Lima

Bolivia

Brasília

La Paz

Sucre

Paraná River

PACIFIC
OCEAN

Paraguay

ANDES MOUNTAINS

Asunción

South America

⊙ National capital

⋀ Mountain

— Border

Uruguay

Santiago

Montevideo

Buenos Aires

Area of detail

Argentina

Chile

N
NW   NE
W   E
SW   SE
S

Miles

0   200   400   600

0   200 400 600

Falkland
Islands (U.K.)

Landforms

Maps are usually drawn on paper, so the land looks flat. But you know that Earth's land is not always flat. In fact, the land takes many shapes called **landforms**. The pictures show some important landforms.

A **plain** is open, flat land.

A **mountain** is very high land with steep slopes.

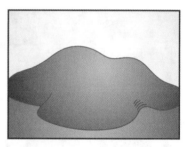

A **hill** is land that is higher than a plain but not as high or steep as a mountain.

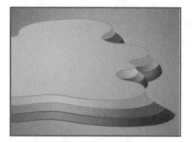

A **plateau** is high, flat land.

A **valley** is low land between mountains or hills. Rivers often run through a valley.

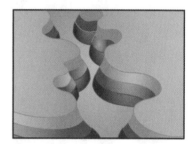

A **canyon** is a narrow valley with high, steep sides. Rivers sometimes flow through canyons, too.

Use the pictures to answer these questions.

1. Which landforms are high land? _____

2. Which landforms are low places? _____

3. How are a canyon and a valley alike? _____

How are they different? _____

More than half of Earth is covered with water.

You have learned about some of these bodies of water such as oceans, rivers, and lakes. The picture shows some other bodies of water and some other landforms.

Use the maps to help answer the questions.

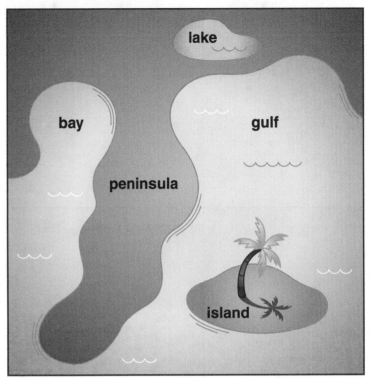

A **gulf** is part of an ocean or sea. A gulf is partly surrounded by land.

A **bay** is like a gulf but smaller.

An **island** is land that is completely surrounded by water.

A **peninsula** is an "almost island." It is land that is surrounded by water on all but one side.

1. Why might a bay be a good place to keep a boat? _____

2. How is a bay like a gulf? _____

3. Find Florida on the map on page 224. What landform is Florida? _____

4. How is a peninsula different from an island? _____

5. In what way are a lake and an island similar? _____

Using a Landform Map

This is a landform map of Arkansas.

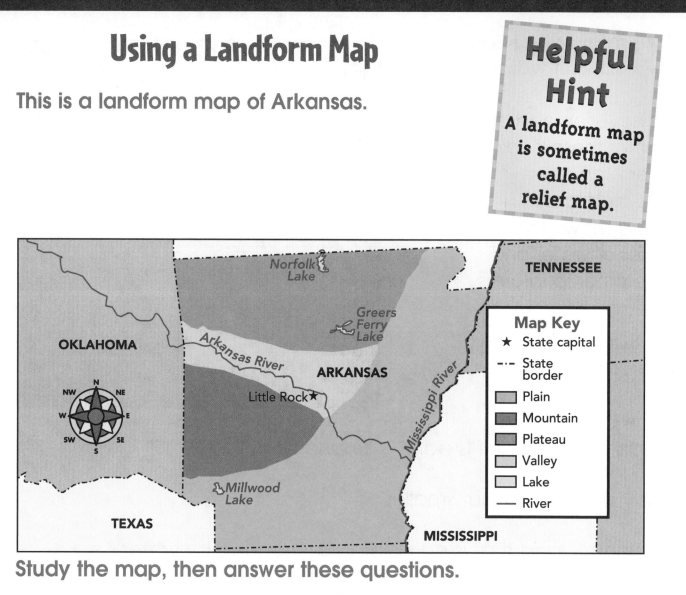

Study the map, then answer these questions.

1. What does the symbol [ ] stand for? _____

2. What is the symbol for mountains? _____

3. What landform covers most of the northern part of the state? _____

4. What body of water forms the eastern border of Arkansas? _____

5. In which parts of the state would you find plains? _____

© Scholastic Inc.

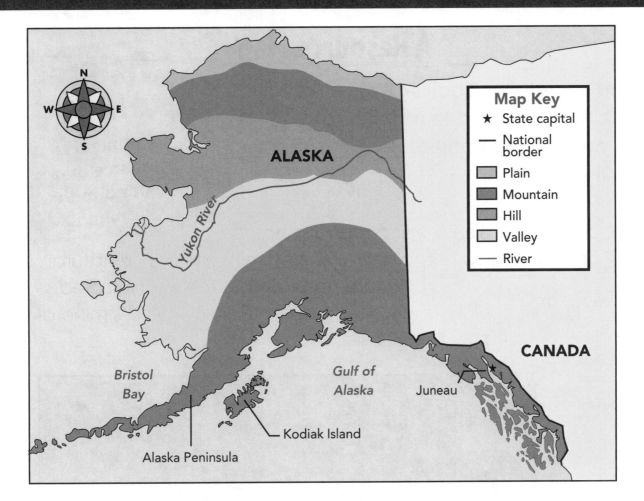

This map shows the landforms of Alaska.
Study the map, then answer these questions.

1. In which part of Alaska are there plains?

    _____

2. Name a large island off the
    southern part of the state.

    _____

3. What is the land that extends from the
    southwest part of the state called?

    _____

4. On what kind of land is Alaska's capital?

    _____

5. What river runs across the state?

    _____

A Resource Map

Do you know what coal is? It's a kind of rock that is burned to make heat and energy. Coal is just one of Pennsylvania's **natural resources**.

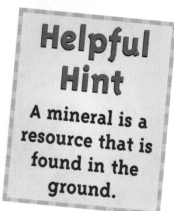

A natural resource is something found in nature that people use. Air, water, plants, soil, and minerals are all natural resources. A map can show where natural resources are located. The map on this page shows where some of Pennsylvania's mineral resources are found.

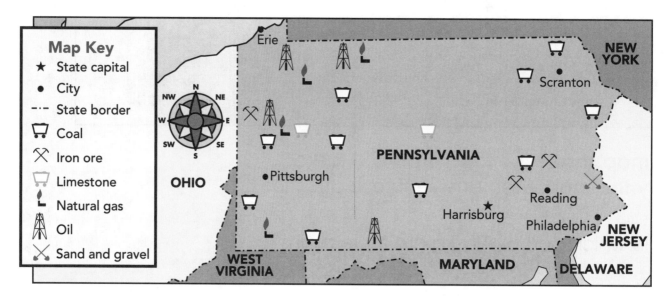

Answer these questions.

1. How are natural resources helpful to people? _____

_____

2. What are some ways people use sand and gravel? _____

3. Why is a flame a good symbol for natural gas? _____

© Scholastic Inc.

Much of Pennsylvania's coal
is burned to make electricity.

**Write TRUE or FALSE on the line.
Use the map on the previous
page to help you.**

_____ 1. Most of Pennsylvania's oil is in the northwest
            part of the state.

_____ 2. Sand and gravel are found in the east.

_____ 3. Most of the state's iron ore is in the north.

_____ 4. Pennsylvania has no natural gas.

_____ 5. Pennsylvania has more coal than oil.

_____ 6. The symbol ⬡ stands for oil.

An Amazing Journey

Use this
Pennsylvania
maze to get
from
Philadelphia
to the oil
field in the
northwest.

FINISH

START

A Rainfall Map

Water is the most important natural resource. Plants, animals, and people all need water. Water falls to Earth as rain, snow, sleet, and hail.

This map is called a rainfall map. It shows how much water falls in the different parts of Maine during one year.

Helpful Hint

Another word for rainfall is precipitation.

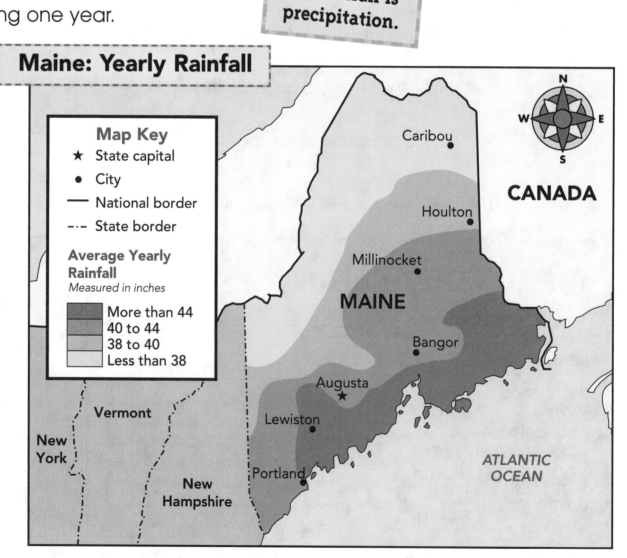

Maine: Yearly Rainfall

Map Key
★ State capital
● City
— National border
-·- State border

Average Yearly Rainfall
Measured in inches
More than 44
40 to 44
38 to 40
Less than 38

Caribou

CANADA

Houlton

Millinocket

MAINE

Bangor

Augusta

Lewiston

Vermont

New York

New Hampshire

Portland

ATLANTIC OCEAN

© Scholastic Inc.

People use water to drink and to bathe. Water is also important for growing crops, washing things, and running machines.

Use the map to answer these questions.

1. This symbol ▭ stands for _____ inches.

2. The least amount of rain in Maine falls in the _____ parts of the state.

3. Bangor gets about _____ inches of rain a year.

4. A city in Maine that gets 38 to 40 inches of rain a year is _____ .

5. The city on this map that gets the most rain is _____ .

6. The rainfall in Houlton is _____ than in Caribou.

7. You can guess that the part of Canada near the northwest part of Maine gets _____ inches of rain a year.

Connect the words to the correct symbols.

1. rain   2. snow   3. sleet   4. hail

A History Map

You can learn about the past from a map. The map below shows the Oregon Trail. This was a route that pioneers followed when they traveled west in the 1840s. A route is a way to go from one place to another.

In the 1840s people did not have airplanes or cars. They traveled in covered wagons pulled by oxen. Some pioneers rode on horses or walked alongside the wagons. Most pioneers met in Independence, Missouri, and formed groups. The groups traveled together in wagon trains.

Oregon Trail

Map Key
- • City or town
- — Oregon Trail
- — River
- ⛰ Mountain

Use the map to answer these questions.

1. In what direction did the trail go
    from Independence to Portland?_____

2. What river flows by Independence?_____

3. After Independence, what was the
    first town along the trail?
    _____

4. What mountains did the Oregon Trail cross? _____

5. Find Three Island Crossing. On what river is it? _____

6. Why do you think the Oregon Trail
    does not follow a straight line? _____

7. The wagon trains left Independence in May for
    the five-month trip. Why do you think it was
    important to start then?_____

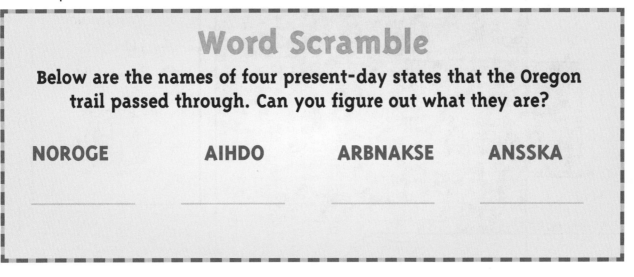

Word Scramble

**Below are the names of four present-day states that the Oregon
trail passed through. Can you figure out what they are?**

NOROGE   **AIHDO**   **ARBNAKSE**   **ANSSKA**

_____   _____   _____   _____

A Tourist Map

A tourist is someone who travels for fun.

If you have ever been a tourist, you know that it is handy to have a map of the place you are visiting. A **tourist map** shows a place of interest and highlights the special things to see and do there.

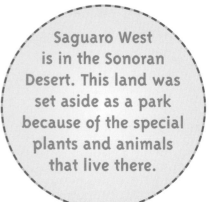

Saguaro West is in the Sonoran Desert. This land was set aside as a park because of the special plants and animals that live there.

This map shows a large park in Arizona called Saguaro West.

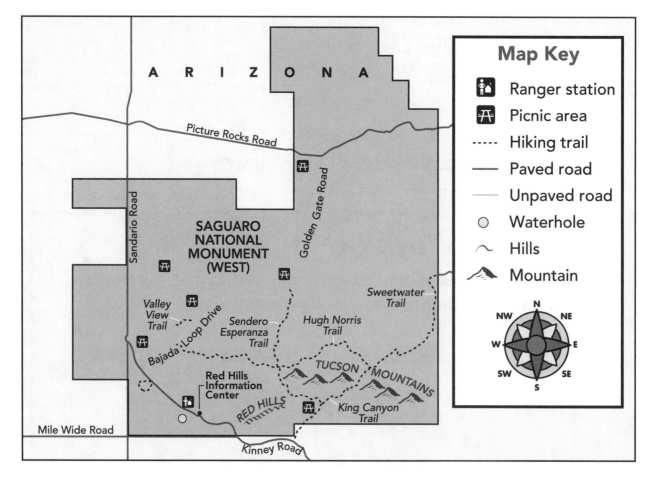

© Scholastic Inc.

Study the map, then answer these questions.

Helpful Hint

Saguaro is the name of a large cactus.

1. What does the symbol ⛺ mean? _____

2. In what part of the park is the Ranger Station? _____

3. From the Ranger Station, how would you drive to the northernmost picnic area? _____

    _____

4. What kind of plants would you expect to see in this park? _____

    _____

5. What does this symbol ○ mean? _____

   Why might animals come there? _____

6. What road cuts through the park on the west side going from north to south? _____

A City Map

Welcome to New York City!
Part of this city is on the island of Manhattan. The map shows some of the main streets in Manhattan. Use the map to answer the questions.

1. What river runs along the west side of Manhattan?

   _____

   Along the east side?

   _____

2. The direction the streets run is from _____ to _____ .

3. The avenues run from

   _____ to _____ .

4. One of the oldest streets is Wall Street. In which part of Manhattan is it?

   _____

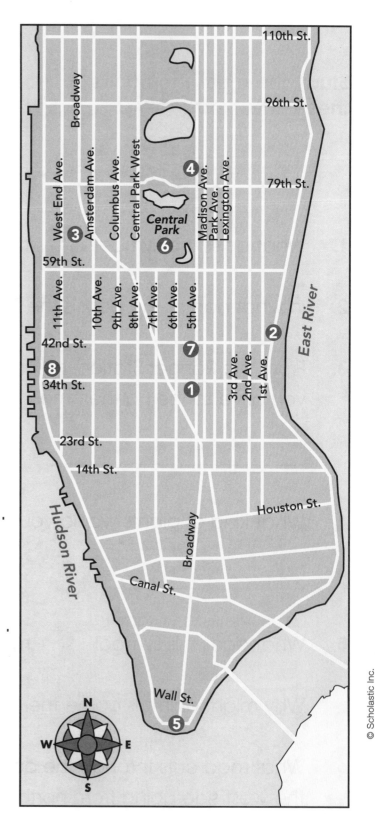

© Scholastic Inc.

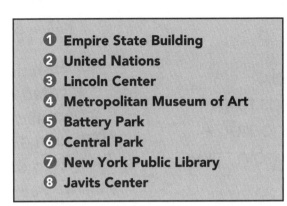

1. Empire State Building
2. United Nations
3. Lincoln Center
4. Metropolitan Museum of Art
5. Battery Park
6. Central Park
7. New York Public Library
8. Javits Center

Helpful Hint

As you move north in Manhattan, the numbers of the streets get higher.

Many of New York's streets form a grid pattern.
This grid makes it easier to find places in the city. For example, the Empire State Building is on the corner of Fifth Avenue and 34th Street. Use the map to answer the questions.

5. What street runs along the southern part of Central Park? _____

   What avenues run along the east and west sides of the park? _____

6. Find the New York Public Library. On what corner is it found? _____

7. On which side of the city is the United Nations? _____

8. Find the Empire State Building. In which direction would you walk to get to the Javits Center? _____

9. Why do you think the streets of New York City are numbered?

   _____

A Transit Map

How do you get to school? How do people in your family get to work?

In many communities people use public transportation. They take buses or trains to get from one part of the community to another. A **transit map** shows the route a bus or train takes.

Helpful Hint

San Francisco is located on a peninsula between San Francisco Bay and the Pacific Ocean.

The transit map on this page shows BART trains in San Francisco, California. BART stands for Bay Area Rapid Transit. The map shows the routes that BART trains take to connect San Francisco to communities around it.

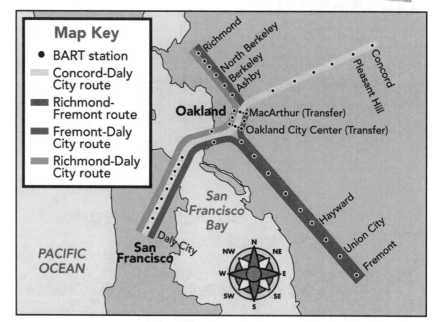

Map Key

- • BART station
- Concord-Daly City route
- Richmond-Fremont route
- Fremont-Daly City route
- Richmond-Daly City route

Use the map to answer these questions.

1. What does this symbol ▬▬▬ stand for on this map? _____

2. What color is the Richmond-Fremont Route? _____

3. On what line is the Pleasant Hill stop? _____

The BART lines come together and form a kind of X.
Find the Oakland City Center stop. Do you see the word "transfer" after it? At a transfer stop, passengers can change from one line to another.

4.   Can you travel on the same train to get from Concord to Daly City? _____

5.   What are the stops at the end of each BART line? _____

_____

6.   What is special about the MacArthur stop? _____

7.   What BART line does not go into San Francisco? _____

8.   In which direction do the BART lines go from Daly City to Oakland? _____

9.   What body of water do three of the BART lines cross? _____

_____

10.   Without BART, how do you think people could get from Oakland to San Francisco? _____

Design a Symbol

BART is looking for a new symbol to show transfer stations on its map. Use this space to draw your own symbol.

Map Review 1

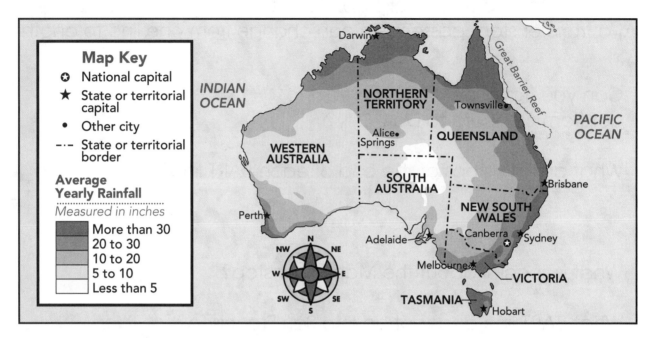

Use the map to answer the questions.

1. What does the symbol ☐ stand for? _____

2. Does Australia get more rain along the coasts or inland?

   _____

3. About how much rain a year does Alice Springs get?

   _____

4. Part of Australia is desert. About how much rain do you think this part of the country gets?

   _____

5. What is the national capital of Australia? _____

6. What oceans surround Australia? _____

7. On which part of the continent is New South Wales?

   _____

8. Check the words that are true for Australia:

   _____ continent
   _____ country
   _____ island

Scholastic Success With
SCIENCE

Fascinating Frogs

Read the article about frogs.
Then follow the directions in the Text Marking box.

In the fairy tale *The Frog Prince*, an ugly frog kisses a princess and then turns into a handsome prince. They marry and live happily ever after. In real life, frogs don't kiss princesses, but they are otherwise remarkable animals.

Frogs are amphibians. All amphibians are cold-blooded—their bodies have the same temperature as the air or water they live in. Amphibians have backbones, no scales, and moist skin. Frogs begin their lives in calm water as eggs and then as tadpoles.

But that just defines frogs. What is interesting is that there are more than 6,300 species of frog! Some are as small as flies, while others are big enough to eat small snakes, mice, and other frogs. Some frogs can jump 10 feet. Some live more than 20 years.

Also interesting is how long frogs have been around. Herpetologists (HUR-puh-tol-oh-jists)—the scientists who study amphibians and reptiles—know that frogs have existed for at least 200 million years! They were here along with the dinosaurs.

European tree frog

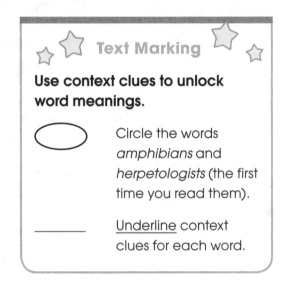

Text Marking

Use context clues to unlock word meanings.

◯ Circle the words *amphibians* and *herpetologists* (the first time you read them).

____ Underline context clues for each word.

© Scholastic Inc.

Answer each question. Give evidence from the article.

1. Which of the following has the same meaning as *moist* (paragraph 2)?

    ○ A. dry   ○ B. damp   ○ C. scaly   ○ D. lumpy

What in the text helped you answer?

_____

_____

2 Which of the following is NOT true about frogs?

    ○ A. They have scales.   ○ C. Young frogs are called tadpoles.

    ○ B. They have backbones.   ○ D. Frogs have been around for millions of years.

What in the text helped you answer?

_____

_____

3. How do you know that frogs are cold-blooded?

_____

_____

_____

4. Why do you think the author began this article by describing a fairy tale?

_____

_____

_____

_____

Which Equine?

**Read the article about horses and ponies.
Then follow the directions in the Text Marking box.**

Ponies are not baby horses, though people often think they are. In fact, horses and ponies are different animals in the same family. Both are *equines* (E-kwīnz). Let's compare them.

All equines are mammals. Horses and ponies are warm-blooded. They have backbones and skin covered with hair. Their babies are born live and nurse on the mother's milk. Both horses and ponies can be used for riding, doing farm work, or pulling wagons. Both graze to eat a plant-based diet. They enjoy hay, grass, leaves, fruits, vegetables, and oats.

But these two equines differ in several ways. The key contrast is in their heights. An equine is a horse if it's 58 or more inches tall at the shoulder. Ponies rarely get that tall. They have shorter legs, necks, and heads, and wider bodies than horses do. Ponies cope with cold weather better than horses do because they have thicker manes and coats.

Horses and ponies do not behave the same either. Both can be smart and stubborn, but ponies usually stay calmer than horses do.

Two full-grown equines—pony (left), horse (right)

Text Marking

Compare and contrast horses and ponies.

☐ Box at least three signal words or phrases such as **both** or **differ** that compare or contrast.

◯ Circle at least three ways they are alike.

_____ Underline at least three ways they are different.

© Scholastic Inc.

Answer each question. Give evidence from the article.

1. Which of the following is not true about *mammals* (paragraph 2)?

○ A. They have hair.   ○ C. They are cold-blooded.

○ B. They have backbones.   ○ D. Their babies drink milk.

What in the text helped you answer?

_____

_____

2. Which is the most important way that horses and ponies are different?

○ A. Ponies have wider   ○ C. Ponies cannot pull wagons.
    bodies than horses do.

○ B. Ponies are shorter than horses.   ○ D. Horses do not eat plants.

What in the text helped you answer?

_____

_____

3. In your own words, explain the difference between a pony and a baby horse.

_____

_____

4. Why don't horses cope as well in cold weather as ponies do?

_____

_____

_____

Animals of Africa

Find these words in the puzzle.

AARDVARK	ANTELOPE	CROCODILE	CHEETAH	
FLAMINGO	GIRAFFE	GORILLA	HYENA	LEOPARD
LION	MEERKAT	OSTRICH	RHINOCEROS	ZEBRA

```
G N M E E R K A T M K N A G K S W A R C
A S W D V F R N F P S C N T H F T A H R
Z Q U E T D S E D I A W T I P A T R B O
N P A D A X I C H L U M E R L I S D O C
A L E R K Y B T H A Y E L S E V H X X O
F L A M I N G O D N E N O Z E B R A P D
X A C O A L O R T A I T P W E C D R F I
Q Y X C D B R H I N O C E R O S I K T L
A D F Y I H I E R T Y H O S G U E T R E
Z L X C O R L F R K D E G P S D N B S M
L I O N D S L P O R A E H G I R A F F E
W O H Y E N A L O R N T C D R C A S A M
M T D N A G T E N O R A T F P R D S W E
A S D E M O S T R I C H U L E O P A R D
```

On a separate sheet of paper write about an African animal that you have seen in real life. For example, you might have seen the animal at an animal sanctuary.

Saving Moto

Read about what a baby wildcat needs to survive on its own. Then try the science investigations.

A wildfire burned through grasslands in Africa. When the fire died out, some people found baby Moto. This little wildcat was all alone and covered in ashes. A wildlife photographer named Suzi took care of him. How did Suzi know what to do? She thought about wildcats and what they need to grow.

Suzi gave Moto milk from a bottle. After a few weeks, she started feeding him raw chicken. She also served him dead rats. That's what he would have eaten in the wild.

Then Suzi taught Moto how to hunt. Soon he could kill his own prey. That's important. Moto needed to do that so he could survive on his own. After six months, Moto went back into the wild.

Investigation 1

Dried yeast is actually a bunch of tiny living things. What does yeast need to live? Find out!

© Scholastic Inc.

1. Gather the materials you will need.

2. Measure ¼ tsp of dried yeast into each of the four sandwich bags.

3. Press out most of the air and seal one bag. Label this bag "Control." Look at the yeast with a magnifying glass. In this form, yeast is not active. What do you think it needs to be active? (**Hint:** What do other living things need?)

4. To another bag, add 1 tsp flour. Press out most of the air and seal the bag. Label it "Food."

5. To another bag, add ¼ cup warm water. Carefully press out most of the air and seal the bag. Label it "Water."

6. To the last bag, add 1 tsp flour. Then add ¼ cup warm water. Press out most of the air and seal the bag. Label it "Food and Water."

7. Gently shake each bag to mix. Then set the bags next to one another on a table. Look at each bag closely. What do you observe? Record on the next page.

8. Wait 15 minutes, then observe. What changes do you see? (**Hint:** When yeast "eats," it gives off gas. Do you see any gas bubbles?)

9. Wait 15 more minutes and observe again. What does yeast need to live?

Materials

- ★ measuring spoons and cups
- ★ 1 packet dried yeast
- ★ 4 zip-top sandwich bags
- ★ marker
- ★ magnifying glass
- ★ 2 tsp flour
- ★ warm water
- ★ clock or watch
- ★ recording sheet (next page)

1. Look at the yeast with a magnifying glass. What do you think yeast needs to be active?

_____

_____

2. Do Steps 2–9 of the investigation. Record your observations below.

Yeast	What I observed	After 15 minutes	After 30 minutes
Control			
Food			
Water			
Food and Water			

3. What does yeast need to live?

_____

_____

Investigation 2

What foods work well for yeast? Try this!

1. Gather the materials you will need.

2. Different animals need different foods. (Could an otter eat the same food as a bee? Could a deer eat the same food as a shark?) What foods would you guess work well for yeast? Write your ideas on your recording sheet.

3. Choose two foods to test. Then make up an experiment to see which food works better.
   Remember: It's important to test only one change at a time. You're changing the kind of food. Other things in your experiment should stay the same. That includes the amount of food you test. Write the steps of your experiment on your recording sheet.

4. How will you tell which food works better? (**Hint:** How could you tell the yeast was "eating" the flour?)

5. Do your experiment! Then tell what happened. Which food was better for your yeast?

Materials
★ dried yeast
★ zip-top sandwich bags
★ measuring spoons
★ measuring cups
★ foods you want to test (for example, milk, ketchup, peanut butter, sugar)
★ recording sheet (next page)

© Scholastic Inc.

1. What foods do you think would work well for yeast?

_____

_____

2. Do Step 3 of the investigation. Write the steps of your experiment.

_____

_____

_____

_____

_____

_____

3. How will you tell which food works better?

_____

_____

4. Which food was better for your yeast?

_____

_____

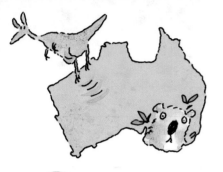

Animals Down Under

What unusual animals live in Australia?
Fill in the blanks in this article to read about them.

Can you find Australia on a world map? It is a very large island.

It is also one of the seven _____. Most of its

people live near the coast. The middle of Australia is very dry. Some

of it is _____. Not too many people live there.

But many unusual animals do!

You may recognize Australia's most famous animals. They are

kangaroos. They have _____ back legs for

hopping. Kangaroos are big, but they can hop very fast. Kangaroo babies are called joeys.

Joeys spend their first few months riding in their mother's _____.

You may also know koalas. Some people think they look like teddy bears! But they're

not bears at all. Koalas spend almost all of their time in trees. They stay there to avoid

bigger animals below.

Now look to the water to find the platypus. Its _____ feet

and flat bill make it look like a duck with fur!

Think About It!

What does the platypus have in common with a duck?

© Scholastic Inc.

Record Breakers

Read the clues for eight animal record breakers. Write the name of the animal that matches each clue. Use the words from the box below.

> blue whale   cheetah   giraffe   Goliath birdeater
>
> Komodo dragon   ostrich   sailfish   sloth

1. The world's heaviest sea mammal weighs over 143 tons.

__ __ __ __   __ __ __ __ __

2. The world's fastest land mammal can run up to 65 miles per hour.

__ __ __ __ __ __ __

3. The world's largest spider can grow to a length of 11 inches.

__ __ __ __ __ __ __   __ __ __ __ __ __ __ __ __

4. The world's slowest land mammal moves at a top speed of .07 miles per hour.

__ __ __ __ __

5. The world's largest bird that cannot fly can grow to 8 feet tall and weigh up to 300 pounds.

__ __ __ __ __ __ __

6. The world's fastest fish can travel at a speed of about 68 miles per hour.

__ __ __ __ __ __ __ __

7. The world's largest lizard can grow up to 10 feet in length.

__ __ __ __ __ __ __   __ __ __ __ __ __

8. The world's tallest land mammal can grow to 18 feet or more in height.

__ __ __ __ __ __ __

Anatomy of a Whale

How do the picture and text together help you understand the whale?

Like most other living creatures, whales have changed over time to adapt to their environment. These magnificent marine mammals spend their entire lives in oceans. Their sleek bodies are perfect for long and deep dives. The way they breathe allows them to stay underwater for more than an hour! Whales' tails help them power through the water.

A sperm whale is a common kind of whale. Read about some features of its large body.

EARS Whales hear very well. They communicate through clicks, whistles, and songs. They navigate through water by listening to their sounds bounce off schools of fish, objects, and structures on the ocean floor.

HEAD It is really an oversized nose. Whales use it to make sounds.

BLOWHOLE This is a nostril that whales use for breathing.

FLUKES Whales move these strong tail parts up and down when they swim. They may also *lobtail*—raise their flukes out of the water into the air, and then slap them down on the water's surface with a loud smack. This might be another way whales communicate.

TEETH Some whales have none, and feed by straining huge gulps of water. Others, like the sperm whale, have teeth and use them to grab prey.

EYES These are small because whales rely more on sounds to move and hunt.

FLIPPERS These help whales steer themselves through the water.

© Scholastic Inc.

Answer each question. Give evidence from the diagram and captions.

1. *Marine* mammals live in _____.

   ○ A. Alaska   ○ B. ponds   ○ C. rivers   ○ D. oceans

What in the text help you answer?

_____

2. Which of the following means about the same as *navigate*?

   ○ A. breathe   ○ B. swim quickly   ○ C. steer   ○ D. communicate

What in the text helped you answer?

_____

_____

3. Why is it important for whales to have sleek bodies?

_____

_____

4. How can such a huge animal manage with such small eyes?

_____

_____

5. Compare and contrast the *flukes* and *flippers* of the sperm whale.
Include their use and location on the body in your answer.

_____

_____

_____

A Prickly Idea

How did an annoying problem lead to a clever idea?

Hiking In 1948, George de Mestral was hiking in the Swiss Alps. He was irritated by all the burrs that stuck to his pants and socks. These prickly, clinging seed cases were annoying. They were hard to pull off. But they gave him an idea. De Mestral, an engineer, wondered if he could make an imitation burr. Maybe it could compete with the zipper as a way to fasten clothing and other things. So he got busy.

Inventing He worked on his idea for several years. Eventually, he produced two cotton strips— one covered with tiny hooks and the other covered with tiny loops. These fabric strips stuck together and stayed that way until pulled apart. De Mestral called his invention *locking tape*. He then improved his idea by using sturdy nylon instead of cotton.

Naming Next, de Mestral formed a company to produce his hook-and-loop fastener. He called the product Velcro. He chose *vel* because he liked the sound of the word *velvet*. He picked *cro* from the French word *crochet*, a hook.

Lasting Today, Velcro products and similar fasteners are used around the world. And it all started with some bothersome burrs.

Clump of burrs

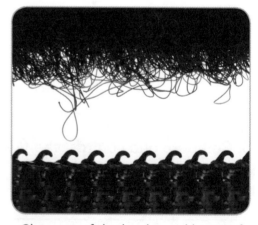

Close-up of the hooks and loops of Velcro®

Answer each question. Give evidence from the article.

1. What are *burrs*?

○ A. clinging seed cases   ○ C. types of fabric

○ B. pants and socks   ○ D. kinds of tape

What in the text helped you answer?

_____

2. Which of the following expressions might make another good title for this article?

○ A. Go Take a Hike!   ○ C. Burrs Under My Saddle

○ B. A Happy Accident   ○ D. Accidentally on Purpose

What in the text helped you answer?

_____

_____

3. Explain the meaning of de Mestral's first name for his new invention, *locking tape*.

_____

_____

4. What features of burrs gave de Mestral a big idea?

_____

5. Based on this article, describe George de Mestral's character.

_____

_____

What Is the Meaning of This?

Do you know the names for the different parts of a tree? Some of the words are **homonyms**, or words that have more than one meaning. Read the words in the Word Bank. Then write a word from the list that matches both definitions below.

Word Bank

stem
leaf
root
bark
trunk

1. _____
   a. the sharp sound that a dog makes
   b. the tough covering of a tree trunk and its branches

2. _____
   c. plant part that grows from the stem and makes food
   d. turn the pages

3. _____
   e. stop the flow of something
   f. the part of a plant that holds it up straight

4. _____
   g. the compartment of a car for storing a tire, luggage, and other items
   h. the main stem of a tree

5. _____
   i. cheer for a team
   j. the part of a plant that grows underground and takes in water and minerals from the soil

© Scholastic Inc.

Stately Trees

Fourteen state trees are listed below. Use them to complete the puzzle. Some letters are filled in to help you figure out where each word belongs.

oak	paloverde	cottonwood	pecan	buckeye
pine	cypress	dogwood	redbud	piñon
kukui	magnolia	hemlock	palmetto	

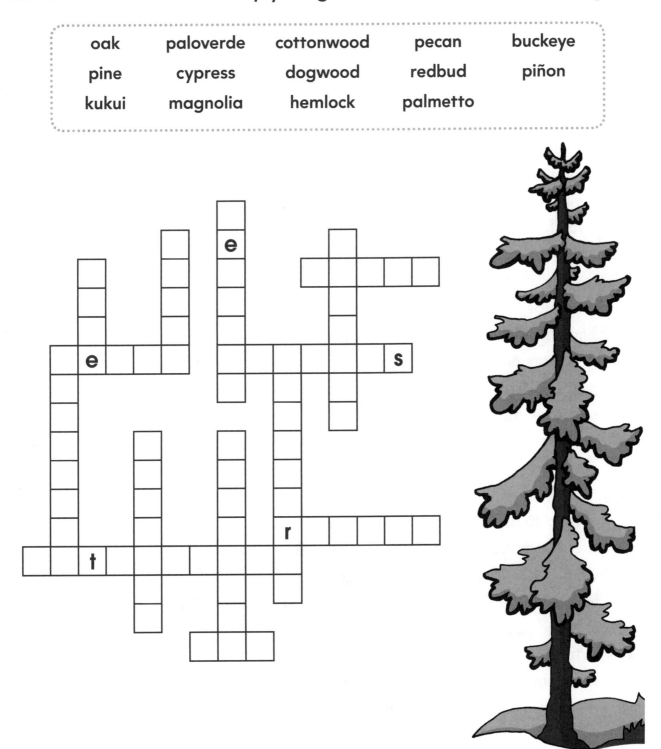

Let's Recycle!

Read the article.
Then answer the questions on the next page.

People, animals, and plants depend on Earth's natural resources to live. Keeping the planet clean and protecting its resources is a big job, but everybody can help. One easy way is to recycle. If every household recycled aluminum, glass, plastic, and paper, we could save natural resources and help clean up Earth. Does your family recycle aluminum cans? Enough aluminum is thrown away in the United States to rebuild our fleet of commercial airlines! So instead of tossing those soft drink cans in the trash, take them to a recycling center.

Did you know that about 41 billion glass containers are made each year? How many of these does your family use and recycle? Maybe you do not use much glass, but recycling just one glass container can save enough energy to light a 100-watt bulb for four hours or an 11-watt compact fluorescent bulb for 20 hours. Every ton of glass made from recycled materials can save 385 pounds of mining waste.

Maybe you use more plastic than glass. Plastic can be recycled, too! Each year in the United States, we use enough plastic wrap to wrap up the whole state of Texas, twice. If we recycled every plastic bottle, we could keep over 25 million tons of plastic out of landfills.

It is not hard to recycle paper, and that, too, can make a big difference. Every year enough paper is thrown away to make a 12-foot wall that stretches from New York to Seattle. Instead of building paper walls and filling landfills, let's recycle! Each pound of recycled paper keeps six pounds of pollutants out of our air. A ton of recycled paper saves 17 trees and 7,000 gallons of water.

Let's all try to clean up Earth and save its resources. Start by recycling at home. Tell your neighbors about recycling. Maybe you could start a recycling club at school. We can all do our part to keep Earth clean and protect its resources.

You just read an article about recycling. What did you learn? What changes can you make to reduce, reuse, and recycle? Answer the questions below. Then think of two ways you can help.

1. What is the main purpose of "Let's Recycle"?

_____

_____

_____

2. Keeping Earth _____ and protecting its _____

are two main reasons to recycle.

3. What specific facts about the benefits of recycling, does the writer include in the article? Give two examples.

_____

_____

Two ways that I can help keep Earth clean and protect its resources are:

1. _____

_____

_____

2. _____

_____

_____

Avalanche!

Read the essay about avalanches.
Then follow the directions in the Text Marking box.

Have you ever watched how snow behaves on a car's windshield? If the temperature stays low, the snow sticks. But if the temperature rises, the snow begins to slide. It moves in chunks down the windshield.

This is a tiny example of an avalanche— a sudden surge of snow and ice down a mountain. A large avalanche might let loose enough snow to cover 20 soccer fields 10-feet deep!

Roaring Snowball Avalanches occur when piled-up layers of snow get too heavy and then weaken. The loosened snow starts to slide down. As it speeds up, it picks up rocks, trees, and even houses, animals, and people in its path. Avalanches grow in size, affecting everything in their way.

Causes Many factors can set off an avalanche. Some are natural causes: heavy rains, warming temperatures, earthquakes, or changes in wind direction. And then there are human causes: snowmobiling, skiing, or explosions.

Danger! Avalanches generally occur in winter or spring. But they can happen any time. And because they start so suddenly, they can be very dangerous.

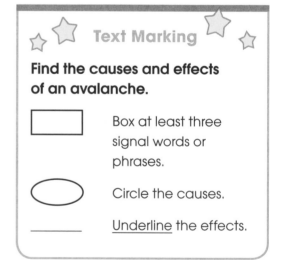

Text Marking

Find the causes and effects of an avalanche.

▭	Box at least three signal words or phrases.
⬭	Circle the causes.
___	Underline the effects.

© Scholastic Inc.

Answer each question. Give evidence from the essay.

1. Which of the following words means the same as *factors* (paragraph 4)?

○ A. dangers   ○ B. seasons   ○ C. causes   ○ D. layers

What in the text helped you answer?

_____

_____

2. According to the essay, which of the following does NOT cause avalanches?

○ A. mountain height   ○ C. earthquakes

○ B. snowmobiling   ○ D. heavy rains

What in the text helped you answer?

_____

_____

3. Why are avalanches so dangerous?

_____

_____

4. Why do you think the author begins the essay by describing how snow acts on a car's windshield?

_____

_____

_____

An American Volcano

**What do you know about volcanoes?
Fill in the blanks in this article to find
out more about one in our country.**

Mount Saint Helens is an active volcano in the state

of Washington. In 1980, this volcano erupted, spewing hot

_____ into the air. Explosions caused a

huge cloud of dust. This gray dust filled the air and settled on

houses and cars many miles away. The thick dust made it hard for

people and animals to _____.

The explosions _____ trees on the side of the mountain.

The hot rocks _____ forest fires. The snow that was on the

mountain melted quickly, causing _____ and mud slides.

Mount Saint Helens still erupts from time to time, but not as badly as it did in 1980.

But who knows when it will blow its top again!

Word Bank

breathe
flattened
floods
ignited
lava

**Think
About It!**

**What effect did the dust from Mt. Saint Helens have
on the area around it?**

© Scholastic Inc.

The Ice Hotel

Read about a hotel made of ice. Then try the science investigations.

There is a hotel in Sweden made out of ice and snow. It is called the Ice Hotel.

In winter, it gets very cold in Sweden. The river slows down and turns into ice. People take the ice from the river and mix it with snow. They call this mixture "snice." They make large blocks out of snice. Then they use the blocks to build the hotel. Even the beds are made of snice. The people who stay there sleep in special, warm sleeping bags.

COOL FACT: How long does it take you to make one snowball? How about 700 million snowballs? That's how much snow is used to build the Ice Hotel!

Investigation 1

When ice is a problem, what's the fastest way to melt it? Find out here!

1. Gather the materials you will need.

2. Put an ice cube in each bag.

3. How can you melt an ice cube fast? Try these:

   • Leave one on a table. (This is your "control." It shows how fast the ice will melt by itself.)

   • Put salt on one ice cube.

   • Crush one ice cube.

   • Think of two other ways.

4. Use the marker to label the bags. Then close them.

5. **Predict:** Which way will melt the ice fastest? Slowest? Record your predictions on the chart on the next page.

6. Wait a few minutes. Check your ice cubes and record what happened.

7. Imagine you are in charge of keeping roads safe. If the roads were covered in slippery ice, what could you do to melt the ice?

Materials

★ 5 ice cubes, same size

★ 5 zip-top plastic sandwich bags

★ ways to melt the ice: 1 tsp salt, something to crush ice with

★ permanent marker

★ recording sheet (next page)

© Scholastic Inc.

1. Do Steps 2–4 of the investigation. **Predict:** Which way will make the ice melt fastest? Slowest? Number these from 1 to 5 (1 for the fastest, 5 for the slowest) on the chart below.

2. Wait a few minutes. Check your ice cubes. Which ice melted fastest? Slowest? Record in the chart. Number these from 1 to 5 (1 for the fastest, 5 for the slowest).

Ice Melters	My prediction	What happened
Control		
Ice with salt		
Crushed ice		
My 1st idea		
My 2nd idea		

3. If the roads were covered in ice, what could you do to melt the ice? Why? Write your answers on a separate sheet of paper.

Investigation 2

What could you use to keep ice from melting?

1. Gather the materials you will need.

2. **Think:** What material could keep heat away from an ice cube and make the best Ice Keeper? Why?

3. Put one ice cube in each sandwich bag. Press out the air, then zip the bags closed.

4. Fill a cup halfway with crumpled aluminum foil. Push one bag into the foil. Then cover it with more foil.

5. Do Step 4 again with crumpled paper and again with the material you chose. Put the fourth bag in a cup by itself. (This is your "control." It shows how fast the ice will melt by itself.) Put all of the cups in a warm place.

6. After 30 minutes, take the ice out of each cup. Record your observations. Then repack the ice in each cup.

7. Look again after 30 minutes. Which Ice Keeper worked best? How can you tell? How could you make an even better Ice Keeper?

Materials

- ★ 4 ice cubes, same size
- ★ 4 zip-top plastic sandwich bags
- ★ 4 plastic cups
- ★ aluminum foil
- ★ notebook paper
- ★ inventor's materials: cotton balls, paper towels, craft feathers, scraps of fabric, foam packing material, empty chip bags
- ★ warm place
- ★ clock or watch
- ★ recording sheet (next page)

foil

paper

my ice keeper

control

© Scholastic Inc.

1. What material do you think would make the best Ice Keeper? Why?

_____

_____

_____

2. Do steps 3–7 of the investigation. Record your observations below.

Ice Keepers	After 30 minutes	After 1 hour
Foil		
Crumpled paper		
Your Ice Keeper		
Control		

3. Which Ice Keeper worked best? How can you tell?

_____

_____

4. How could you make an even better Ice Keeper?
    Write your ideas on a separate sheet of paper.

Words for the Weather-Wise

Choose a word from the box below to complete the crossword puzzle.

tornado	drought	flood	gale	sleet
hurricane	blizzard	frost	hail	thunderstorm

Across
1. a storm with strong winds, rain, lightning, and thunder
4. moisture that is frozen on the surface of something
5. a blinding snowstorm with strong winds and very cold temperatures
7. small pieces of frozen rain
8. a very strong wind
10. snow mixed with rain

Down
2. a severe tropical storm with violent winds and very heavy rain
3. a violent and destructive whirlwind
6. a long period of very dry weather
9. an overflow of water onto what is usually dry land

© Scholastic Inc.

Waiting Out Winter

You will read about what it is like for animals in winter on the next page. Below are some of the names of the animals you will be read about.

bears	birds	chipmunks	deer
foxes	mice	Monarch butterflies	rabbits
rodents	skunks	squirrels	weasels

First, think about the questions below. Write your answer on the lines.

How would you behave if it was very cold? Imagine the winds are blowing and snow is falling. What would you do to make sure your house was warm and cozy?

_____

_____

How would you dress if you had to go outside on a very cold day?

_____

_____

What kinds of food sound good to eat on a cold wintry day?

_____

_____

Now think about what a cold winter would be like if you had no house and no clothes. What would you eat if the only food you had was what you could find in the woods? Think about what winter must be like for animals.

Waiting Out Winter

In the winter when it grows very cold and snow covers the ground, you have to make some changes in your life. You do not play outside as much when the cold winds are blowing. Instead, you stay in a warm house and play games, read books, and watch television. You cannot wear shorts and sandals in the wintertime. When you do go out, you wear a heavy coat, gloves, and boots. There are no more picnics when the weather turns cold. Soup and hot chocolate taste best on wintry days.

Did you ever wonder what animals do during winter? Animals do not have warm houses or stores where they can buy heavy clothes and hot food, but, like you, they must make changes in the winter.

Animals find special shelters in the winter to protect them from the cold. Squirrels, mice, and rabbits find holes in trees and logs or even burrow underground. Their fur grows thicker in the winter to help keep them warm. Some animals, like rabbits and weasels, grow special white fur, so they can hide in the snow. Even the animals' food is different in the winter. Rabbits and deer have to eat twigs, tree bark, and moss because there are no green plants. Red foxes eat insects and fruit during the warm months but in the cold winter must hunt small rodents for food.

Did you ever wish you could just leave during the winter and take a long vacation in someplace warm? Well, some animals do just that. They **migrate**. That means they travel to someplace warm where they can find food. Many birds migrate in the fall. Monarch butterflies also migrate and spend the winter in sunny Mexico.

Sometimes on a very cold morning when the wind is howling, you may want to snuggle under the covers and just stay in bed. Some animals spend part or all of the winter in a special, deep sleep called **hibernation**. Bears, skunks, and chipmunks eat a lot of extra food in the fall and store up fat in their bodies. Then in the winter, they curl up and hibernate until the weather turns warm.

The writer of "Waiting Out Winter" compares and contrasts what people do in winter with what animals do in winter. To **compare** is to identify similarities and to **contrast** is to identify differences.

Are there similarities with how people and animals behave in winter? Are there differences?

Complete the chart.

People	Animals
People stay in warm houses.	
	Animals grow thicker fur.
	Rabbits and deer eat twigs, bark, and moss. Foxes eat rodents.
People go on vacation to places that are warm.	
People snuggle under the covers and stay in bed a little longer on cold mornings.	

Animal Weather Forecasters?

Read the article.
Then follow the directions in the Text Marking box.

Will earthworms wriggle out of the ground prior to a flood? Will sharks swim to deeper waters before a hurricane? Do animals actually have the power to predict natural disasters like earthquakes or hurricanes? The short answer is probably "No." But the long answer is more complex.

Scientists are skeptical that animals have a special sense that enables them to predict the weather. But they know that many animals have more highly developed senses than humans do, and are capable of detecting signals of impending weather change sooner than we can. Some, like dogs, pick up infrasonic sound waves—sounds that are at lower frequencies than we can hear. Others, like the frogs that go silent before a storm, can detect differences in air pressure. Animals learn to associate these signals with danger. They alert the animals to move to a safer area.

Changes in air pressure may cause seagulls to seek shelter on land.

⭐ Text Marking ⭐

Summarize the text.

⬭   Circle the topic.

___   <u>Underline</u> important details.

Answer each question. Give evidence from the article.

1. Which is the best synonym for the word *impending* in paragraph 2?

○ A. major   ○ B. distant   ○ C. natural   ○ D. coming

What in the text helped you answer?

_____

_____

2. Which statement is NOT supported by information in the text?

○ A. Changes in air pressure may help some animals detect signals
of weather change.

○ B. Animals can probably predict weather patterns.

○ C. Many animals have sharper senses than humans do.

○ D. Some frogs stop croaking when they sense a storm is coming.

What in the text helped you answer?

_____

_____

3. Look back at your text markings. Write a one-paragraph summary of the key
information provided in the article.

_____

_____

4. Why does the author use words like *probably* and *skeptical* when discussing views
on animal behaviors involving weather change?

_____

_____

Weather Watchers

How does the weather change from place to place and day to day? Find out!
Choose two cities. Find their high temperature every day for five days. Mark this
on the graph. Connect the marks with lines. Use a different color for each city.

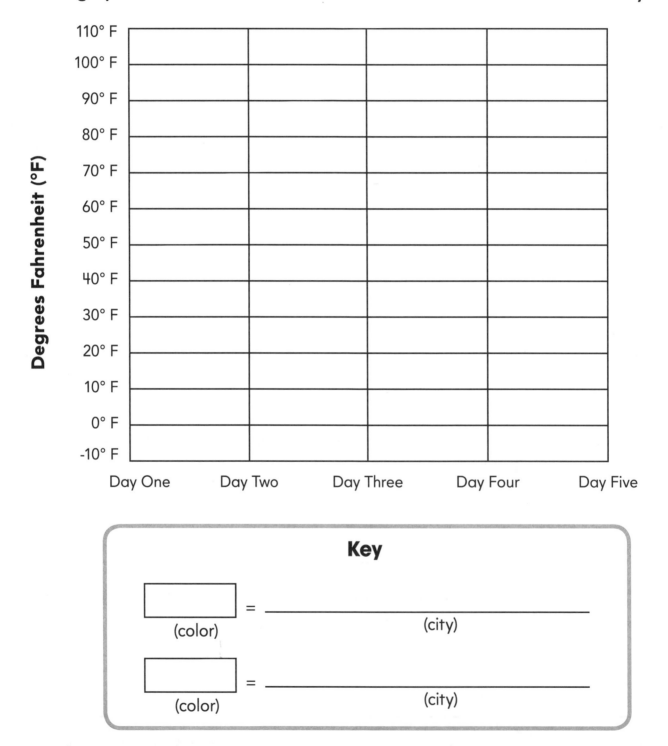

Hello, Sun

Read about the sun. Then try the science investigations.

Did you know our sun is actually a star? It is the closest star to Earth. No wonder it looks so much bigger and brighter than other stars in the sky! Like other stars, our sun is a giant superhot ball of gas. It gives us heat and light.

Can you imagine what Earth would be like if there were no sun? It would be cold and dark! No living thing could survive on this planet! We all need the sun to stay alive. Thank you, sun!

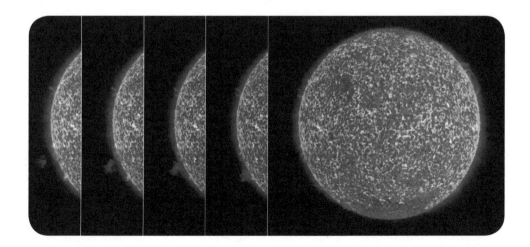

Investigation 1

Track the sun's movement by looking at shadows!

1. Gather the materials you will need.

2. Make a Sun Tracker. Follow the directions on your recording sheet.

3. Take your Sun Tracker outside on a sunny day. Place it on a flat surface. Use a compass to find north. (An adult can help you.) Turn your paper so the word **North** points north. Tape your tracker down.

4. Find the shadow cast by your triangle. Use a dark marker to trace around the shadow. Write the time next to it.

5. Where do you think the shadow will be in 30 minutes? Use a pencil to draw your guess.

6. In 30 minutes, find the shadow again. Trace it with the dark marker. Write the time next to it.

7. Do Steps 5 and 6 again. Which of your predictions was more correct? What do you think will happen to the shadow over the rest of the day?

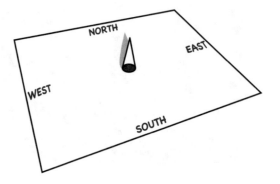

Materials
★ sheet of tracing paper
★ pencil scissors
★ masking tape
★ sunny day
★ compass
★ dark marker
★ recording sheet (next page)

© Scholastic Inc.

1. Make a Sun Tracker:

- Trace the square and rectangle below onto a separate sheet of paper. Copy all markings.

- Cut out your Sun Tracker (the square).

- Cut out the rectangle. Fold on the solid lines. Overlap the two ends and tape them together.

- Tape the triangle to the middle of the Sun Tracker.

2. Do Steps 3–7 of the investigation. What do you think will happen to the shadow over the rest of the day? Record on a separate sheet of paper.

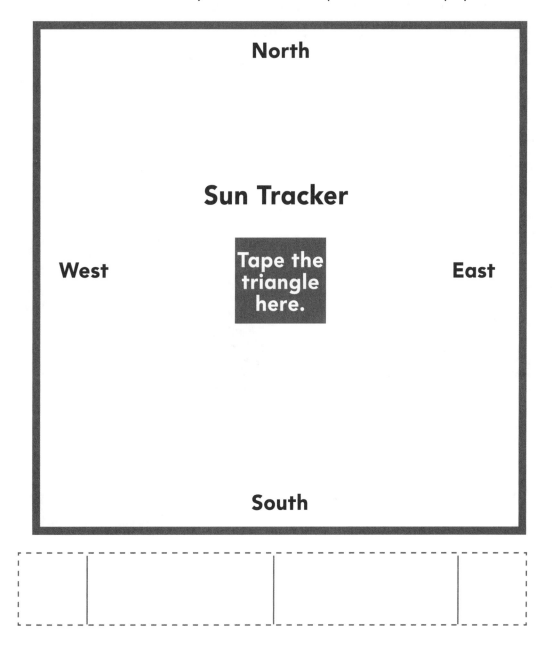

Investigation 2

Where does the sun go at night? Find out!

1. Gather the materials you will need.

2. Have a partner hold the flashlight and turn it on.
   Your partner is the "sun."

3. Stand two steps away from the "sun." You are the "Earth."
   Your chest is the side of the Earth you live on. Have your
   partner point the flashlight at your body. Turn so that your left arm
   is toward the sun. How is this like sunrise? Record your answer on the next page.

4. Slowly turn to your left until you are facing the sun.
   Which part of the day is this like? Why do you think so?

5. Turn to your left again so your right arm is toward the sun.
   Which part of the day is this like?

6. Turn left again so your back is now
   toward the sun. How is this
   like nighttime?

7. Switch roles with your partner.
   Now you are the "sun," and your
   partner is the "Earth." Repeat
   Steps 2–6.

8. Does the sun go away at night?
   Why do we have day and night?
   Record your answers on the next page.

Materials

★ a partner

★ flashlight

★ recording sheet
(next page)

© Scholastic Inc.

1. Do Steps 2 and 3 of the investigation. How is Step 3 like sunrise?

_____

_____

2. Now do Step 4 of the investigation. Which part of the day is this like? Why do you think so?

_____

_____

3. Do Step 5 of the investigation. Which part of the day is this like?

_____

_____

4. Do Step 6 of the investigation. How is this like nighttime?

_____

_____

5. Does the sun go away at night? Why do we have day and night?

_____

_____

Hello, Roy G. Biv!

What helps you understand the meaning of the title of this article?

Dorothy in *The Wizard of Oz* longed to be "over the rainbow." The perfect place she imagined wasn't real. But rainbows are.

A rainbow is a colorful arc in the sky. You might see one when the sun comes out after it rains. You also might see one in the mist from a hose. You can *see* rainbows but you can't *touch* them. Rainbows don't take up space. So what makes them real?

The great scientist Sir Isaac Newton discovered important ideas about light 450 years ago. He observed light to determine how it moved. Newton figured out that light is made of fast-moving bits of energy. Light can move through air. It also moves through water and other materials.

One day, Newton used an object called a prism to look at light. A *prism* is a wedge-shaped piece of clear glass. When he held his prism up to the sun, its visible (white) light passed through the glass. It came out the other side. But the light was no longer white. The prism *refracted*, or bent, the white light. It broke the light apart into colors called the *spectrum*. These are the same colors you see in a rainbow.

> **Do you know ROY G. BIV?**
>
> He's not a person. Roy G. Biv is a memory shortcut. Each letter in the "name" means a color of the spectrum in order: **R**ed, **O**range, **Y**ellow, **G**reen, **B**lue, **I**ndigo, and **V**iolet.

© Scholastic Inc.

Answer each question. Give evidence from the article.

1. What is NOT true about a rainbow?

○ A. It is shaped like an arc.   ○ C. You can see it in the sky.

○ B. You can grab hold of it.   ○ D. Its colors appear in the same order.

What in the text helped you answer?

_____

_____

2. Which of the following means the same as *refracted*?

○ A. bent   ○ B. visible   ○ C. touched   ○ D. energetic

What in the text helped you answer?

_____

3. Who is Roy G. Biv? Explain.

_____

_____

4. Why does the author include Sir Isaac Newton in this article?

_____

_____

5. Why did the author begin the article with Dorothy from *The Wizard of Oz*?

_____

_____

Our Solar System

A **solar system** is made up of a sun and all of the objects that travel around that sun. In addition to comets, meteors, and other objects, our solar system includes the sun, the moon, Earth, and seven other planets.

Find the objects in our solar system in the puzzle below.

EARTH	JUPITER	MARS	MERCURY	MOON
NEPTUNE	SATURN	SUN	URANUS	VENUS

```
P  Z  B  E  L  H  M  J  U  P  I  T  E  R
Y  X  M  A  R  S  U  G  W  S  Z  L  U  F
I  R  I  M  U  J  A  S  A  T  U  R  N  U
M  E  X  C  L  N  F  M  H  F  X  G  M  F
M  M  L  F  F  E  E  X  K  K  F  S  H  N
E  S  I  H  Y  P  X  M  O  O  N  O  S  Q
R  Z  C  C  S  T  U  L  I  I  C  L  V  D
C  G  Z  Y  E  U  A  Q  M  N  W  C  E  A
U  J  E  S  D  N  Z  N  Q  J  V  X  N  L
R  J  L  G  U  E  C  C  U  R  A  N  U  S
Y  P  W  Y  U  F  U  A  Y  L  L  G  S  B
Y  N  U  E  A  R  T  H  Z  M  G  N  A  L
S  U  N  K  V  V  M  D  T  Y  M  O  Y  I
```

Moon Shapes

Read about why the moon seems to change its shape.
Then try the science investigations.

The moon is our closest neighbor in space. We often see it in the night sky. Sometimes the moon looks big and round. Other times it looks like the tip of your fingernail. Does the moon actually change its shape?

The moon is round like a ball. It **orbits** (travels around) Earth. The sun shines on the moon, just like it shines on Earth. As the moon moves around Earth, we see a different part of the moon's sunlit surface. When the moon's lit-up side faces away from us, we call it the **new moon**. When its whole lit-up side faces us, we call it the **full moon**.

The different shapes of the moon are called **phases**. What phase is the moon tonight?

Investigation 1

**Why does the moon look like it changes shape?
Find out here.**

Materials
★ Styrofoam ball
★ craft stick
★ flashlight
★ recording sheet (next page)

1. Gather the materials you will need.

2. To make your model moon, insert the craft stick into the Styrofoam ball. The flashlight will serve as your sun.

3. Have a partner turn on your model sun. Dim other lights. Stand three big steps from the model sun. Turn so your back is toward the sun.

4. Your head is the model Earth. Hold the model moon in front of you at arm's length. Lift it high enough so your shadow doesn't cover it.

5. Look at the light on your moon. Compare it to the four moon pictures on the next page. Which picture does it look most like? Write "full moon" in the box under that picture.

6. Turn left until the sun is directly on your left. Look at the light and shadow on your moon. Which picture does it most look like? (Notice which side is lit up.) Write "last quarter" in its box.

7. Turn left until you're facing the sun. Which picture does your moon look most like? Write "new moon" in its box.

8. Turn left until the sun is directly on your right. Which picture does your moon look most like? Write "first quarter" in its box.

9. Turn left until the sun is directly behind you again. Your model moon just made one full trip around your model Earth. The real moon takes about a month to orbit Earth.

© Scholastic Inc.

Investigation 2

You have learned about the four moon phases: Full Moon, Last Quarter, New Moon, and First Quarter. Now learn about the other phases too!

Materials

★ Styrofoam ball

★ craft stick

★ flashlight

★ recording sheet (next page)

1. Gather the materials you will need.

2. To make your model moon, insert the craft stick into the Styrofoam ball. The flashlight will serve as your sun.

3. Use your finger to trace the arrows on your recording sheet. The arrows show the order of the moon phases.

4. Look at the four pictures at the bottom of your recording sheet. Each one shows another moon phase. These phases happen between the first four phases you observed.

5. Ask a partner to turn on your model sun. Dim other lights. Stand three big steps from the model sun. Turn so your back is toward the sun. Hold the model moon in front of you at arm's length. Lift it high enough so your shadow doesn't cover it. You are modeling a Full Moon.

6. Slowly turn to your left until your moon is halfway between the Full Moon and Last Quarter phases. Look at the light and shadow on your moon. Which cutout picture is it most like? Draw that picture in the box between the Full Moon and the Last Quarter.

7. Keep turning left and observing your model. Figure out which picture you should draw in each of the other three boxes.

8. **Think:** Why does the shape of the moon seem to change as it orbits the Earth? Write your ideas on the back of your sheet.

© Scholastic Inc.

Full Moon

Last Quarter

First Quarter

New Moon

Waxing Crescent

Waning Crescent

Waning Gibbous

Waxing Gibbous

Life in Space

What would it be like to live in space? Fill in the blanks in this article to find out about some of the things that affect life in space.

When astronauts go to work in space, they are too far away

to _____ home each night. They have to live

in space for a short time to do their work. But life in space is

different from life on Earth! The main reason is that there is less

gravity. Gravity is the _____ force that holds

everything—even you—to the earth. With less gravity, astronauts'

feet don't stay on the ground, so they float instead of walk. It feels

a bit like _____. At night, astronauts sleep in sleeping bags strapped

to the walls so they don't float around. To eat without pots and pans flying, astronauts

have special food like freeze-dried _____ eggs. To get clean,

astronauts rub soap and water on their bodies and _____ it off.

That's because a shower would spray all over.

Word Bank

commute
invisible
scrambled
sponge
swimming

Think About It!

What effect does less gravity have on astronauts working in space?

Let's Roll

**Read about a race car that has no motors.
Then try the science investigations.**

Every summer in Akron, Ohio, children race in the All-American Soap Box Derby. They race in cars they built themselves.

Every racer gets a kit from the Soap Box Derby. The kit comes with the car's body, brakes (for stopping), a steering wheel (to turn the car), and a helmet. Wheels come separately.

But the cars don't have motors. So what makes them move? **Gravity**—the force that pulls down on us—pulls the cars down the hill!

Racers have to figure out how to make their cars go fast. They can ask an adult for help. What do you think can help these cars go faster?

Did you know?
Force is a push or a pull that makes something move. **Gravity** is a force.

Investigation 1

Find out if an empty bottle has more or less push than a full bottle!

1. Gather the materials you will need.

2. Make a ramp using a folded game board and blocks. Tape the pieces in place.

3. Hold your hand at the bottom of the ramp.
   Have a partner roll the empty bottle down the ramp. Let the bottle push your hand. How did the push feel?

4. Repeat Step 3 with the full bottle. Which bottle gave your hand a bigger push? Why?

5. Place the cereal box in front of the ramp, as shown. **Predict:** What will happen if you roll the empty bottle down the ramp? Test your prediction. Record your results.

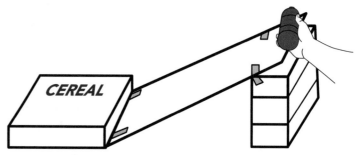

6. Put the cereal box back in front of the ramp.
   Predict: What will happen if you roll the full bottle down the ramp? Test your prediction. Record your results. How much did the box move with the bigger push? Why do you think this happened?

Materials

★ game board

★ blocks

★ masking tape

★ 2 plastic bottles, one full and one empty

★ empty cereal box

★ recording sheet (next page)

1. Do Steps 2 and 3 of the investigation. How did the push feel?

_____

_____

2. Now do Step 4 of the investigation. Which bottle gave your hand a bigger push? Why do you think that is?

_____

_____

3. Do Step 5 of the investigation. **Predict:** What will happen if you roll the empty bottle down the ramp?

_____

_____

4. What happened when you rolled the empty bottle?

_____

_____

5. Do Step 6. **Predict:** What will happen if you roll the full bottle down the ramp?

_____

_____

6. How much did the box move with this bigger push? Check one:

☐ farther   ☐ the same   ☐ not as far

Why do you think this happened? Write your answer on a separate sheet of paper.

Investigation 2

How can you make a bigger push? Try this!

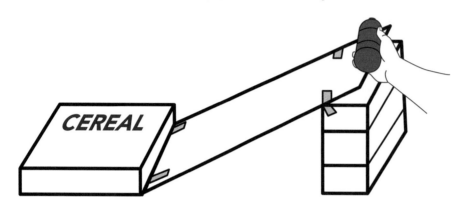

Materials

★ game board

★ blocks

★ masking tape

★ full plastic bottle

★ empty cereal box

★ recording sheet (next page)

1. Gather the materials you will need.

2. Make a ramp using a folded game board and blocks. Tape the pieces in place. Put the cereal box in front of the ramp. Roll the full plastic bottle down the ramp. If the box moves, put a piece of tape on the floor to mark its new position.

3. **Think:** What one thing could you change to make the box move farther? Think about the box, the bottle, and the ramp. What could be changed about each one? (For instance, in Investigation 1 you used a light, empty bottle, then changed to a heavy, full bottle.) Pick one idea to try.

4. Now make up an experiment to test the change. It's important to test only one change at a time. Everything else in your experiment should stay the same. What one thing will you change? What will you keep the same?

5. Write the steps of your experiment on your recording sheet. Then do your experiment! Record what happened.

© Scholastic Inc.

1. Do Steps 2 and 3 of the investigation. What could you change to make the box move farther? List your ideas.

_____

_____

2. Pick one idea. I will try this change:

_____

3. Write down the steps of your experiment.

_____

_____

_____

_____

4. Do your experiment. Record what happened.

_____

_____

_____

_____

As Fit as a Clown

Read the physical education article.
Then follow the directions in the Text Marking box.

Are you "circus fit"? Big-top performers are. They need to be in peak condition. How else could they perform all those wacky stunts? How do they juggle while balancing on a rope? How do they ride around backwards on a unicycle?

To do all this nutty stuff, circus performers exercise a lot. They must be as strong as they are silly. They must be as fit as they are funny. One major circus now shares its fitness secrets with kids. Clowns, dancers, and acrobats visit schools to teach what they do to stay in shape.

Kids who take part may not learn to prance about in huge flapping shoes. But they will learn how to be strong and flexible. They will get tips for keeping fit and staying safe. Plus, they may learn riddles like this one:

Q: Why do lions like to eat high-wire artists?

A: Because they want a well-balanced meal!

When that circus comes to town, the kids get to attend. Some lucky ones may even step into the ring and perform!

Text Marking

Check to identify the author's <u>two</u> purposes in this article.

☐ to entertain (E)

☐ to inform (I)

☐ to persuade (P)

_____ <u>Underline</u> text clues for this purpose. Write E, I, or P in the margin beside each clue.

Answer each question. Give evidence from the article.

1. Which person below must be in *peak condition* (paragraph 1) for his or her job?

○ A. a librarian   ○ C. a school nurse

○ B. a bank teller   ○ D. a professional athlete

What in the text helped you answer?

_____

_____

2. Based on the article, what do circus performers teach when they visit schools?

○ A. how to walk on a high wire   ○ C. how to exercise to build strength

○ B. how to put on clown makeup   ○ D. how to twirl plates on a long stick

What in the text helped you answer?

_____

_____

3. Reread the riddle. What makes it funny? Why did the author include it?

_____

_____

4. Review your text markings for author's purpose. Summarize why the author wrote this article. Use another sheet of paper if you need more space.

_____

_____

Food for Thought

Read the nutrition article.
Then follow the directions in the Text Marking box.

Does it matter how much fat, salt, and sugar children eat? Should kids avoid fatty foods like chicken fingers and French fries? Should they steer clear of salty junk foods, like puffed cheese sticks? Should they stay away from foods loaded with chemicals and dyes? Soda has both.

Fat, salt, and sugar make foods taste good. But too much of a good thing can harm you. That's why food scientists strongly support healthy eating. They want to direct children and parents toward wiser food choices. Teachers, school nurses, doctors, and many parents agree. They hope schools will share the responsibility of keeping kids fit and strong.

So, many school communities urge cafeteria lunches to be both tasty *and* nourishing. They encourage serving wholesome, natural foods. They don't want kids eating foods with unhealthy ingredients in them. And scientists and educators want school lunches to be varied. They suggest that menus celebrate cultural differences.

Teachers and principals care deeply about how kids learn best. Science shows that a healthy diet increases a child's ability to stay alert for learning. That is surely food for thought.

A healthy salad

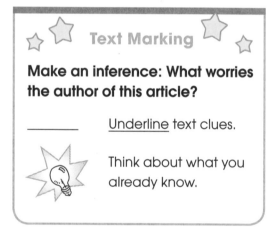

☆ ★ **Text Marking** ★ ☆

Make an inference: What worries the author of this article?

_____ <u>Underline</u> text clues.

Think about what you already know.

Answer each question. Give evidence from the article.

1. Foods with too much sugar, fat, or salt are called _____.

    ○ A. junk foods   ○ C. school food

    ○ B. sandwiches   ○ D. wholesome choices

What in the text helped you answer?

_____

_____

2. Which word means the same as *steer clear* (paragraph 1)?

    ○ A. encourage   ○ B. direct   ○ C. avoid   ○ D. vary

What in the text helped you answer?

_____

_____

3. Look back at your text markings. Think about what you already know. What does the writer think about how kids eat?

_____

_____

_____

4. Why would educators support wholesome school lunches?

_____

_____

Healthy and Crispy

Why are only the directions given in number order?

Sesame seeds are very healthy to eat. They supply fiber, protein, and vitamins. Best of all, they are available all over the world. The Bantu people of Africa call sesame seeds *benne*. Make these simple benne wafers for a sweet and tasty treat.

Benne Wafers   Makes 24 thin wafers

Ingredients

cooking spray

½ cup sesame seeds

6 tablespoons unsalted butter, soft

1 cup brown sugar, packed

1 beaten egg

½ cup flour

¼ teaspoon salt

½ teaspoon baking powder

1 teaspoon vanilla extract

Utensils

- cookie sheets
- measuring spoons and cups
- frying pan
- mixing bowl, fork, and spoon
- spatula
- cooling rack

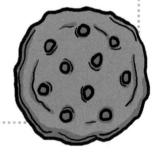

Directions

1. Preheat oven to 350°F. Spray cookie sheets with cooking spray.

2. Gently toast sesame seeds in a dry frying pan.
   Stir until they turn golden. Don't let them scorch.

3. Blend butter and brown sugar together in a bowl.
   Add egg, flour, salt, baking powder, and vanilla. Combine until smooth.

4. Add toasted sesame seeds. Mix well.

5. Drop spoonfuls of dough onto cookie sheets.
   Allow room between wafers because they spread as they bake.

6. Bake 12–13 minutes, or until the wafers turn golden brown.
   Wait a few minutes. Then transfer them to a rack to cool. ENJOY!

Answer each question. Give evidence from the recipe.

1. Which of the following is NOT true about sesame seeds?

   ○ A. They are healthy to eat.   ○ C. They supply fiber and vitamins.

   ○ B. They are available everywhere.   ○ D. They were discovered in Africa.

What in the text helped you answer?

_____

2. If you *scorch* the sesame seeds, they will _____,

   ○ A. turn dark brown   ○ B. taste better   ○ C. feel cold   ○ D. spread

What in the text helped you answer?

_____

_____

3. Why are the Directions numbered, but the Ingredients or Utensils are not?

_____

_____

4. Why do the directions appear *last* in the recipe?

_____

_____

5. What about the ingredients, utensils, and directions tell you that *wafers* are
   a kind of cookie?

_____

Chocolate Lover's Experiment

There are so many tasty varieties of chocolate: plain, candy-coated, cups with peanut-butter centers. But which one will last longest under the heat of the sun? Design an experiment to find out. Then answer the questions below.

1. What is your independent variable, or the detail you would change on purpose?

_____

2. What is your dependent variable, or the variable you would measure?

_____

3. State your research question for this experiment.

_____

4. State your hypothesis.

_____

5. List the materials you'll need for this experiment.

_____

6. On a separate sheet of paper, write a detailed procedure to test your hypothesis. Remember: Other people should be able to follow your instructions exactly.

7. Identify your control.

_____

8. What variables should you hold constant?

_____

9. On a separate sheet of paper, design a data table for recording your results.

10. What kind of graph or chart would you use to present your data? Draw your graph or chart on a sheet of graph paper.

Scholastic Success With

ADDITION & SUBTRACTION

On the *Mayflower*

Add or subtract. Write the Pilgrims' names in alphabetical order by sequencing the answers from greatest to smallest.

Resolve	$14 - 7 =$
Susan	$13 - 9 =$
Jasper	$6 + 7 =$
Priscilla	$8 + 2 =$
Edward	$9 + 6 =$
Solomon	$11 - 6 =$
Prudence	$18 - 9 =$
Constance	$8 + 8 =$
Remember	$17 - 9 =$
Oceanus	$7 + 5 =$
Thomas	$15 - 12 =$
Samuel	$14 - 8 =$
Charity	$6 + 12 =$
Peregrine	$16 - 5 =$
Humility	$9 + 5 =$

_____

_____

_____

_____

_____

_____

_____

_____

_____

_____

Which name would your name follow in the alphabetical list of names? Write a number sentence to show where your name would follow.

Great States

Add or subtract. Connect the matching answers to find each state's shape.

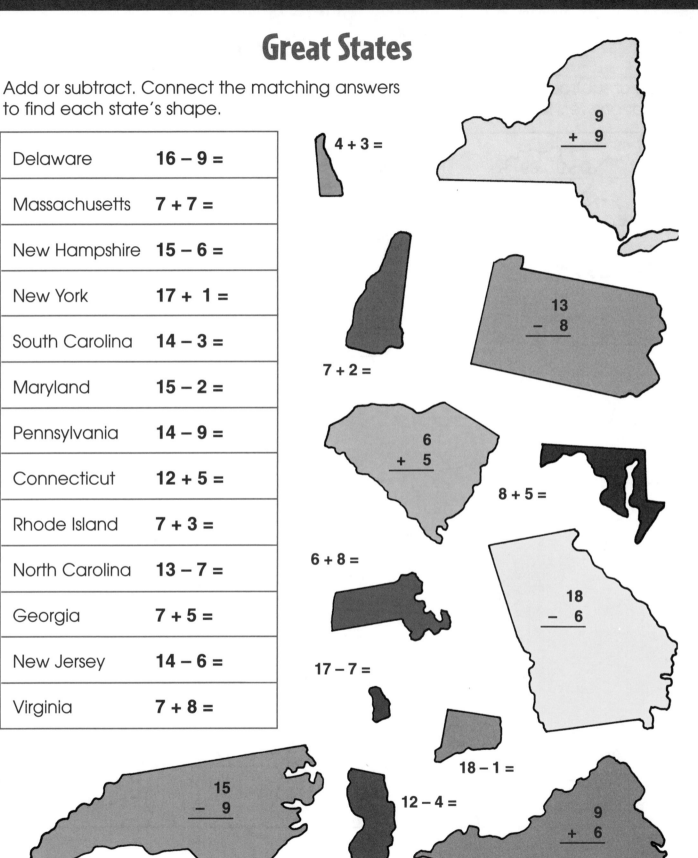

Delaware	**16 – 9 =**
Massachusetts	**7 + 7 =**
New Hampshire	**15 – 6 =**
New York	**17 + 1 =**
South Carolina	**14 – 3 =**
Maryland	**15 – 2 =**
Pennsylvania	**14 – 9 =**
Connecticut	**12 + 5 =**
Rhode Island	**7 + 3 =**
North Carolina	**13 – 7 =**
Georgia	**7 + 5 =**
New Jersey	**14 – 6 =**
Virginia	**7 + 8 =**

4 + 3 =

$$9 + 9$$

7 + 2 =

$$13 - 8$$

$$6 + 5$$

8 + 5 =

6 + 8 =

$$18 - 6$$

17 – 7 =

18 – 1 =

12 – 4 =

$$15 - 9$$

$$9 + 6$$

© Scholastic Inc.

United We Stand

Add or subtract. Color answers greater than 50 green to show the United States.
Color answers less than 50 blue.

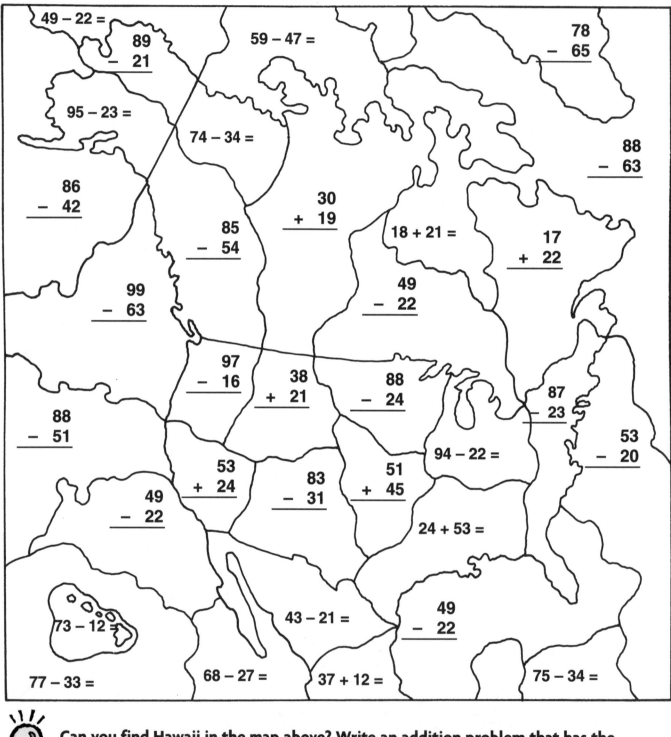

$49 - 22 =$

$$\begin{array}{r} 89 \\ -\ 21 \\ \hline \end{array}$$

$59 - 47 =$

$$\begin{array}{r} 78 \\ -\ 65 \\ \hline \end{array}$$

$95 - 23 =$

$74 - 34 =$

$$\begin{array}{r} 88 \\ -\ 63 \\ \hline \end{array}$$

$$\begin{array}{r} 86 \\ -\ 42 \\ \hline \end{array}$$

$$\begin{array}{r} 85 \\ -\ 54 \\ \hline \end{array}$$

$$\begin{array}{r} 30 \\ +\ 19 \\ \hline \end{array}$$

$18 + 21 =$

$$\begin{array}{r} 17 \\ +\ 22 \\ \hline \end{array}$$

$$\begin{array}{r} 99 \\ -\ 63 \\ \hline \end{array}$$

$$\begin{array}{r} 49 \\ -\ 22 \\ \hline \end{array}$$

$$\begin{array}{r} 97 \\ -\ 16 \\ \hline \end{array}$$

$$\begin{array}{r} 38 \\ +\ 21 \\ \hline \end{array}$$

$$\begin{array}{r} 88 \\ -\ 24 \\ \hline \end{array}$$

$$\begin{array}{r} 87 \\ -\ 23 \\ \hline \end{array}$$

$$\begin{array}{r} 88 \\ -\ 51 \\ \hline \end{array}$$

$$\begin{array}{r} 53 \\ -\ 20 \\ \hline \end{array}$$

$94 - 22 =$

$$\begin{array}{r} 53 \\ +\ 24 \\ \hline \end{array}$$

$$\begin{array}{r} 83 \\ -\ 31 \\ \hline \end{array}$$

$$\begin{array}{r} 51 \\ +\ 45 \\ \hline \end{array}$$

$$\begin{array}{r} 49 \\ -\ 22 \\ \hline \end{array}$$

$24 + 53 =$

$73 - 12 =$

$43 - 21 =$

$$\begin{array}{r} 49 \\ -\ 22 \\ \hline \end{array}$$

$77 - 33 =$

$68 - 27 =$

$37 + 12 =$

$75 - 34 =$

© Scholastic Inc.

Can you find Hawaii in the map above? Write an addition problem that has the same answer.

Stars and Stripes Forever

Circle groups of 10. Write the number of tens and ones. Write the number in the star.

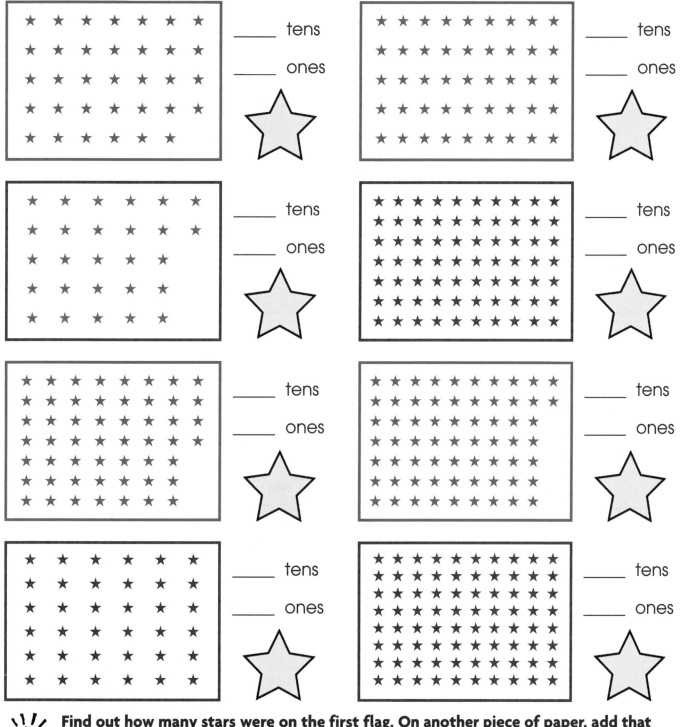

_____ tens

_____ ones

_____ tens

_____ ones

_____ tens

_____ ones

_____ tens

_____ ones

_____ tens

_____ ones

_____ tens

_____ ones

_____ tens

_____ ones

_____ tens

_____ ones

Find out how many stars were on the first flag. On another piece of paper, add that number to the number of stars on the United States flag today. How many groups of tens and ones are there?

The U.S. Capital

Add. Match each building to the correct sum.

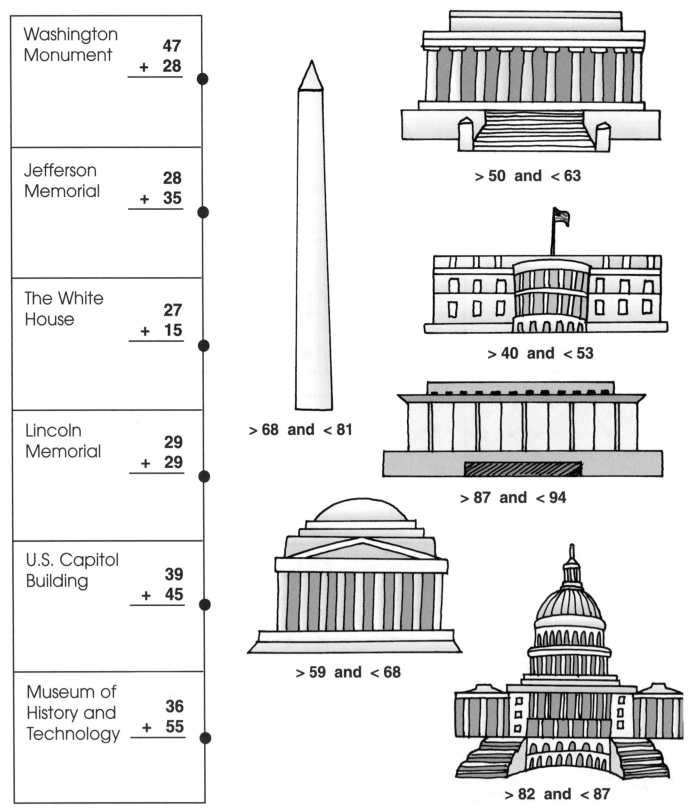

Washington Monument	47 + 28
Jefferson Memorial	28 + 35
The White House	27 + 15
Lincoln Memorial	29 + 29
U.S. Capitol Building	39 + 45
Museum of History and Technology	36 + 55

> 50 and < 63

> 40 and < 53

> 87 and < 94

> 68 and < 81

> 59 and < 68

> 82 and < 87

© Scholastic Inc.

Mr. President

Add. Write the letters in the circles to identify each president.

I was a leader in the Civil War.

39 + 13	38 + 15	56 + 26	26 + 35	29 + 67	27 + 25	43 + 39

◯ ◯ ◯ ◯ ◯ ◯ ◯

I helped write the Declaration of Independence.

19 + 18	28 + 55	24 + 18	19 + 23	17 + 66	59 + 19	49 + 15	78 + 18	48 + 34

◯ ◯ ◯ ◯ ◯ ◯ ◯ ◯ ◯

I was a leader in the American Revolutionary War.

59 + 39	48 + 24	27 + 37	19 + 46	27 + 26	38 + 44	27 + 18	18 + 29	38 + 58	27 + 55

◯ ◯ ◯ ◯ ◯ ◯ ◯ ◯ ◯ ◯

Code

61 C	98 W	55 Y	83 E	45 G	82 N	78 R	65 H	52 L
96 O	42 F	86 K	47 T	72 A	37 J	64 S	53 I	36 D

On another piece of paper, make a code and write problems for the name of our current president.

Travel the Nation

Look at the number on each form of transportation. Write the number of tens and ones. Regroup. Write the new number.

___3___ tens
___7___ ones

Trade 1 ten for 10 ones.

___2___ tens
__17__ ones

___ tens
___ ones

Trade 1 ten for 10 ones.

___ tens
___ ones

___ tens
___ ones

Trade 1 ten for 10 ones.

___ tens
___ ones

___ tens
___ ones

Trade 1 ten for 10 ones.

___ tens
___ ones

___ tens
___ ones

Trade 1 ten for 10 ones.

___ tens
___ ones

___ tens
___ ones

Trade 1 ten for 10 ones.

___ tens
___ ones

___ tens
___ ones

Trade 1 ten for 10 ones.

___ tens
___ ones

Great Vacations

Subtract. Draw a line from each difference to the vacation spot on the map.

Mount Rushmore	Niagara Falls	Gateway Arch	Four Corners Monument	Statue of Liberty
72 − 27	57 − 29	58 − 39	93 − 19	94 − 29

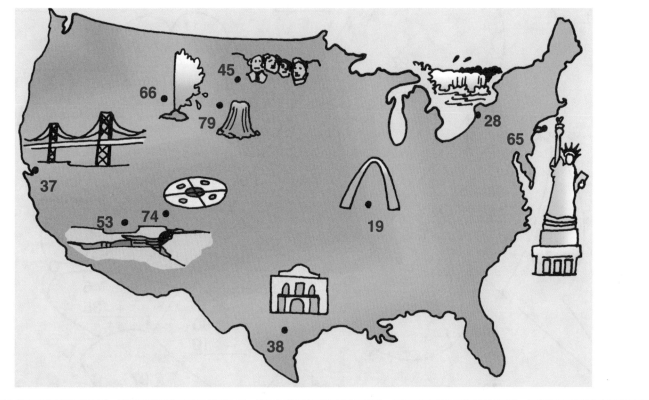

Grand Canyon	Devil's Tower	Golden Gate Bridge	The Alamo	Old Faithful
82 − 29	93 − 14	64 − 27	66 − 28	94 − 28

On the map above, mark and write the name of a vacation spot in the United States you would like to visit. Write a subtraction problem for it.

America's Favorite Pastime

Add or subtract. Use the chart to color the picture.

white	blue	brown	red	yellow
0–20	21–40	41–60	61–80	81–100

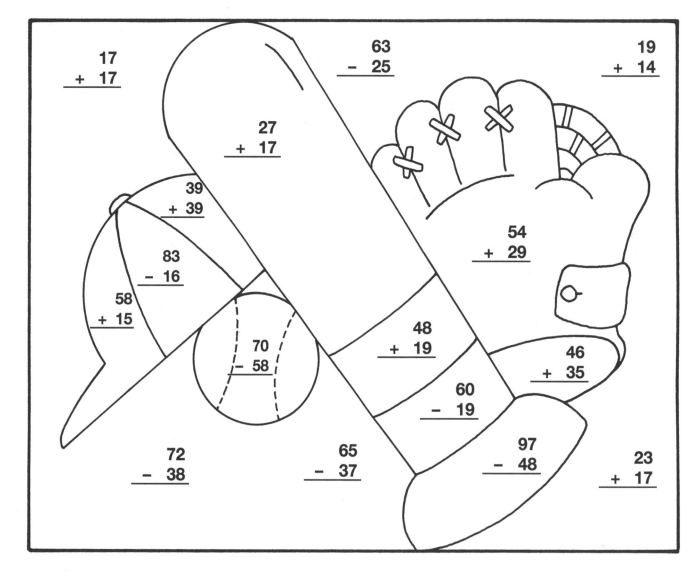

$$\begin{array}{r} 17 \\ + 17 \\ \hline \end{array}$$

$$\begin{array}{r} 63 \\ - 25 \\ \hline \end{array}$$

$$\begin{array}{r} 19 \\ + 14 \\ \hline \end{array}$$

$$\begin{array}{r} 27 \\ + 17 \\ \hline \end{array}$$

$$\begin{array}{r} 39 \\ + 39 \\ \hline \end{array}$$

$$\begin{array}{r} 54 \\ + 29 \\ \hline \end{array}$$

$$\begin{array}{r} 83 \\ - 16 \\ \hline \end{array}$$

$$\begin{array}{r} 58 \\ + 15 \\ \hline \end{array}$$

$$\begin{array}{r} 70 \\ - 58 \\ \hline \end{array}$$

$$\begin{array}{r} 48 \\ + 19 \\ \hline \end{array}$$

$$\begin{array}{r} 46 \\ + 35 \\ \hline \end{array}$$

$$\begin{array}{r} 60 \\ - 19 \\ \hline \end{array}$$

$$\begin{array}{r} 72 \\ - 38 \\ \hline \end{array}$$

$$\begin{array}{r} 65 \\ - 37 \\ \hline \end{array}$$

$$\begin{array}{r} 97 \\ - 48 \\ \hline \end{array}$$

$$\begin{array}{r} 23 \\ + 17 \\ \hline \end{array}$$

Finish the pattern.

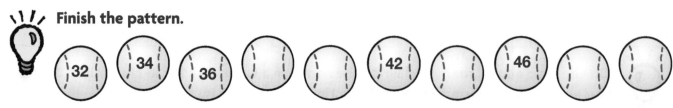

32   34   36   ___   ___   42   ___   46   ___   ___

© Scholastic Inc.

High-Scoring Game

	1	2	3	4	5	6	7	8	9
Cardinals	16	57	91	39	68	25	83	44	72
Blue Jays	87	11	45	94	29	73	32	58	66

Find the total number of runs in each inning.

Add.

1	2	3	4	5	6	7	8	9
16 + 87								

Find the difference in runs in each inning.

Subtract.

1	2	3	4	5	6	7	8	9
87 - 16								

Solve.

A. How many runs did the Cardinals score altogether in the first and sixth inning?

_____ runs

B. How many runs did the Blue Jays score altogether in the seventh and eighth inning?

_____ runs

C. How many more runs did the Cardinals score in the third inning than the second inning?

_____ runs

D. How many more runs did the Blue Jays score in the first inning than the fifth inning?

_____ runs

© Scholastic Inc.

More Fun Sports

Add or subtract.

91 − 67	48 + 43	92 − 45	70 − 17	63 − 47	38 + 54	29 + 36	80 − 42
skating	football	hockey	volleyball	basketball	soccer	tennis	track

Complete the puzzle with the sport that goes with each answer.

Down

1. 47
2. 53
3. 24
5. 38

Across

3. 92
4. 16
5. 65
6. 91

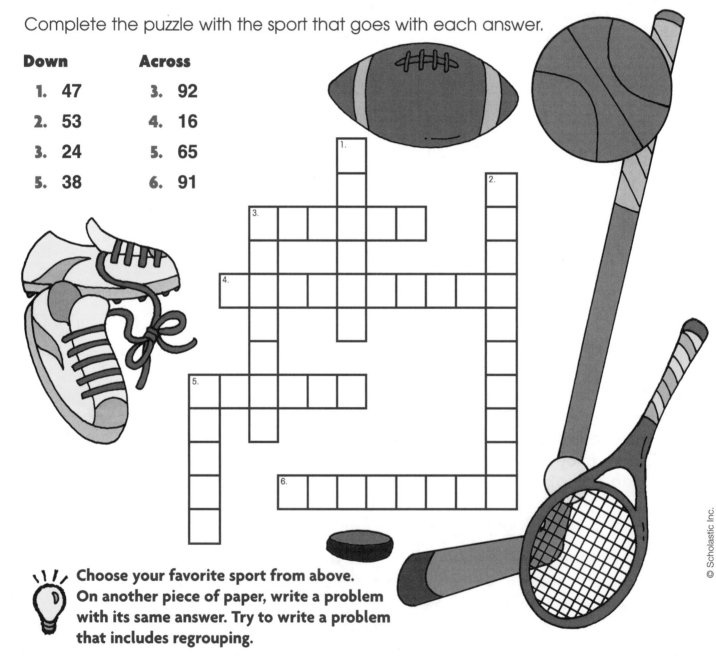

Choose your favorite sport from above.
On another piece of paper, write a problem
with its same answer. Try to write a problem
that includes regrouping.

Skating Shapes

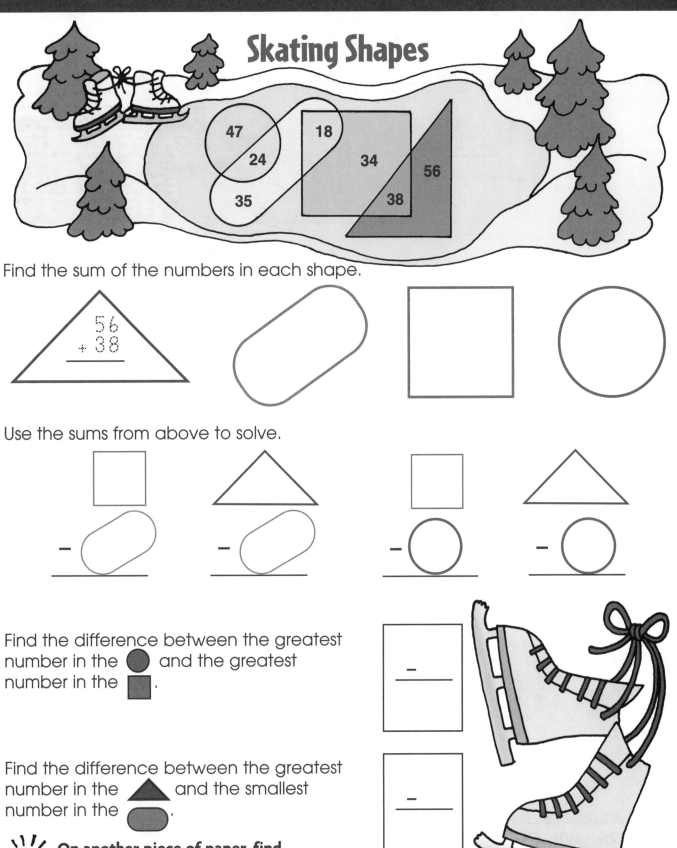

Find the sum of the numbers in each shape.

$$\begin{array}{r} 56 \\ +38 \\ \hline \end{array}$$

Use the sums from above to solve.

Find the difference between the greatest
number in the ⬤ and the greatest
number in the ◼.

Find the difference between the greatest
number in the ▲ and the smallest
number in the ⬭.

💡 **On another piece of paper, find
the sum of all the numbers in the
shapes on the skating pond.**

Great Math Inventions

Add or subtract. Then write the problem's letter above its matching answer below.

S.   29
    + 46

I.   48
    − 24

A.   27
    + 38

R.   56
    − 18

R.   37
    + 47

W.   81
    − 24

H.   23
    + 35

I.   90
    − 26

U.   52
    − 19

O.   37
    + 35

L.   70
    − 19

M.   82
    − 48

B.   23
    + 48

L.   52
    + 28

G.   91
    − 22

U.   73
    − 25

___ ___ ___ ___ ___ ___ ___   ___ ___ ___ ___ ___ ___ ___ ___ ___
57   24   80   51   64   65   34   71   48   84   38   72   33   69   58   75

invented and patented the adding machine in St. Louis, Missouri, in 1888.

It All Adds Up!

Add. Fill in the missing numbers.

3 2 4 + 6 3 □ ——— □ □ 6	2 4 □ + □ 5 1 ——— 7 □ 2	□ 5 5 + 3 □ 1 ——— 4 8 □	2 □ 3 + □ 1 3 ——— 5 2 □
4 1 □ + 3 □ 2 ——— □ 3 7	□ 4 3 + 1 4 □ ——— 2 □ 9	2 □ □ + 2 1 6 ——— □ 1 8	□ 3 1 + 4 □ □ ——— 8 5 3
1 □ 2 + □ 3 3 ——— 3 7 □	□ 4 1 + 1 3 □ ——— 6 □ 5	3 3 □ + □ □ 3 ——— 6 6 8	□ 1 2 + 2 □ 2 ——— 9 4 □
2 2 □ + 3 1 4 ——— □ □ 4	5 □ 4 + □ 3 4 ——— 8 4 □	2 2 4 + 1 □ 3 ——— □ 6 □	□ 1 6 + 1 3 □ ——— 5 □ 8

Joe and Ellie were going to the movies. Joe brought \$5.□0, and Ellie brought \$□.35. If they had \$9.75 altogether, how much money did they each have? Show your work.

It's Electrifying!

Regroup tens into hundreds. Draw a line to connect.

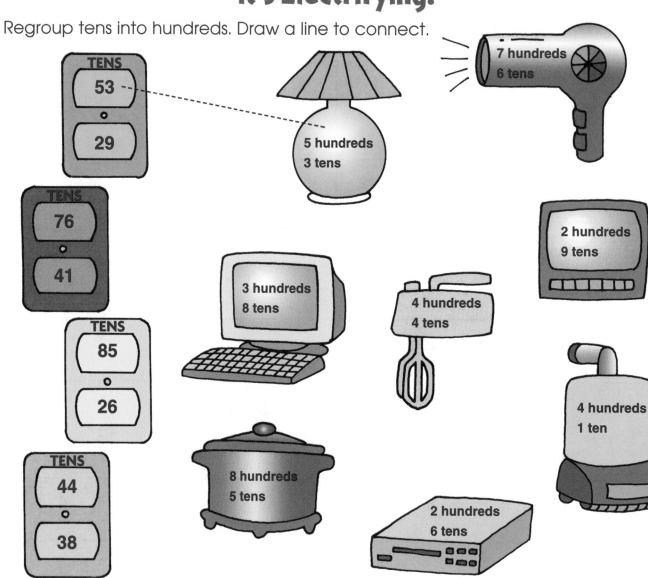

Fill in each missing number.

hundreds	tens	ones	number
200	40	7	2 4 7
400	70	6	__ __ __
300		2	__ 9 __
100	90		__ __ 3
500		1	__ 6 __

Let the Light Shine

Regroup hundreds to tens.

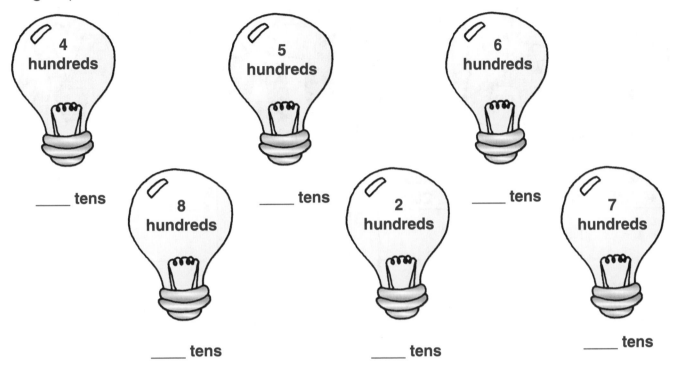

4 hundreds ____ tens

5 hundreds ____ tens

6 hundreds ____ tens

8 hundreds ____ tens

2 hundreds ____ tens

7 hundreds ____ tens

Circle the lightbulb in each box with the greater value yellow.

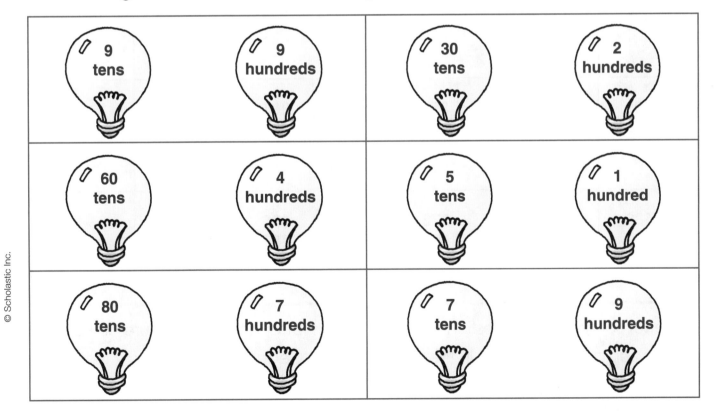

9 tens — 9 hundreds

30 tens — 2 hundreds

60 tens — 4 hundreds

5 tens — 1 hundred

80 tens — 7 hundreds

7 tens — 9 hundreds

A, B, C, . . .

Add.

286 + 668	138 + 289	285 + 269
496 + 188	159 + 190	175 + 189
499 + 446	375 + 469	183 + 289
299 + 158	196 + 378	657 + 285
186 + 287	157 + 267	276 + 566

295 + 675	188 + 185	487 + 385
284 + 439	389 + 188	595 + 289
128 + 379	297 + 179	198 + 199
365 + 378	192 + 579	123 + 589
386 + 189	295 + 379	436 + 538

This letter sounds like a question.

Color each answer with a 4 in the ones place to see!

This letter names a feature on your face.

Color each answer with a 7 in the tens place to see!

© Scholastic Inc.

...X, Y, and Z

Add.

298 + 276	191 + 343	269 + 289
157 + 189	137 + 369	278 + 485
395 + 457	244 + 279	499 + 446
288 + 664	236 + 288	577 + 388
498 + 399	399 + 164	284 + 439

259 + 467	364 + 258	487 + 436
199 + 128	199 + 89	238 + 287
255 + 373	509 + 315	117 + 304
257 + 569	276 + 566	149 + 279
339 + 385	258 + 467	179 + 348

This letter names an icy drink.

Color each answer with a 5 in the
hundreds place to see!

This letter names an insect that stings.

Color each answer with a 2 in the
tens place to see!

Number Decoder

Find the number that goes with each letter
in the problems below. Then subtract.

1	2 ABC	3 DEF
4 GHI	5 JKL	6 MNO
7 PQRS	8 TUV	9 WXYZ
*	0	#

JDH − APL	−

GMQ − CSV	−

EWA − BYN	−

MAL − FNO	−

WTU − JVW	−

REK − DMP	−

TJI − EXQ	−

KNH − HZU	−

FDX − BGY	−

Find the numbers for your name. Add to find the sum of the numbers.

Out of This World

Subtract. Use the chart to color the picture.

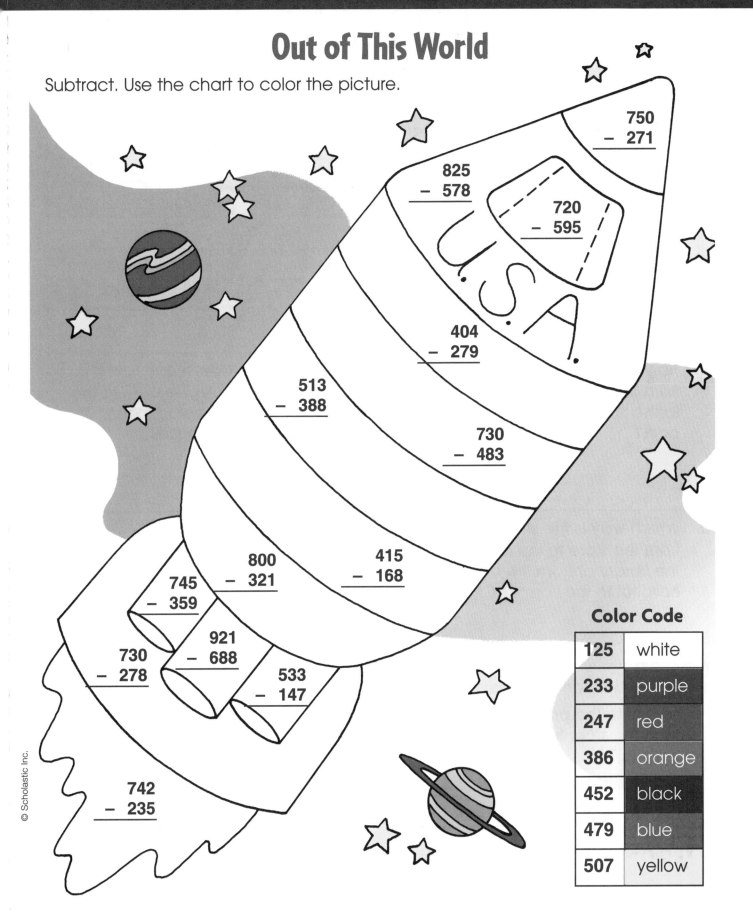

750
− 271

825
− 578

720
− 595

404
− 279

513
− 388

730
− 483

800
− 321

415
− 168

745
− 359

921
− 688

730
− 278

533
− 147

742
− 235

Color Code

125	white
233	purple
247	red
386	orange
452	black
479	blue
507	yellow

© Scholastic Inc.

Your Part of the World

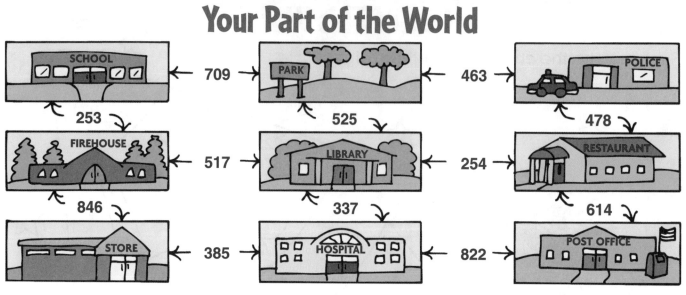

Use the distance between each building to solve each problem.

A. How many feet is it from the firehouse to the library to the park?	B. How many feet is it from the post office to the restaurant to the police station?	C. How many feet is it from the park to the school to the firehouse?

D. Which way is the shortest route—from the store to the firehouse to the library or from the store to the hospital to the library? Circle.

$$846$$
$$+ \ 517$$

$$385$$
$$+ \ 337$$

E. How much farther is the

school to the park than the store to the hospital?

firehouse to the library than the park to the police station?

library to the park than the hospital to the store?

 On another piece of paper, find which route is the shortest way from the school to the post office. Trace this route on the map above.

Home Sweet Home

Use the coordinates to find each number. Add or subtract.

A	496	723	379
B	162	215	956
C	547	834	688
	1	2	3

E	668	884	345
F	239	716	188
G	422	578	957
	4	5	6

A. (A, 1)

(F, 6) − _____

B. (B, 3)

(E, 4) − _____

C. (C, 1)

(F, 4) + _____

D. (A, 3)

(E, 6) + _____

E. (A, 2)

(B, 1) − _____

F. (G, 4)

(B, 2) − _____

G. (G, 6)

(C, 3) − _____

H. (E, 5)

(C, 2) + _____

I. (B, 3)

(G, 5) − _____

Color the largest number on each house orange. Color the smallest number on each house purple.

What a Beautiful World!

Add or subtract.

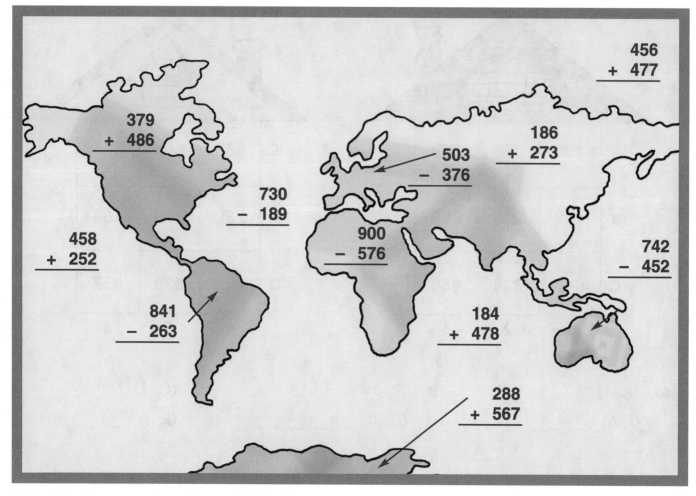

$$456 + 477$$

$$379 + 486$$

$$186 + 273$$

$$503 - 376$$

$$730 - 189$$

$$900 - 576$$

$$458 + 252$$

$$742 - 452$$

$$841 - 263$$

$$184 + 478$$

$$288 + 567$$

Label the map using the code below.

North America	> 860 and < 927	**Atlantic Ocean**	> 496 and < 560
South America	> 571 and < 658	**Indian Ocean**	> 581 and < 672
Australia	> 189 and < 293	**Pacific Ocean**	> 671 and < 732
Asia	> 423 and < 538	**Arctic Ocean**	> 867 and < 948
Europe	> 85 and < 266		
Antarctica	> 748 and < 864		
Africa	> 297 and < 334		

Add the answers for the oceans together.

Majestic Mountains

Add or subtract. Use the code to name four
different mountain ranges.

N	6,348
R	8,789
A	5,063
I	7,695
O	2,429
K	5,642
E	7,483
C	3,012
Y	2,351
Z	5,234
L	3,721
U	6,704
P	3,827
S	8,749
D	4,907

```
  2,033        2,411        2,504        4,328
+ 3,030      + 1,310      + 1,323      + 4,421
```

( )   ( )   ( )   ( )

```
  4,258        1,326        1,012        2,321        1,231
+ 4,531      + 1,103      + 2,000      + 3,321      + 1,120
```

( )   ( )   ( )   ( )   ( )

```
  1,204        2,113        2,042        3,746        4,131
+ 1,225      + 3,121      + 3,021      + 5,043      + 1,511
```

( )   ( )   ( )   ( )   ( )

```
  4,053        2,216        2,506        6,471        7,326
+ 1,010      + 4,132      + 2,401      + 1,012      + 1,423
```

( )   ( )   ( )   ( )   ( )

Reach for the Top

Add. Then starting at the bottom
row, add the digits in each sum. If
the digits total 9, color the box to
find your way to the top!

1,021
+ 1,031

3,432
+ 1,154

2,130
+ 1,200

1,423
+ 1,322

2,423
+ 1,520

4,000
+ 4,010

4,024
+ 3,012

5,010
+ 1,011

3,011
+ 4,000

2,240
+ 1,232

1,412
+ 1,351

4,201
+ 1,100

2,431
+ 3,132

4,631
+ 3,210

4,302
+ 5,502

3,243
+ 4,200

2,031
+ 1,200

4,084
+ 2,011

1,362
+ 1,202

3,025
+ 1,312

6,434
+ 3,251

**Write an addition problem with four numbers in the answer so the sum of the digits
equals 12.**

One in a Thousand

Add. Write the letters on the lines below in order from the smallest to the largest sums to find out whose face is on the hundred-dollar bill.

F. $27.41	**N.** $59.63	**N.** $85.42	**R.** $31.75
+ $12.55	+ $20.33	+ $14.06	+ $35.24

K. $64.84	**A.** $29.35	**L.** $46.96	**I.** $73.57
+ $22.15	+ $50.42	+ $42.03	+ $23.43

___ ___ ___ ___ ___ ___ ___ ___

If you have **50** hundred-dollar bills, you have _____ thousand dollars!

If you have **20** hundred-dollar bills, you have _____ thousand dollars!

If you have **80** hundred-dollar bills, you have _____ thousand dollars!

If you have **10** hundred-dollar bills, you have _____ thousand dollars!

If you have **30** hundred-dollar bills, you have _____ thousand dollars!

If you have **70** hundred-dollar bills, you have _____ thousand dollars!

If you have **90** hundred-dollar bills, you have _____ thousand dollars!

If you have **40** hundred-dollar bills, you have _____ thousand dollars!

If you have **60** hundred-dollar bills, you have _____ thousand dollars!

© Scholastic Inc.

Great Beginnings

Add. Look at each sum. Use the code below to color the picture.

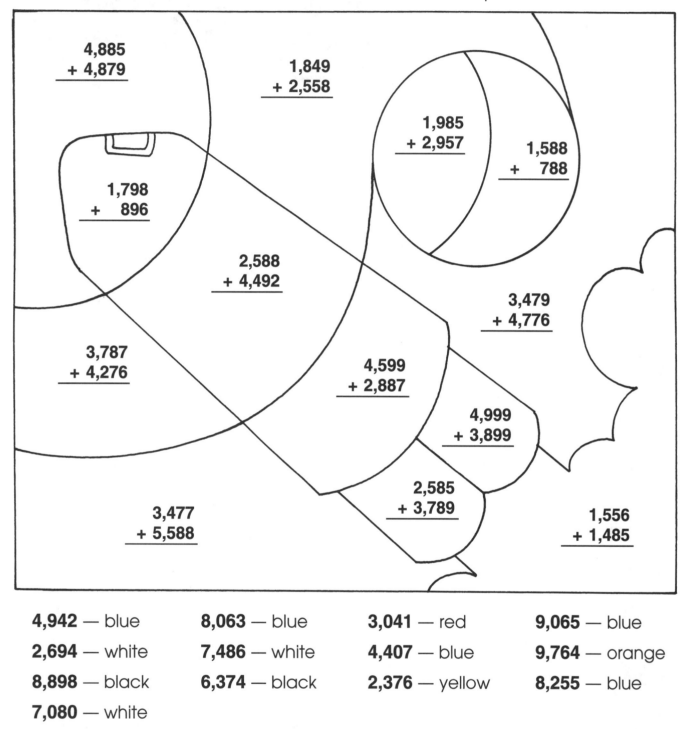

4,885
+ 4,879

1,849
+ 2,558

1,985
+ 2,957

1,588
+   788

1,798
+   896

2,588
+ 4,492

3,479
+ 4,776

3,787
+ 4,276

4,599
+ 2,887

4,999
+ 3,899

3,477
+ 5,588

2,585
+ 3,789

1,556
+ 1,485

4,942 — blue   **8,063** — blue   **3,041** — red   **9,065** — blue

2,694 — white   **7,486** — white   **4,407** — blue   **9,764** — orange

8,898 — black   **6,374** — black   **2,376** — yellow   **8,255** — blue

7,080 — white

Find the year man first walked on the moon. Add that number to the year it is now.

Styles Change

Add. Match the sums to show the hats and shoes that go together.

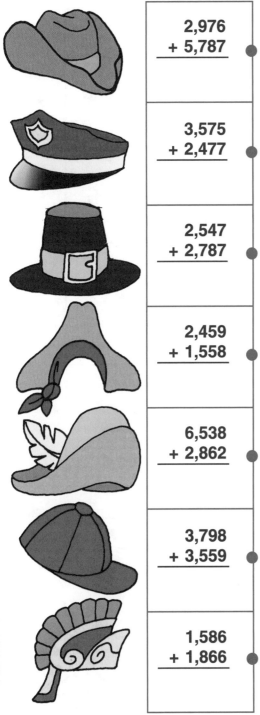

2,976 + 5,787
3,575 + 2,477
2,547 + 2,787
2,459 + 1,558
6,538 + 2,862
3,798 + 3,559
1,586 + 1,866

2,386 + 3,666
1,278 + 2,739
2,645 + 4,712
3,885 + 4,878
1,665 + 1,787
3,655 + 1,679
2,766 + 6,634

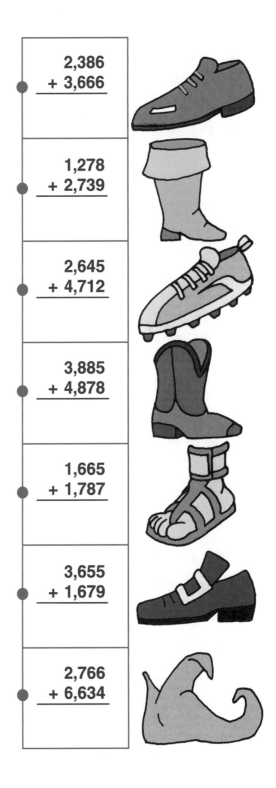

Dynamite Dominoes

Color the connecting squares that equal the same amount the same color.
Remember, 1 thousand equals 10 hundreds.

thousands	**20 hundreds**	**10 hundreds**	**thousand**	**thousands**
50 hundreds	**thousands**	**90 hundreds**	**thousands**	**40 hundreds**
30 hundreds	**70 hundreds**	**thousands**	**10 hundreds**	**20 hundreds**
thousands	**thousands**	**thousands**	**60 hundreds**	**thousands**

Add. Write the number.

thousands		hundreds		tens		ones		
3	+	1	+	6	+	7	=	
5	+	7	+	0	+	3	=	
6	+	0	+	3	+	9	=	
4	+	5	+	8	+	4	=	
9	+	9	+	4	+	0	=	

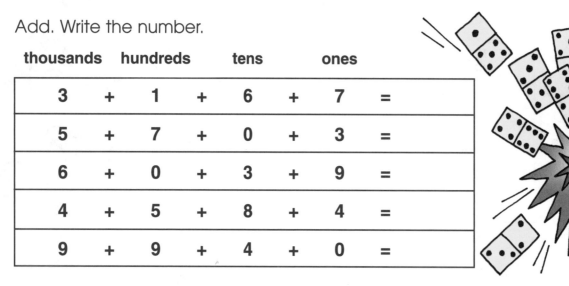

Pictures in the Sky

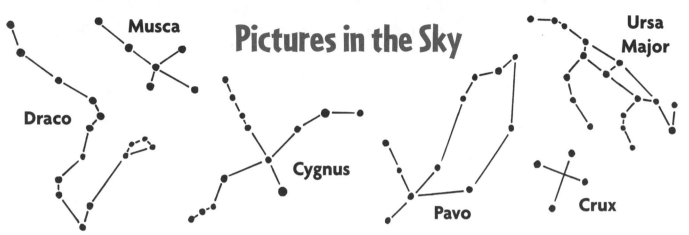

Subtract. Draw a line between matching sums to connect the Latin and English names for each constellation.

Latin		English	
Draco	7,621 − 5,586	8,533 − 2,074	**Swan**
Pavo	7,340 − 3,758	7,662 − 2,678	**Cross**
Cygnus	9,317 − 2,858	8,403 − 6,368	**Dragon**
Ursa Major	8,332 − 3,579	6,441 − 2,859	**Peacock**
Musca	7,015 − 1,739	7,031 − 2,278	**Great Bear**
Crux	8,150 − 3,166	8,133 − 2,857	**Fly**

© Scholastic Inc.

Fun With Numbers

Add or subtract. Then write the problem's letter above its matching answer below.

W.
2,376
+ 2,784

O.
8,500
− 2,763

T.
4,401
− 2,550

A.
2,763
+ 3,857

E.
6,345
− 2,660

H.
8,455
− 1,867

!
4,672
+ 3,885

M.
8,304
− 2,541

M.
2,463
+ 4,908

A.
1,074
+ 5,988

E.
4,365
− 1,478

S.
3,453
+ 2,778

_____ _____ _____ _____ **is**
5,763 7,062 1,851 6,588

_____ _____ _____ _____ _____ _____ _____ _____
6,620 5,160 2,887 6,231 5,737 7,371 3,685 8,557

© Scholastic Inc.

Space Chase Place Value

Use strategies to capture creepy space creatures while learning about place value.

Directions

1. Review place value to the hundred thousands place. You will need this knowledge if you want to do well in the Space Chase game.

2. Partner up with a friend or family member. To make your own spinner, spin a paper clip around a pencil placed at the spinner's center. Players should spin to see who goes first, with the higher spin going first. Players then take turns spinning.

3. On each turn, a player spins and lands on a number. The player then says which creepy space creature he or she will capture on that turn. Players write the number they landed on in the blank that corresponds with the place value of the space creature. (For example: In round 1, Player 1 spins a 5. She decides to capture a Kerpew on this turn. Kerpews represent the ten thousands place. So Player 1 writes a 5 in the ten thousands place of her Round 1 score blanks.) Players record their numbers in the score blanks of the round they are playing.

4. A particular space creature can be captured only once per round. The round ends when both players have captured all six space creatures. Play continues for three rounds. The winner of each round is the player who has written the greater 6-digit number.

Space Chase Place Value

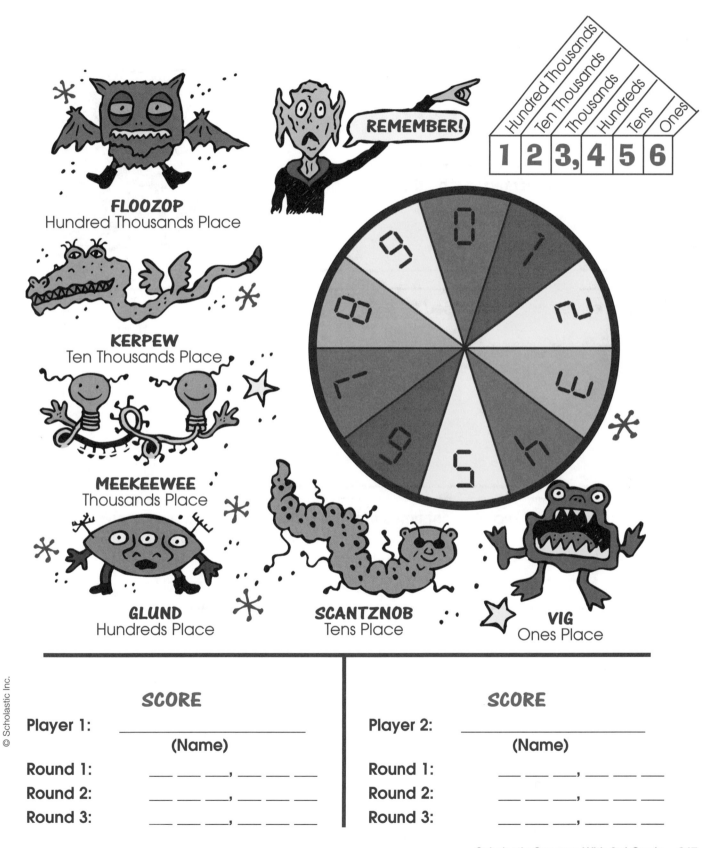

Hundred Thousands	Ten Thousands	Thousands	Hundreds	Tens	Ones
1	2	3,	4	5	6

REMEMBER!

FLOOZOP
Hundred Thousands Place

KERPEW
Ten Thousands Place

MEEKEEWEE
Thousands Place

GLUND
Hundreds Place

SCANTZNOB
Tens Place

VIG
Ones Place

SCORE

Player 1: _____
(Name)

Round 1: __ __ __, __ __ __
Round 2: __ __ __, __ __ __
Round 3: __ __ __, __ __ __

SCORE

Player 2: _____
(Name)

Round 1: __ __ __, __ __ __
Round 2: __ __ __, __ __ __
Round 3: __ __ __, __ __ __

Newspaper Math

What to Do:

Use a newspaper to find the numbers listed below. Cut out your answers from the newspaper and tape them in the box with each question.

1. **From the weather report, find the temperature in two cities.**

2. **Pick three items advertised for sale.**

3. **Find two different times that the same movie is playing.**

4. **From the TV listings, pick three programs that you would like to watch. Include the channels that those programs will be on.**

5. **Choose two numbers from an article of your choice.**

Place-Value Puzzler

What is too much fun for one, enough for two, and means nothing to three?

Find the answer to this riddle by using place value! Take a look at each number below. One digit in each number is underlined. Circle the word in each line that tells the place value of the underlined number. Write the letters next to each correct answer in the blanks below. The first one is done for you.

A.	15,209	**a** thousands	**i** hundreds
B.	4,729	**n** hundreds	**s** tens
C.	425	**e** hundreds	**o** tens
D.	7,618	**c** tens	**g** ones
E.	1,112	**p** thousands	**r** hundreds
F.	8,636	**a** hundreds	**e** ones
G.	222	**t** tens	**m** ones

a
—— ———— ———— ———— ———— ———— ————
A   B   C   D   E   F   G

Bee Riddle

Riddle: What did the farmer get when he tried to reach the beehive?

Round each number. Then use the Decoder to solve the riddle by filling in the spaces at the bottom of the page.

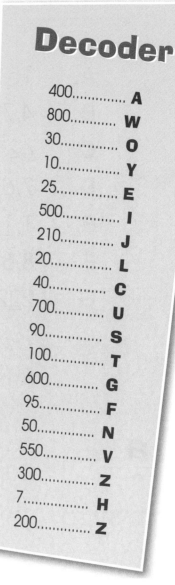

Decoder

400............ **A**
800........... **W**
30............. **O**
10............. **Y**
25.............. **E**
500............. **I J**
210............. **J**
20.............. **L**
40.............. **C**
700............. **U**
90.............. **S**
100............. **T**
600............ **G**
95.............. **F**
50.............. **N**
550............. **V**
300............. **Z**
7.............. **H**
200............. **Z**

❶ Round 7 to the nearest ten   _____
❷ Round 23 to the nearest ten   _____
❸ Round 46 to the nearest ten   _____
❹ Round 92 to the nearest ten   _____
❺ Round 203 to the nearest hundred _____
❻ Round 420 to the nearest hundred_____
❼ Round 588 to the nearest hundred_____
❽ Round 312 to the nearest hundred_____
❾ Round 549 to the nearest hundred_____
❿ Round 710 to the nearest hundred_____

A "B __ __ __ __" __ __ __ __ __ __
    10 5 8 1   4 9 7 3 6 2

Discover Coordinates!

Follow the coordinates to the correct box, then draw in the underlined treasures

on this treasure map.

C3   A <u>jeweled crown</u> sparkles.
B1   A <u>ruby necklace</u> can be found.
C5   A <u>golden cup</u> awaits you.
D4   An <u>X</u> marks the spot!
A4   A <u>wooden treasure chest</u> you'll find.
E1   A <u>silvery sword</u> lies here.

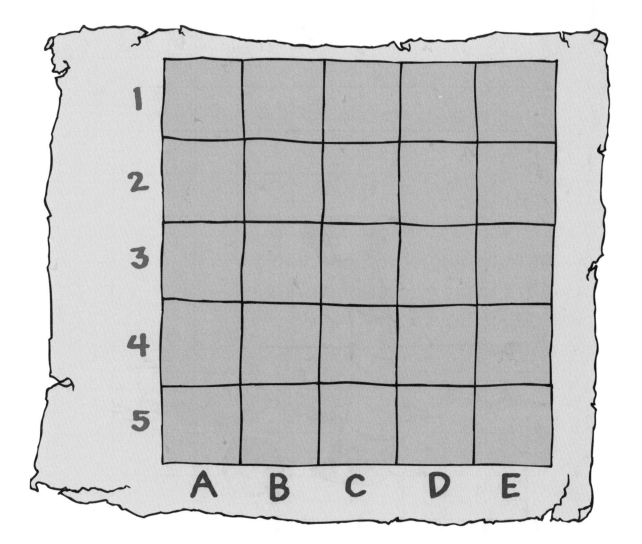

Tropical Tree

1. Solve the problems.

2. Find each number pair on the graph. Make a dot for each.

3. Connect the dots in the order that you make them.

4. What picture did you make?

_____

	Across	Up
1.	10 – 5 = ____	7 – 0 = ____
2.	19 – 12 = ____	9 – 4 = ____
3.	10 – 4 = ____	18 – 11 = ____
4.	20 – 12 = ____	8 – 2 = ____
5.	9 – 3 = ____	17 – 9 = ____
6.	18 – 10 = ____	15 – 8 = ____

	Across	Up
7.	17 – 11 = ____	19 – 10 = ____
8.	20 – 16 = ____	11 – 2 = ____
9.	19 – 18 = ____	13 – 5 = ____
10.	20 – 17 = ____	15 – 7 = ____
11.	20 – 19 = ____	14 – 8 = ____
12.	18 – 15 = ____	20 – 13 = ____
13.	13 – 12 = ____	16 – 11 = ____
14.	17 – 13 = ____	16 – 9 = ____

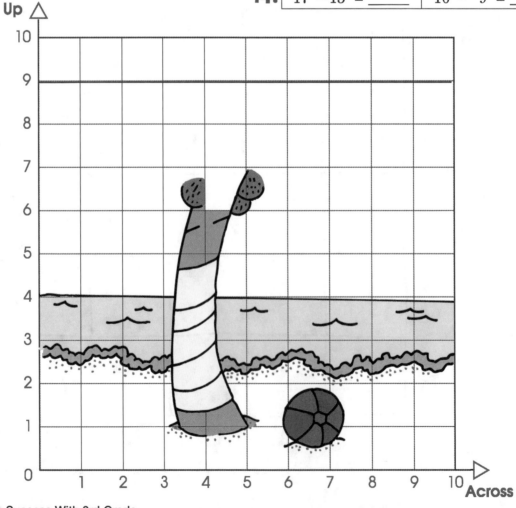

Animal Caller

A bar graph shows information. This bar graph shows the speeds of animals in miles per hour. Use the graph to answer the questions.

WHICH ANIMAL IS...

1. THE FASTEST?

_____

2. THE SLOWEST?

_____

3. GOING 40 mph?

_____

4. 20 mph FASTER THAN A CAT?

_____

5. HOW MANY 4-FOOTED ANIMALS ARE LISTED?

_____

DO THE BARS SHOW...

6. ANIMAL NAMES AND mph?

_____

7. SPEED OR WEIGHT?

_____

8. INFORMATION ABOUT TIGERS?

_____

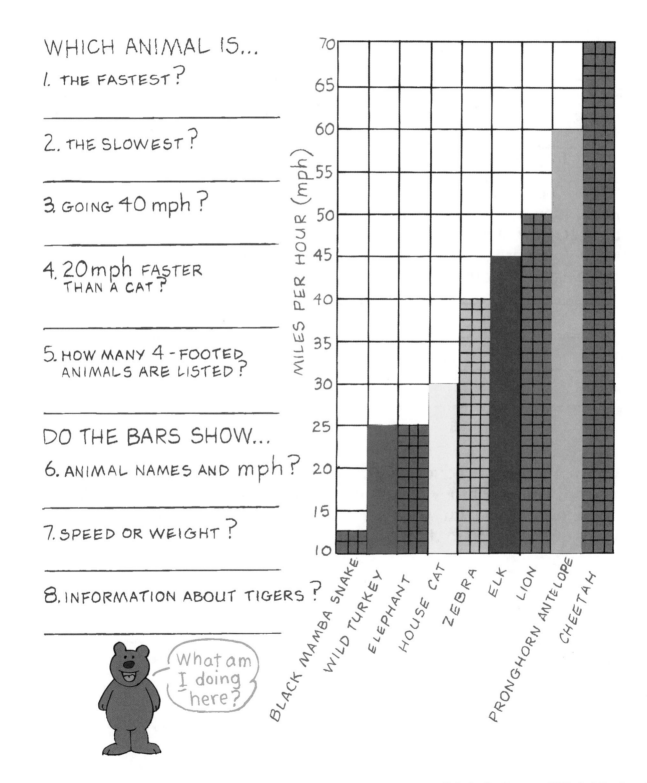

What am I doing here?

Great Graphing

How many pennies equal 5¢? Color in the boxes on the graph to show your answer. How many nickels equal 5¢? Color in the boxes on the graph to show your answer.

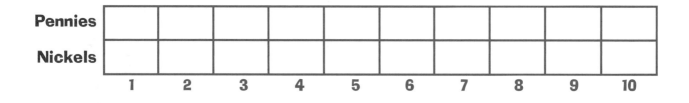

How many pennies equal 10¢? Color in the boxes on the graph to show your answer. How many nickels equal 10¢? Color in the boxes on the graph to show your answer. How many dimes equal 10¢? Color in the boxes on the graph to show your answer.

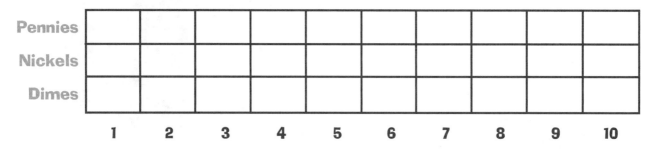

How many pennies equal 25¢? Color in the boxes on the graph to show your answer. How many nickels equal 25¢? Color in the boxes on the graph to show your answer. How many quarters equal 25¢? Color in the boxes on the graph to show your answer.

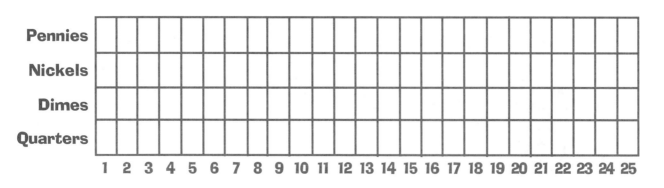

Graph Drafter

A line graph shows how something changes over time. This line graph shows temperature changes during a year in New York City. Use the graph to answer the questions below.

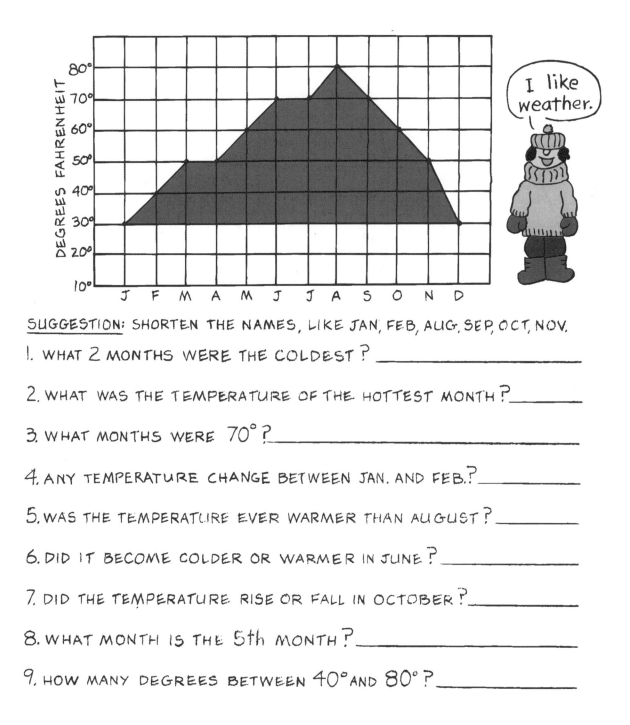

SUGGESTION: SHORTEN THE NAMES, LIKE JAN, FEB, AUG, SEP, OCT, NOV.

1. WHAT 2 MONTHS WERE THE COLDEST ? _____

2. WHAT WAS THE TEMPERATURE OF THE HOTTEST MONTH ?_____

3. WHAT MONTHS WERE 70° ?_____

4. ANY TEMPERATURE CHANGE BETWEEN JAN. AND FEB.?_____

5. WAS THE TEMPERATURE EVER WARMER THAN AUGUST ?_____

6. DID IT BECOME COLDER OR WARMER IN JUNE ?_____

7. DID THE TEMPERATURE RISE OR FALL IN OCTOBER ?_____

8. WHAT MONTH IS THE 5th MONTH ?_____

9. HOW MANY DEGREES BETWEEN 40° AND 80° ?_____

Code Zero! Code One!

When a number is multiplied by 0, the product is always 0.
When a number is multiplied by 1, the product is always the number being multiplied.

Multiply. Shade all products of 0 yellow. Shade all other products green.

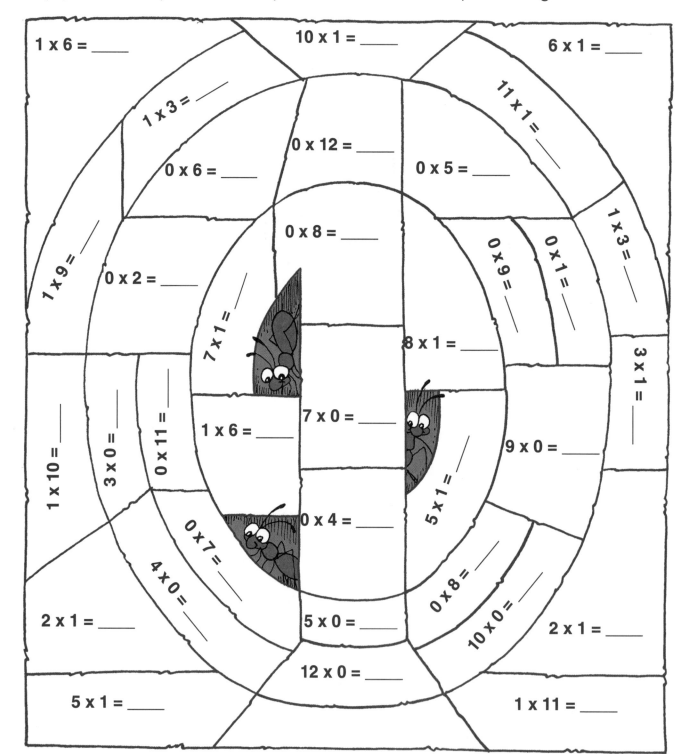

© Scholastic Inc.

Two, Four, Six, Eight, Who Do We Appreciate?

When multiplying by 2, skip count by 2, or think of number line jumping!

Multiply.

A. 2 x 3 = _____   2 x 8 = _____   11 x 2 = _____   2 x 7 = _____

B. 8 x 2 = _____   4 x 2 = _____   2 x 2 = _____   2 x 4 = _____

C. 12 x 2 = _____   5 x 2 = _____   10 x 2 = _____   2 x 12 = _____

D. 9 x 2 = _____   2 x 1 = _____   2 x 10 = _____   7 x 2 = _____

E. 2 x 0 = _____   2 x 6 = _____   3 x 2 = _____   0 x 2 = _____

F. 2 x 5 = _____   2 x 9 = _____

G. 6 x 2 = _____   1 x 2 = _____

H. 2 x 11 = _____   2 x 2 = _____

On another piece of paper, write a rhyme to go with each multiplication fact for 2.
Examples: "2 x 4 = 8, I love math, can you relate?" Or, "2 x 4 = 8, I've got to go, and shut the gate!"

A Positive Answer

What should you say if you are asked, "Do you want to learn the 3s?"

To find out, look at each problem below. If the product is correct, color the space green. If the product is incorrect, color the space yellow.

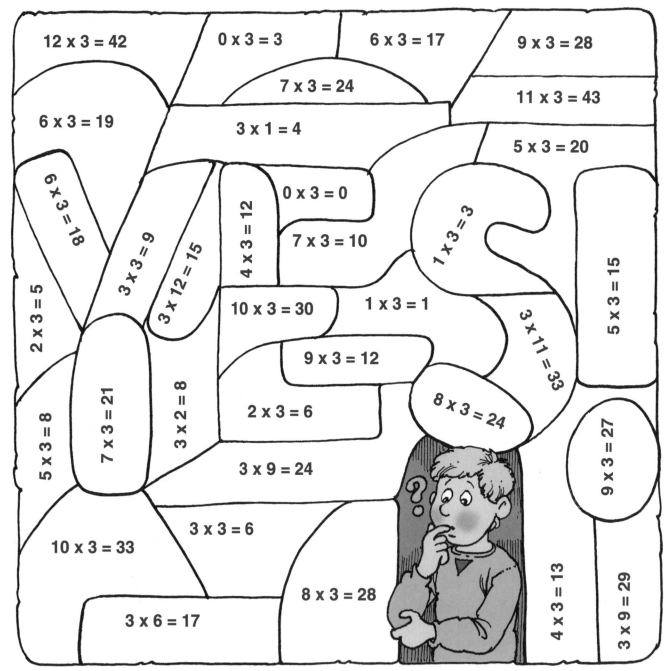

💡 **How many letters are in the answer to the puzzle? If you wrote this word ten times, how many letters would you write altogether?**

Puzzling Facts

Multiply. Write the number word for each product in the puzzle. Don't forget the hyphens!

Across

2. 4 x 9 = _____

4. 4 x 5 = _____

7. 4 x 3 = _____

8. 4 x 7 = _____

9. 4 x 10 = _____

11. 4 x 0 = _____

12. 4 x 11 = _____

Down

1. 4 x 4 = _____

2. 4 x 8 = _____

3. 4 x 12 = _____

5. 4 x 2 = _____

6. 4 x 6 = _____

10. 4 x 1 = _____

Tracy was missing 4 buttons on 11 different shirts. How many buttons does she need to fix all the shirts?

How Many Can You Find?

Complete each multiplication sentence. Then circle each answer in the picture.

A. 2 x 5 = _____

B. 5 x _____ = 5

C. _____ x 5 = 35

D. 10 x 5 = _____

E. _____ x 5 = 60

F. 5 x 6 = _____

G. _____ x 5 = 55

H. 5 x 3 = _____

I. 8 x 5 = _____

J. _____ x 5 = 45

K. 2 x _____ = 10

L. _____ x 5 = 25

M. 7 x 5 = _____

N. 5 x 12 = _____

O. 5 x _____ = 20

Squeaky Squirrel lived in a tree with 4 squirrel friends. If each squirrel collected 12 nuts, how many nuts altogether did the squirrels collect?

Mathematics Fireworks

Multiply. On another piece of paper, find the sum of the products of each star trail. Then use the key to color each star to match its star trail sum.

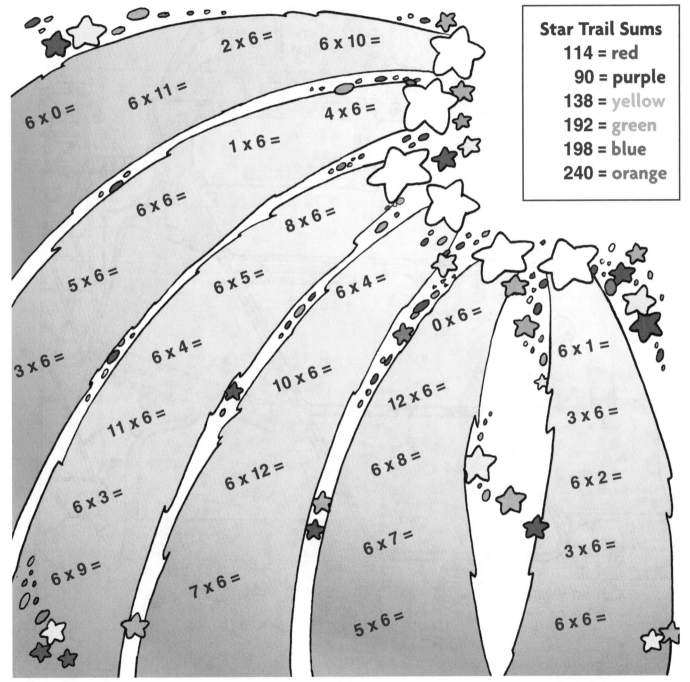

Star Trail Sums
114 = red
90 = purple
138 = yellow
192 = green
198 = blue
240 = orange

2 x 6 =
6 x 10 =
6 x 0 =
6 x 11 =
4 x 6 =
1 x 6 =
6 x 6 =
8 x 6 =
5 x 6 =
6 x 5 =
6 x 4 =
3 x 6 =
6 x 4 =
0 x 6 =
6 x 1 =
11 x 6 =
10 x 6 =
12 x 6 =
3 x 6 =
6 x 3 =
6 x 12 =
6 x 8 =
6 x 2 =
6 x 9 =
6 x 7 =
3 x 6 =
7 x 6 =
5 x 6 =
6 x 6 =

Emma counted the fireworks she watched on the Fourth of July. She counted 6 different fireworks every 15 minutes. The firework show lasted 2 hours. How many fireworks did Emma see?

Flying Sevens

Multiply.

7 x 9 = _____

11 x 7 = _____

6 x 7 = _____

7 x 4 = _____

3 x 7 = _____

7 x 7 = _____

7 x 10 = _____

7 x 0 = _____

5 x 7 = _____

7 x 12 = _____

7 x 2 = _____

4 x 7 = _____

7 x 11 = _____

1 x 7 = _____

0 x 7 = _____

7 x 8 = _____

2 x 7 = _____

7 x 1 = _____

7 x 6 = _____

8 x 7 = _____

9 x 7 = _____

10 x 7 = _____

12 x 7 = _____

7 x 3 = _____

7 x 5 = _____

Cassandra's space mission is to orbit Earth seven times, as quickly as she can a total of seven times. How many times altogether will she orbit Earth?

The Ultimate Eight Track

Use a stopwatch to time how long it takes to multiply around the track.

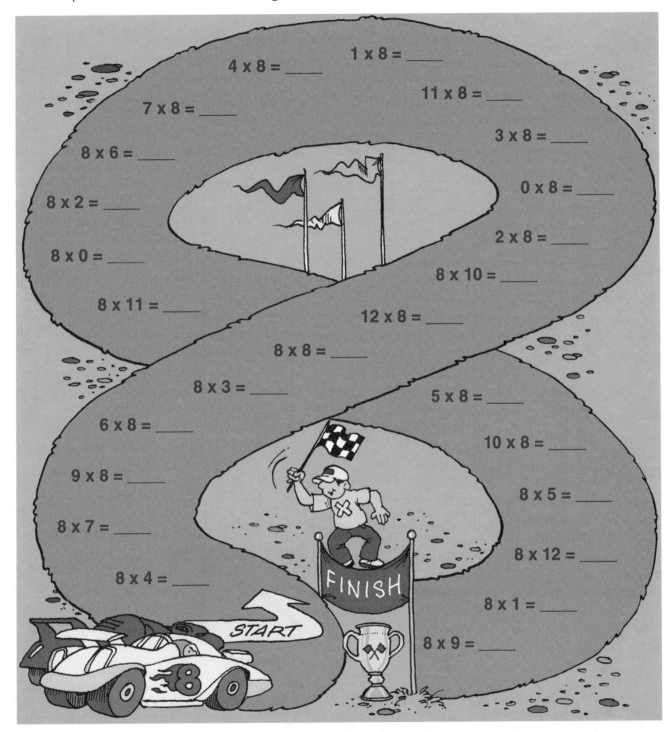

4 x 8 = ____

1 x 8 = ____

7 x 8 = ____

11 x 8 = ____

8 x 6 = ____

3 x 8 = ____

8 x 2 = ____

0 x 8 = ____

8 x 0 = ____

2 x 8 = ____

8 x 11 = ____

8 x 10 = ____

12 x 8 = ____

8 x 8 = ____

8 x 3 = ____

5 x 8 = ____

6 x 8 = ____

10 x 8 = ____

9 x 8 = ____

8 x 5 = ____

8 x 7 = ____

8 x 12 = ____

8 x 4 = ____

8 x 1 = ____

8 x 9 = ____

START

FINISH

Racing Ricardo rapidly raced 8 times around the Eight Track. It took him 12 seconds to rapidly race one time around the track. How many seconds did it take him to complete the race?

Cross-Number Puzzle

Multiply. Write the number word for each product in the puzzle. Don't forget the hyphens!

Across

1. 9 x 5 = ____
5. 1 x 9 = ____
7. 9 x 12 = ____
9. 4 x 9 = ____
10. 9 x 10 = ____
12. 2 x 9 = ____
13. 9 x 11 = ____

Down

2. 9 x 3 = ____
3. 6 x 9 = ____
4. 0 x 9 = ____
6. 9 x 8 = ____
8. 7 x 9 = ____
11. 9 x 9 = ____

Justin just finished putting together a puzzle of a castle and wants to know how many pieces are in the puzzle. He knows he put together nine pieces every five minutes. If Justin worked for one hour, how many pieces does the puzzle have?

© Scholastic Inc.

Around Town

Multiply.

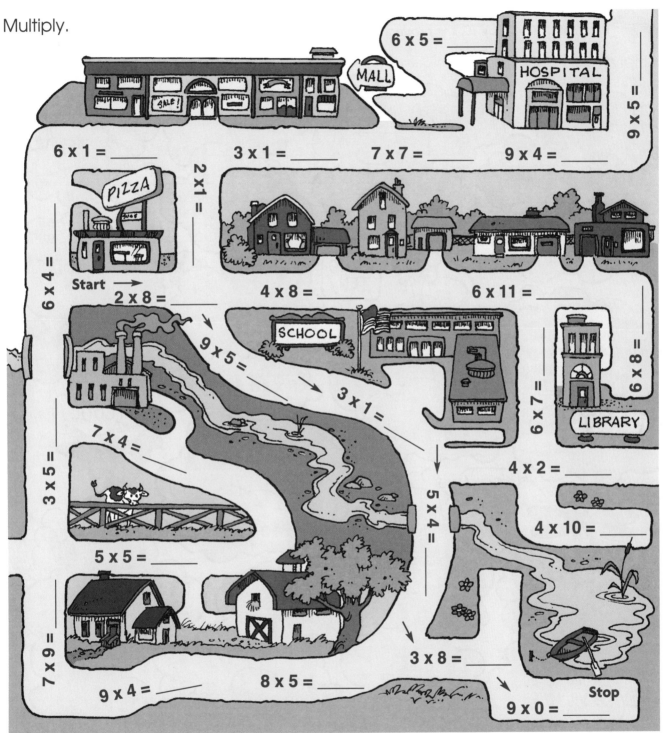

After finishing three slices of pizza at the restaurant, James walked to the pond to meet his dad. James and his dad were going to go canoeing. Add the products on the road James walked along from the pizza restaurant to the pond. Follow the arrows. What multiplication fact has a product equal to this sum?

Cloud Ten

When multiplying by 10, the product always ends in 0.

Multiply.

1 x 10 = _____

10 x 9 = _____

9 x 10 = _____

7 x 10 = _____

10 x 0 = _____

3 x 10 = _____

10 x 8 = _____

10 x 5 = _____

HANG TEN!

10 x 4 = _____

10 x 2 = _____

10 x 3 = _____

10 x 10 = _____

6 x 10 = _____

8 x 10 = _____

WAY COOL!

0 x 10 = _____

4 x 10 = _____

10 x 7 = _____

COOL!

11 x 10 = _____

10 x 1 = _____

10 x 12 = _____

10 x 10 = _____

10 x 11 = _____

2 x 10 = _____

12 x 10 = _____

5 x 10 = _____

10 x 6 = _____

Every morning Miranda chose her favorite ten clouds in the sky. She especially liked clouds which looked like animals. If Miranda did this every morning for a week, how many clouds did she choose altogether?

Eleven! Eleven!

When multiplying the factor 11 by a number from 1 to 9, double the number to find the product.

Examples: 11 x 5 = 55   11 x 7 = 77

Look at each multiplication sentence. If the product is correct, circle it. If the product is incorrect, cross it out and write the correct product above it.

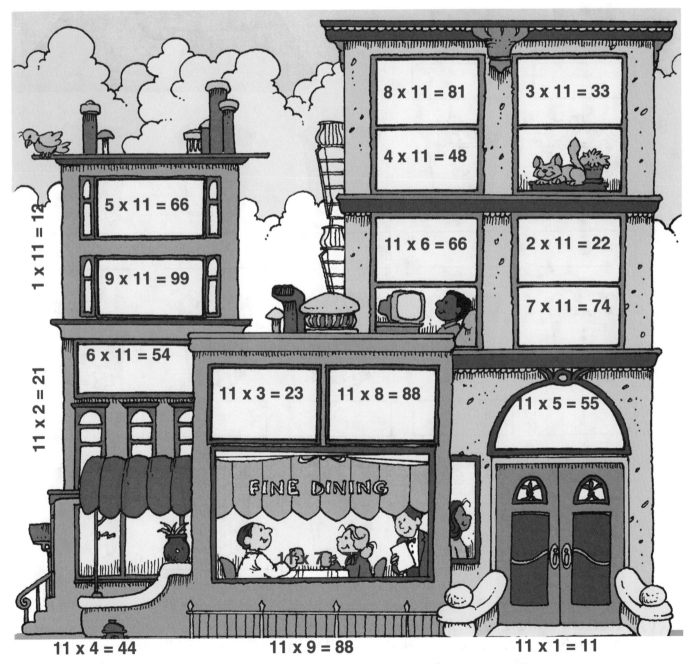

8 x 11 = 81

3 x 11 = 33

4 x 11 = 48

5 x 11 = 66

11 x 6 = 66

2 x 11 = 22

9 x 11 = 99

7 x 11 = 74

1 x 11 = 11

6 x 11 = 54

11 x 3 = 23   11 x 8 = 88

11 x 5 = 55

11 x 2 = 21

FINE DINING

11 x 7

11 x 4 = 44   11 x 9 = 88   11 x 1 = 11

Thinking Thoughts of Twelve

Write a multiplication fact in each box using 12 as a factor for the product on each wastebasket. Use a different sentence for each product.

A.

84   0

B.

96   132   72   144   36

C.

12   60   84   108   48

D.

120   48   96   132   24

Elizabeth wrote 12 different multiplication sentences on each of 6 different pieces of paper. After solving all the problems, she discovered 5 of the problems had the same product. On another piece of paper, show how many multiplication sentences Elizabeth wrote in all. Then write 5 multiplication sentences with the same product.

There Are No Obstacles Too Big for You!

Use a stopwatch to time how long it takes to multiply around the obstacle course.

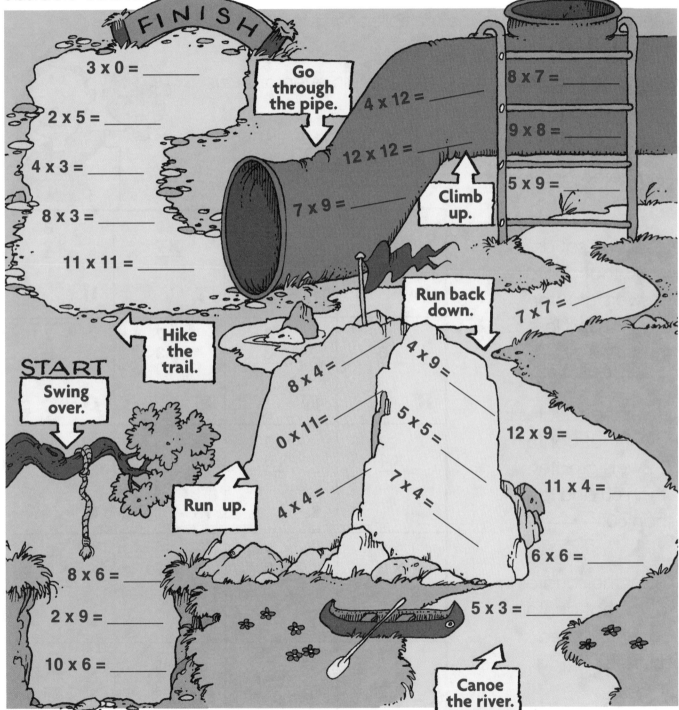

FINISH

3 x 0 = _____

2 x 5 = _____

4 x 3 = _____

8 x 3 = _____

11 x 11 = _____

Go through the pipe.

4 x 12 = _____

12 x 12 = _____

7 x 9 = _____

8 x 7 = _____

9 x 8 = _____

5 x 9 = _____

Climb up.

Run back down.

7 x 7 = _____

Hike the trail.

START

Swing over.

Run up.

8 x 4 = _____

0 x 11 = _____

4 x 4 = _____

4 x 9 = _____

5 x 5 = _____

7 x 4 = _____

12 x 9 = _____

11 x 4 = _____

6 x 6 = _____

8 x 6 = _____

2 x 9 = _____

10 x 6 = _____

5 x 3 = _____

Canoe the river.

In the morning, four students completed the obstacle course. In the afternoon, five students completed the same course. If each student completed the course seven times, how many times altogether was the course completed?

Friendship

You always have something to give a friend. What is it? _____

To find the answer, do the multiplication problems and then follow the directions below.

Color the squares in row 1 that contain even answers.

Color the squares in row 2 that contain odd numbered answers.

Color the squares in row 3 that contain answers greater than 30 and less than 40.

Color the squares in row 4 that contain answers greater than 50 and less than 60.

Color the squares in row 5 that contain odd-numbered answers.

The letters in the colored squares spell the answer.

6 X 1 Y	6 X 4 O	7 X 7 T	6 X 2 U
7 X 9 R	6 X 3 W	7 X 3 S	7 X 6 O
7 X 4 C	6 X 5 E	6 X 6 M	6 X 9 L
7 X 8 I	7 X 0 F	6 X 7 R	6 X 0 B
7 X 5 L	6 X 8 J	7 X 2 S	7 X 1 E

Eager Seeker

Divide the objects and food equally among the groups of people shown below. How many will each person receive? How much will be left over?

ITEM	NUMBER OF PEOPLE	EACH	LEFT OVER
1. 28 MARBLES			
2. 15 STICKS OF BUBBLE GUM			
3. 8 ONE DOLLAR BILLS			
4. 15 SLICES OF PIZZA			
5. 4 BALLOONS			
6. 25 MARSHMALLOWS			
7. 6 TOY DINOSAURS			
8. 29 FRENCH FRIES			
9. 12 STRAWBERRIES			
10. 19 COOKIES			

Introducing division with remainders

Scholastic Success With 3rd Grade   373

Exploding Star

Solve the problems. If the answer is even, color the shape blue.
If the answer is odd, color the shape orange.

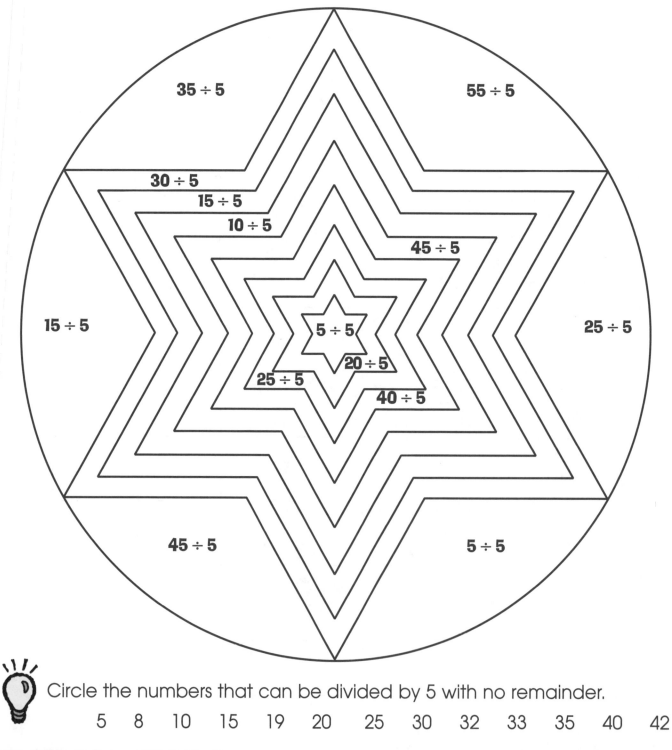

Circle the numbers that can be divided by 5 with no remainder.

5   8   10   15   19   20   25   30   32   33   35   40   42

Flying Carpet

Solve the problems. If the answer is between 100 and 250, color the shape red. If the answer is between 251 and 900, color the shape blue. Finish the design by coloring the other shapes with the colors of your choice.

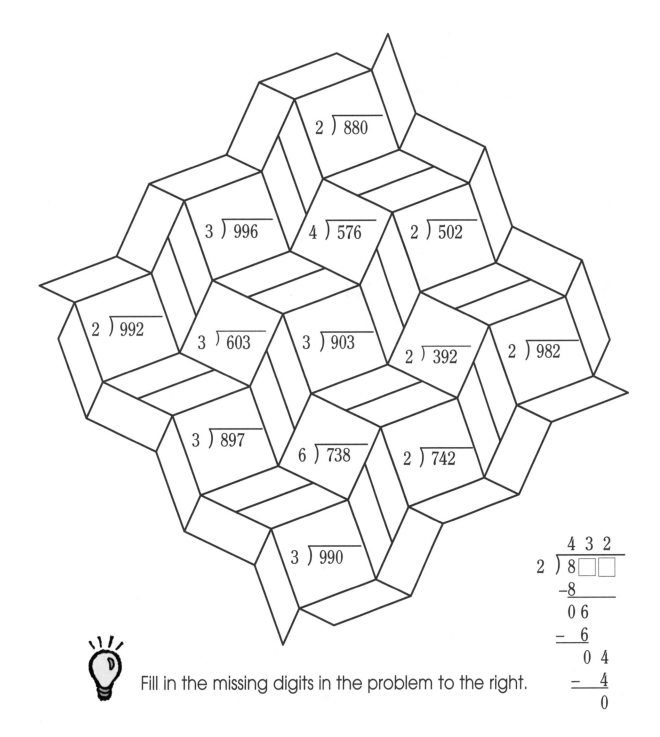

Fill in the missing digits in the problem to the right.

$$2 \overline{)8 \square \square} \begin{array}{r} 4\ 3\ 2 \\ \hline \end{array}$$

$$\begin{array}{r} 4\ 3\ 2 \\ 2\ )\ 8\ \square\ \square \\ -8 \\ \hline 0\ 6 \\ -\ 6 \\ \hline 0\ 4 \\ -\ 4 \\ \hline 0 \end{array}$$

Who's Got the Button?

Figure it out!

1. If a button is lost every 3 seconds, how many buttons are lost in 60 seconds?

_____

2. Ant Betty finds some buttons. She gives 7 buttons to each of her 8 nieces. How many buttons did she find? _____

3. Molly Mouse organizes 6 groups of mice to look for lost buttons. Each group has 5 mice. How many mice are there in all? _____

4. One group of mice finds many buttons and they put them into 9 bags. Each bag contains 14 buttons. How many buttons did the mice find? _____

5. A second group of mice collects 20 bags containing a total of 160 buttons. Each bag contains the same number of buttons. How many buttons are in each bag? _____

Suppose 20 mice want to form teams with an equal number of mice on each team. How many different-size teams can they form?

Problems and More

Put on your thinking cap to solve these problems.

1. Magic Square

Using the numbers 1 to 9, fill in the squares so the rows across, down, and diagonally all add up to 15.

2. Pocket Change

I have 19 coins in my pocket. I have twice as many dimes as nickels, three more pennies than nickels, and one more dime than the number of pennies. My coins add up to $1.07. How many of each coin do I have?

 _____ dimes

_____ nickels

_____ pennies

3. Connect the Dots

Can you connect all of the dots with four straight lines? Here's the catch: You can't lift your pencil!

4. A Sneaky Puzzle

Something is hiding under your bed! To find out what it is, do this problem on a calculator:

5,000 + 45,842 + 2,203.

Turn the calculator upside down to reveal the answer.

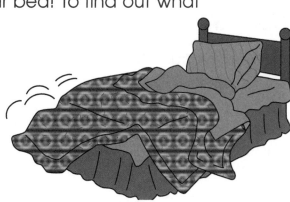

More Problems and More

1. Tricky Triangles

How many triangles can you find
in this shape?

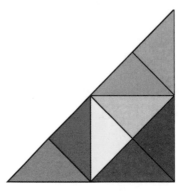

2. Time After Time

How are the clocks the same?
How are they different?

3. Half Again

Draw the missing half
of each shape.

4. A Code for You!

ABC	DEF	GHI	JKL	MNO	PQR	STU	VWX	YZ
1	2	3	4	5	6	7	8	9

Use the code. Write your name. Then add to find the value of all the
letters in your name.

Name _____ Value _____

Find the value of some other words you know.

Brain Power!

Put on your thinking cap to solve these problems!

1. **How Many Students?**

   Estimate the number of students in your school. How did you do it?

   _____

   _____

   _____

2. **Upside Down**

   What two-digit number reads the same upside down as it does right side up?

   _____

3. **Cats In Line**

   One cat walked in front of two cats. One cat walked behind two cats. One cat walked between two cats. How many cats were there? (Hint: Draw a picture!)

   _____

4. **Number Pattern**

   Here are the first five figures in a pattern. Draw the next figure.

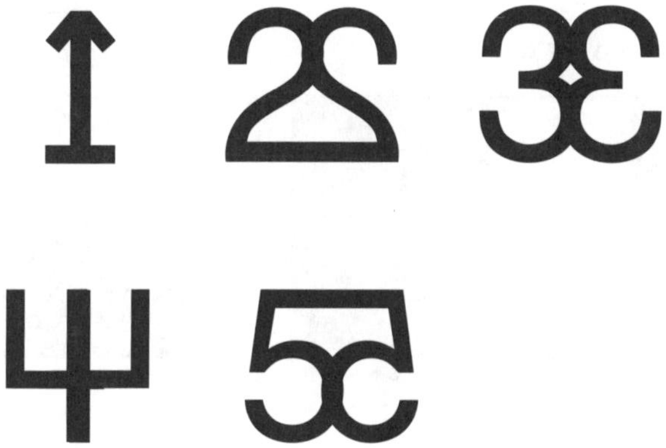

5. **Cutting The Cake!**

   What is the fewest number of cuts you could make in order to cut a cake into six slices? (Hint: Draw a picture!)

   _____

Flag Wagger

Write a fraction for the section of the flag next to the arrow.

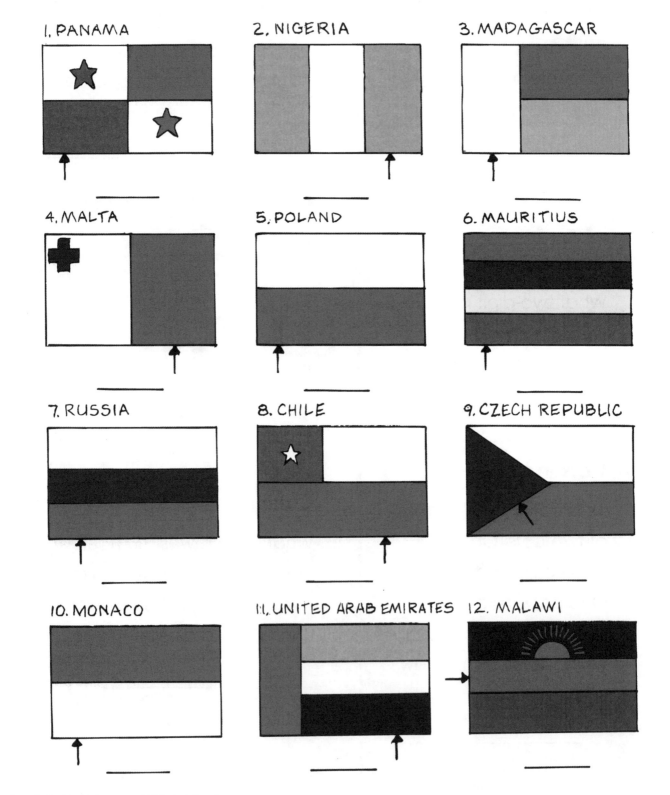

1. PANAMA

2. NIGERIA

3. MADAGASCAR

4. MALTA

5. POLAND

6. MAURITIUS

7. RUSSIA

8. CHILE

9. CZECH REPUBLIC

10. MONACO

11. UNITED ARAB EMIRATES

12. MALAWI

Goody for Fractions!

Wash your hands, then gather the recipe ingredients and equipment listed below. To prepare the peanut butter–oatmeal drops, simply mix the ingredients together, roll the dough into balls, and place the balls on the wax paper. Chill the finished drops for about an hour, then enjoy your tasty "fractions" with family or friends!

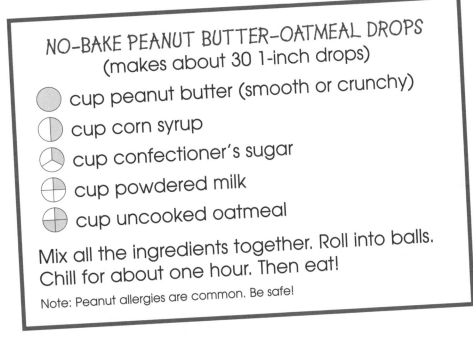

NO-BAKE PEANUT BUTTER-OATMEAL DROPS
(makes about 30 1-inch drops)

cup peanut butter (smooth or crunchy)

cup corn syrup

cup confectioner's sugar

cup powdered milk

cup uncooked oatmeal

Mix all the ingredients together. Roll into balls. Chill for about one hour. Then eat!

Note: Peanut allergies are common. Be safe!

Now try these fraction pictures. Can you write the fraction each picture shows?

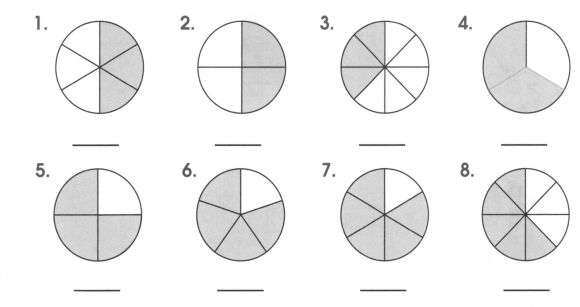

1.

2.

3.

4.

5.

6.

7.

8.

Flower Shop Fractions

Choose 2 colors for each bunch of flowers. Color some
of the flowers one color. Color the rest of the flowers
the other color. Write a fraction to tell how many
flowers there are of each color.

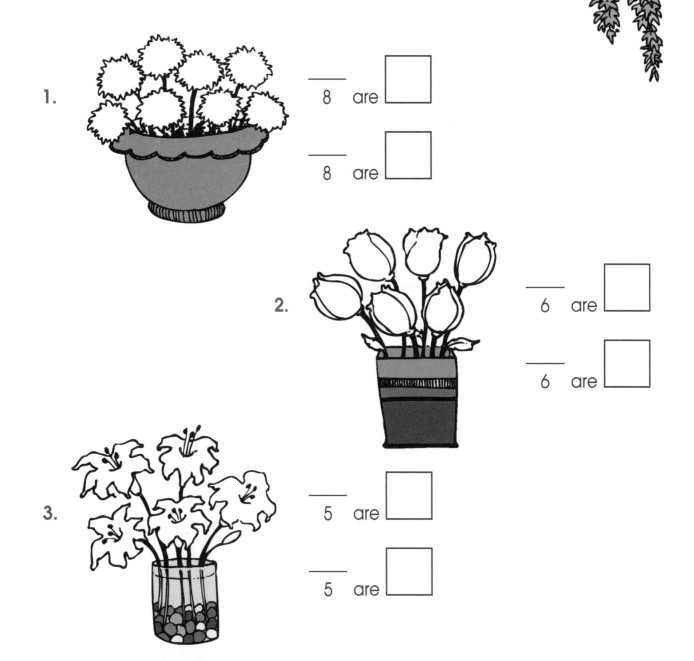

1.

$\dfrac{}{8}$ are ☐

$\dfrac{}{8}$ are ☐

2.

$\dfrac{}{6}$ are ☐

$\dfrac{}{6}$ are ☐

3.

$\dfrac{}{5}$ are ☐

$\dfrac{}{5}$ are ☐

Cooking With Fractions

The recipe below explains how to make peanut-butter balls.

Read the recipe. Then answer the questions.

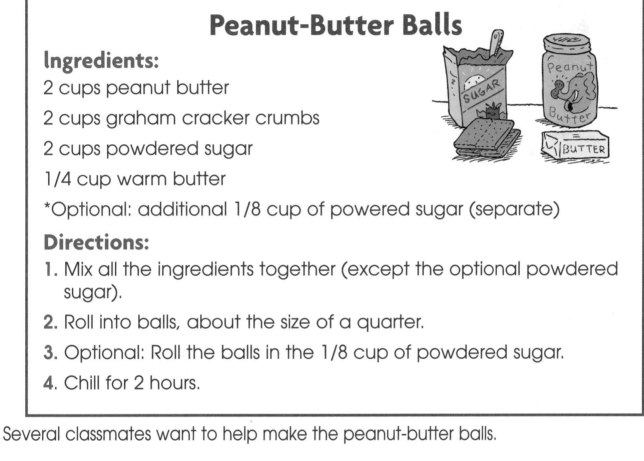

Peanut-Butter Balls

Ingredients:

2 cups peanut butter

2 cups graham cracker crumbs

2 cups powdered sugar

1/4 cup warm butter

*Optional: additional 1/8 cup of powered sugar (separate)

Directions:

1. Mix all the ingredients together (except the optional powdered sugar).

2. Roll into balls, about the size of a quarter.

3. Optional: Roll the balls in the 1/8 cup of powdered sugar.

4. Chill for 2 hours.

Several classmates want to help make the peanut-butter balls.

1. How many students would be needed if each measured 1/2 cup of the peanut butter?

   _____

2. How many students would be needed if each measured 1/4 cup of the graham cracker crumbs?

   _____

3. How many students would be needed if each measured 1/3 cup of the powdered sugar?

   _____

Into Infinity

Solve the problems. Then rename the answers in lowest terms.

If the answer is $\frac{1}{4}$, $\frac{1}{8}$, or $\frac{1}{16}$, color the shape purple.

If the answer is $\frac{1}{2}$, $\frac{1}{3}$, or $\frac{1}{7}$, color the shape blue.

If the answers $\frac{2}{3}$, $\frac{3}{4}$, or $\frac{7}{8}$, color the shape green.

If the answer is $\frac{3}{5}$, $\frac{4}{5}$, or $\frac{5}{7}$, color the shape yellow.

If the answer is $\frac{9}{10}$ or $\frac{11}{12}$, color the shape red.

Finish the design by coloring the other shapes with colors of your choice.

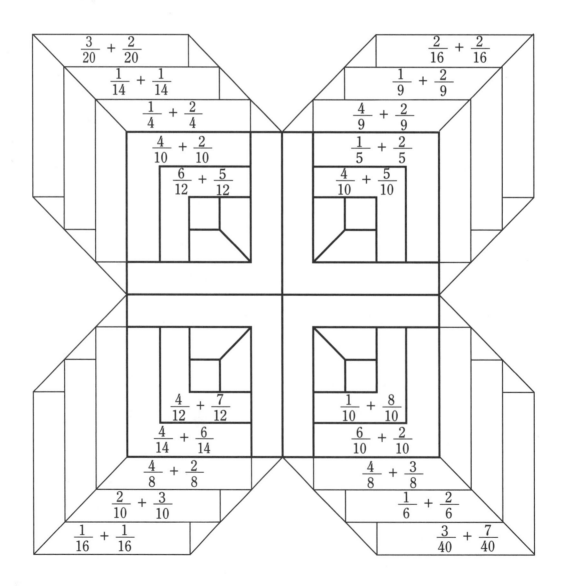

Put the Brakes on Math Mistakes!

Take a look at the signs on Bob's store. Circle any mistakes you see.
Then fix the mistakes so that the signs are correct.

BOB'S BIKE BARN

Bike Helmets $14.999

OPEN 9:30AM–8:75PM

OPEN 8 DAYS A WEEK

SALE
$10 off selected Mountain Bikes
Were $139.99
Now $129.00

Handlebar Tape
$3.99 a roll
Buy two for $7.97
SAVE $1.00

Bicycle Baskets
$12.99 each
Two for $25.00
SAVE $.98

FREE
Bicycle Stickers
$.10 each

Bicycle Chain
$.50 an inch
That's only $5.00 a foot

½ off all Bicycle Seats
Were $17.00
Now $9.50

Autumn Harvest

Circle the coins that you need to pay for each thing in the picture on the next page.

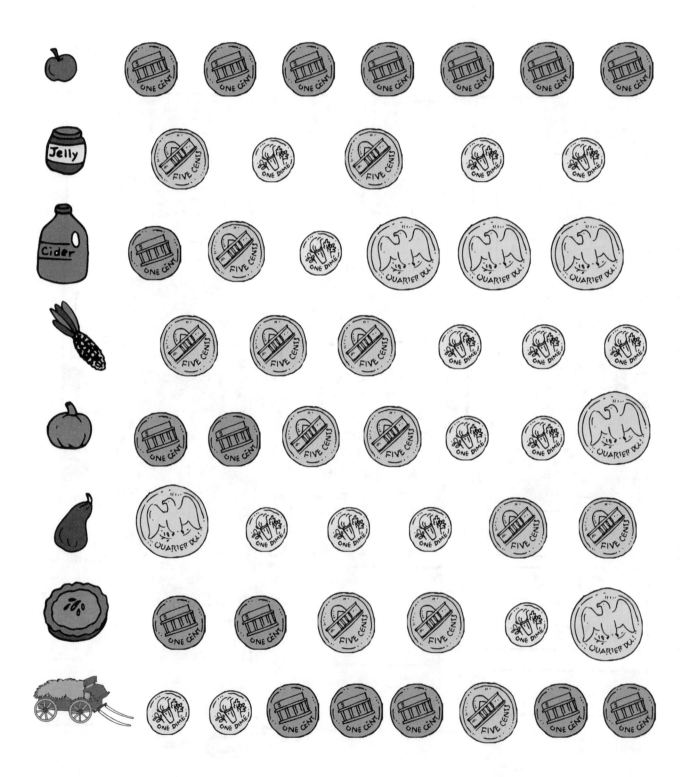

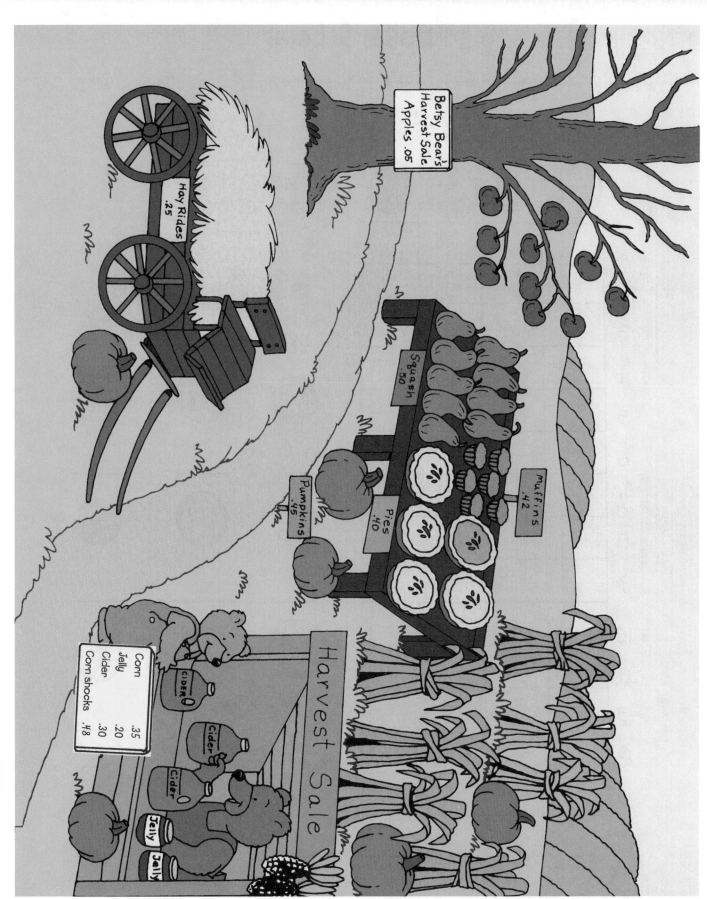

Dollar Scholar

How many ways can you make a dollar? Write the number of coins you will need.

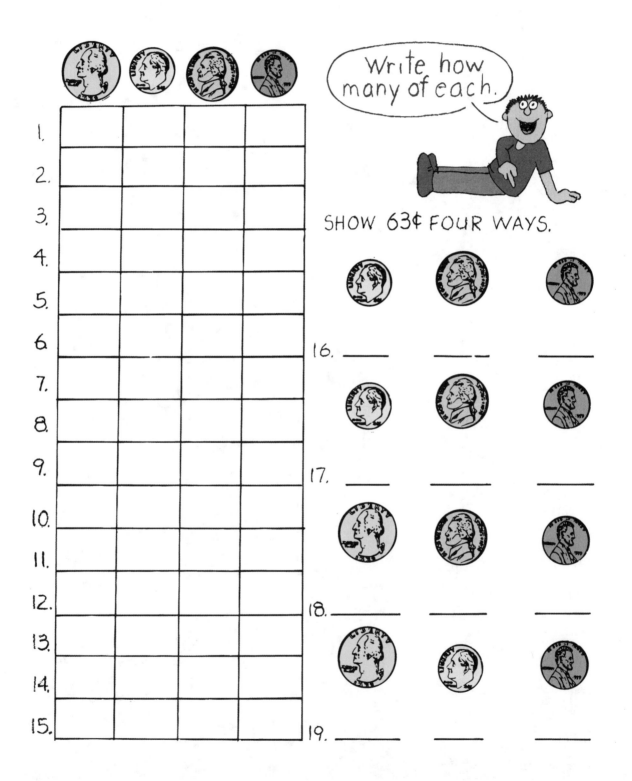

Write how many of each.

SHOW 63¢ FOUR WAYS.

16. _____ _____ _____

17. _____ _____ _____

18. _____ _____ _____

19. _____ _____ _____

Time for a Riddle!

Read the riddle. To find the answer, find the clockface that matches the time written under each blank line. Then write the letter under that clockface on the blank line.

Riddle: What did the little hand on the clock say to the big hand?

Answer. " _____ _____ _____ _____ _____ _____ _____
      10:00   3:30   3:30   6:05   2:25   3:45   6:15

_____ _____   _____ _____ _____ _____ !"
 4:45   6:05   2:55   3:45   3:45   2:55

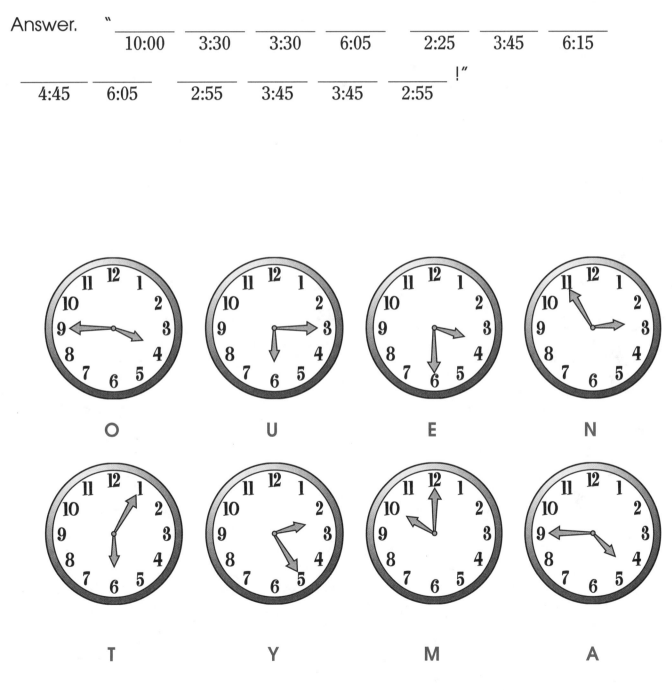

O   U   E   N

T   Y   M   A

Curves Ahead!

How long is each curved line? Guess. Then check by measuring.

1. My guess _____

   Actual length _____

2. My guess _____

   Actual length _____

3. My guess _____

   Actual length _____

4. My guess _____

   Actual length _____

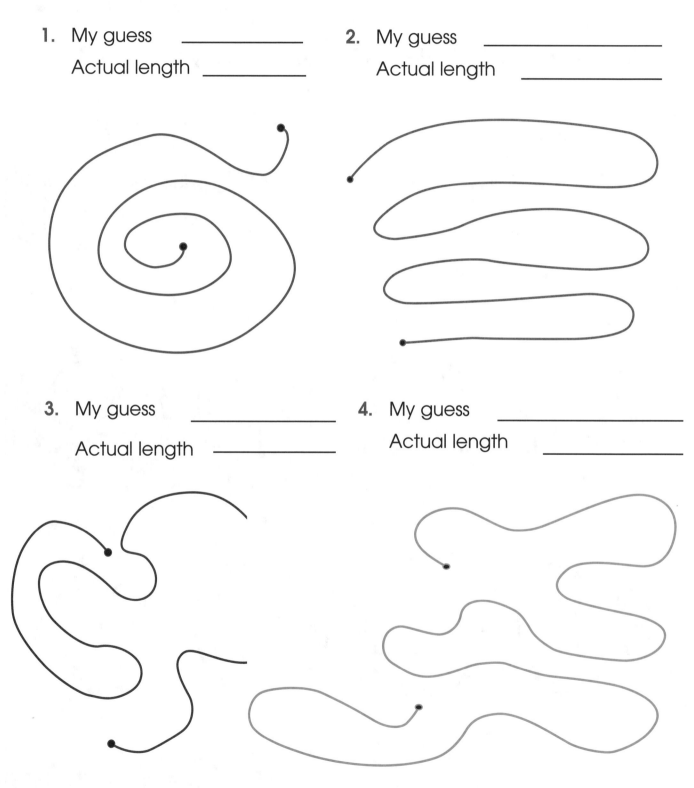

Measure With Me

Cut a piece of string or yarn that is equal to your height. Measure each object below and check the correct box.

Object	Longer than my string	Shorter than my string	The same as my string
(door)			
(chair)			
(table)			
(chair height)			
(window)			

◎ Measure something else. Draw a picture of it on another piece of paper. Write a sentence to show what you found out.

_____

_____

◎ Have someone measure you. Who measured you? _____

How tall are you? _____

Weight Watcher

Weight can be measured in ounces (oz.) and pounds (lb.). 16 oz. = 1 lb. Which unit of measure would you use to weigh the items below? Underline the more sensible measure.

1. An apple

        ounces   pounds

2. A pair of sneakers

        ounces   pounds

3. A bar of soap

        ounces   pounds

4. A bicycle

        ounces   pounds

5. A watermelon

        ounces   pounds

6. A baseball player

        ounces   pounds

7. A balloon

        ounces   pounds

8. A jam sandwich

        ounces   pounds

9. A baseball bat

        ounces   pounds

10. A pair of socks

        ounces   pounds

11. A slice of pizza

        ounces   pounds

12. A full backpack

        ounces   pounds

13. A large dog

        ounces   pounds

14. A loaf of bread

        ounces   pounds

15. A paintbrush

        ounces   pounds

Put me down!

Degree Overseer

Temperature is measured in degrees. Fahrenheit (°F) is a common measure. Celsius (°C) is a metric measure. Circle the more sensible temperature in which to do the activities below.

1. FRY AN EGG

90°F
50°F

2. ICE SKATE

0°C
30°C

3. GO TO THE BEACH

60°C
30°C

4. RAKE LEAVES

55°F
75°F

5. BUILD A SNOWMAN

30°F
50°F

°C   °F

50—   —120
45—   —110
40—   —100
35—   —90
30—   —80
25—
20—   —70
15—   —60
10—   —50
5—   —40
0—   —30
-5—   —20
-10—   —10
           —0

6. DRINK HOT COCOA

75°F
40°F

7. STUDY IN SCHOOL

68°F
40°F

8. FLY A KITE

40°C
20°C

9. DRINK COLD JUICE

75°F
25°F

10. EAT ICE CREAM

30°F
80°F

Fact Finder

Numbers can be used to count and to measure. Complete the measures below by writing how many are in each.

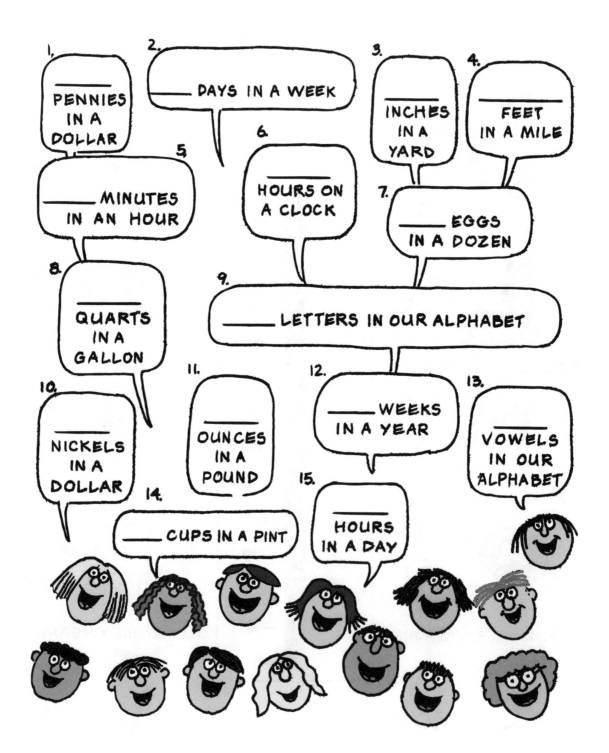

1. _____ PENNIES IN A DOLLAR

2. _____ DAYS IN A WEEK

3. _____ INCHES IN A YARD

4. _____ FEET IN A MILE

5. _____ MINUTES IN AN HOUR

6. _____ HOURS ON A CLOCK

7. _____ EGGS IN A DOZEN

8. _____ QUARTS IN A GALLON

9. _____ LETTERS IN OUR ALPHABET

10. _____ NICKELS IN A DOLLAR

11. _____ OUNCES IN A POUND

12. _____ WEEKS IN A YEAR

13. _____ VOWELS IN OUR ALPHABET

14. _____ CUPS IN A PINT

15. _____ HOURS IN A DAY

Amount Counter

How many triangles and squares can you count in these geometric figures?

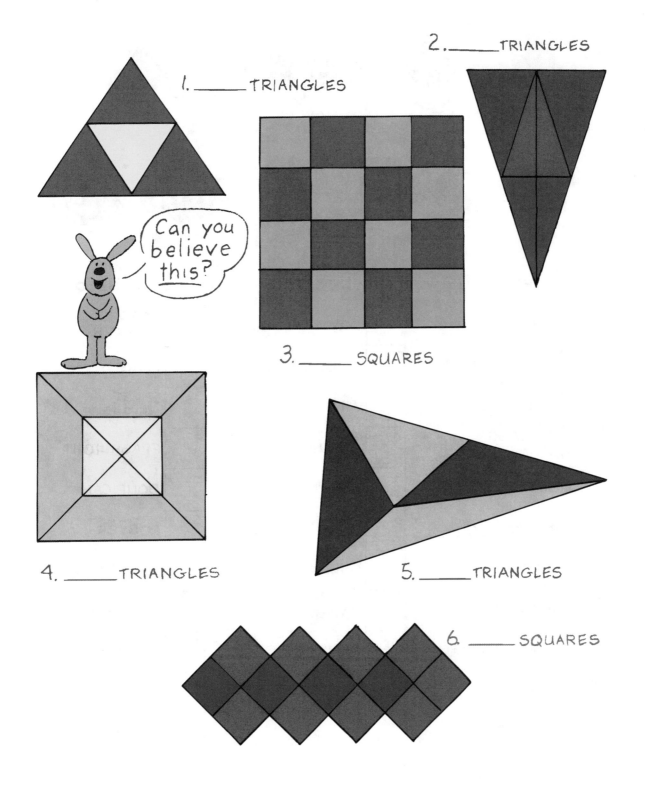

2. _____ TRIANGLES

1. _____ TRIANGLES

Can you believe this?

3. _____ SQUARES

4. _____ TRIANGLES

5. _____ TRIANGLES

6. _____ SQUARES

Shape Gaper

FLAT SHAPES HAVE LENGTH AND WIDTH.

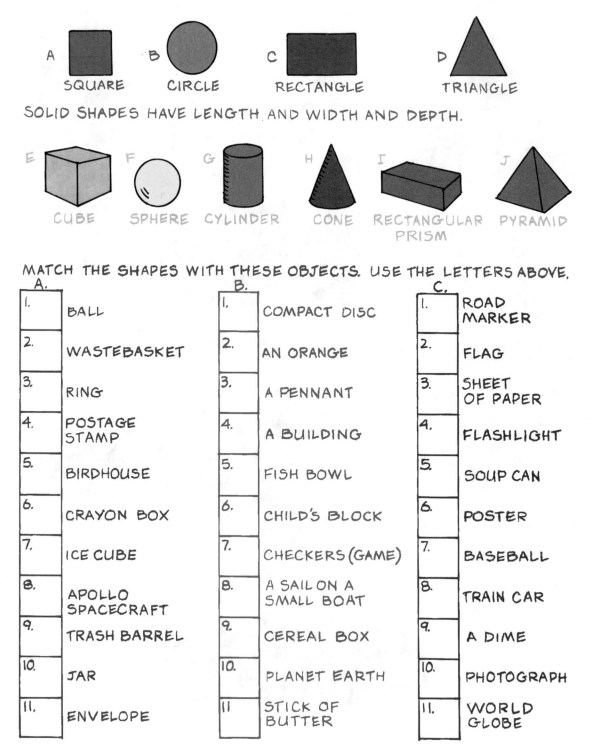

A SQUARE   B CIRCLE   C RECTANGLE   D TRIANGLE

SOLID SHAPES HAVE LENGTH AND WIDTH AND DEPTH.

E CUBE   F SPHERE   G CYLINDER   H CONE   I RECTANGULAR PRISM   J PYRAMID

MATCH THE SHAPES WITH THESE OBJECTS. USE THE LETTERS ABOVE.

A.		B.		C.	
1.	BALL	1.	COMPACT DISC	1.	ROAD MARKER
2.	WASTEBASKET	2.	AN ORANGE	2.	FLAG
3.	RING	3.	A PENNANT	3.	SHEET OF PAPER
4.	POSTAGE STAMP	4.	A BUILDING	4.	FLASHLIGHT
5.	BIRDHOUSE	5.	FISH BOWL	5.	SOUP CAN
6.	CRAYON BOX	6.	CHILD'S BLOCK	6.	POSTER
7.	ICE CUBE	7.	CHECKERS (GAME)	7.	BASEBALL
8.	APOLLO SPACECRAFT	8.	A SAIL ON A SMALL BOAT	8.	TRAIN CAR
9.	TRASH BARREL	9.	CEREAL BOX	9.	A DIME
10.	JAR	10.	PLANET EARTH	10.	PHOTOGRAPH
11.	ENVELOPE	11	STICK OF BUTTER	11.	WORLD GLOBE

Riddle Teller

Read the riddle. Then draw the shape it describes.

I have 3 sides and 3 corners. One of my corners is at the top.

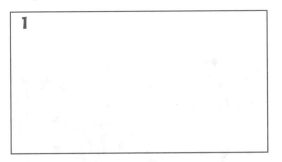

I have no corners. One half of me is like the other half.

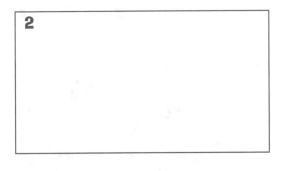

I have 4 corners and 4 sides. You can draw me by joining 2 triangles.

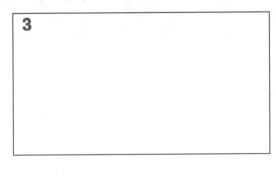

I have 5 sides and 5 corners. Draw a square and a triangle together.

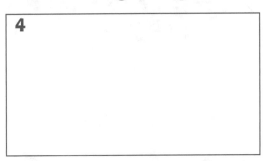

I am not a square, but I have 4 sides and 4 corners.

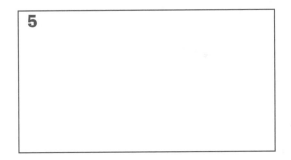

I have 4 sides and 4 corners. My 2 opposite sides are slanted.

Terrific Tessellations

What do math and art have in common?
Everything—if you're making tessellations!

A **tessellation** (tess-uh-LAY-shun) is a design made of shapes that fit together like puzzle pieces. People use tessellations to decorate walls and floors, and even works of art.

This sidewalk is formed from rectangles.

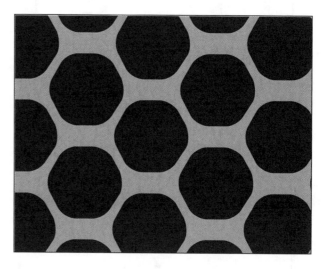

Hexagons form this beehive.

Here is a tessellation made from more than one shape.

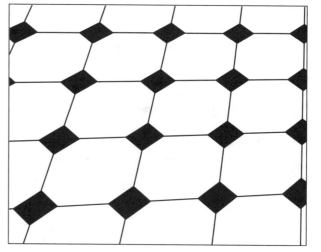

Squares and octagons form a tile floor.

Terrific Tessellations

You Need:
heavy paper • scissor
tape • crayons

What to Do:
Here's how you can make
your own tessellation.

1. Start with a simple shape
   like a square. (Cut your
   shape from the heavy
   paper). Cut a piece out of
   side A . . .

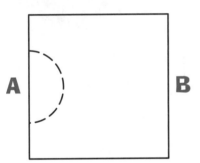

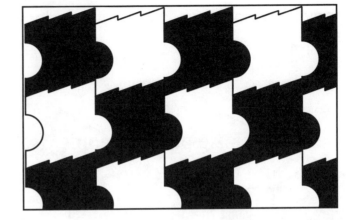

2. . . . and slide it over to side B. Make
   sure it lines up evenly with the cut
   out side, or your tessellation won't
   work. Tape it in place on side B.

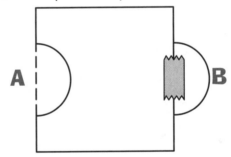

3. If you like, do the same
   thing with sides C and D.
   Now you have a new
   shape.

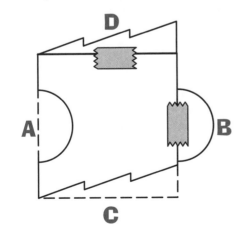

4. Trace your new shape on paper. Then
   slide the shape so it fits together with the
   one you just traced. Trace it again. Keep
   on sliding and tracing until your page is
   filled. Decorate your tessellation.

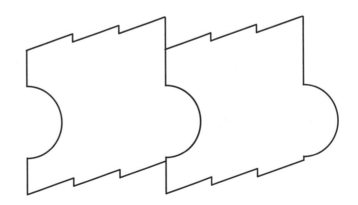

Pattern Block Design

How many total pieces are in this pattern block design?

2 + 2 + 2 + 4 = _____

Now make your own design. Use 10 pattern blocks different from those used above. Cut out the shapes and trace or glue them in the space below. You may need to use a shape more than once.

Write an equation to show how many of each shape you used.

Equation: _____

Answer Key

READING COMPREHENSION

Page 13
1. Alexander Graham Bell;
2. teacher of the deaf; 3. "Mr. Watson, come here! I want to see you!";
4. Mr. Bell's assistant; 5. Bell demonstrated it to many people.

Page 14
Main Idea: The Milky Way is our galaxy.; Details: 1. stars; 2. outer; 3. spiral; 4. white; 5. sun; 6. billions

Page 15
Life on a wagon train was hard and dangerous.; 1. oiling; 2. gathering; 3. cooking; 4. hauling; 5. hunting; 6. watching; 7. waiting; 8. crossing; 9. getting

Page 16
Main Idea: Elephants have very useful noses.; Sentences that do not belong: Some people like to ride on elephants.; Giraffes are the tallest animals in the world.; (The rest of the sentences are details.)

Page 17
The answer is 20.

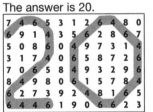

1. Mr. Jefferson, Riley, Rhonda;
2. C; 3. B; 4. Riley

Page 19
1. B; 2. E, A, D; 3. G; 4. F; 5. C, F

Page 20
1. land by the sea; 2. weather;
3. happens regularly; 4. outer covering of trees; 5. illness; 6. wood cut into boards; 7. no longer existing

Page 21

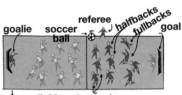

Page 22
A. 2, 1, 3; B. 1, 3, 2; C. 3, 2, 1;
D. 2, 1, 3; E. 3, 1, 2; F. 3, 1, 2;
G. 1, 3, 2; H. 2, 1, 3; I. 2, 1, 4, 3;
J. 2, 4, 1, 3

Page 23
4, 6, 1, 3, 5, 2

Page 24
7, 4, 8, 1, 5, 3, 6, 2

Page 25
Check your child's pages.

Page 26
1. venomous; 2. sneaky; 3. camouflage;
4. jungle; 5. rattlesnakes; 6. sand;
7. coral snake;
Watch out for sneaky snakes!

Page 27
1. The palindromes are wow, dad, mom, noon, deed. (The other words are not.); 2. screech, pow, slurp, boom, click, sizzle, crunch; 3. knot–not; break–brake; flu–flew; sore–soar; right–write; rode–road; 4. pear, shoe, soccer, like, oven, hen, neither

Pages 28–29
1. Holly was being so quiet.
2. Holly's voice sounded so far away.
3. She thought Holly might be hiding.
4. She had fallen headfirst into the toy box and couldn't get out. 5. The piano was at the bottom of the toy box.
6. Mom and Holly will play on the swings in the park.

Page 30
1. Potato chips were invented by accident. 2. George Crum was a chef in Saratoga Springs. 3. The complaining diner actually caused something good to happen. 4. Mr. Crum was angry when the diner sent the potatoes back, but he was probably glad later on because his chips became famous. 5. Saratoga Chips were named after the town where they were invented. 6. The reason we have potato chips today is because of what happened at Moon's Lake House in 1853.

Page 31
Check your child's drawings.

Page 33
1. way back yonder—many years ago;
2. buckboard—wagon; 3. Lend me your ears.—Listen to me.; 4. Put a spring in your step.—makes you feel peppy;
5. heavenly elixir—wonderful tonic;
6. special blend of secret ingredients —I won't tell what's in it.; 7. bustin' broncs—making wild horses gentle;
8. war whoop—loud yell; 9. It's a steal!—You are getting it for a low price.; 10. mosey—walk slowly;
11. kept my eye on him—watched him closely; 12. hornswoggled—cheated; tricked; 13. hightailed it—ran quickly;
14. no-good varmint—evil creature;
15. behind bars—in jail

Page 34
1. an illness; 2. shoreline of a river or creek; 3. a measurement;
4. a small, furry animal; 5. hot bread;
6. applause; 7. am able to;
8. area that is fenced in

Page 35
1. in a cave; 2. at a movie; 3. on a roller coaster; 4. on an airplane; 5. at a wedding; 6. at the vet; 7. at a candy store; 8. in a garden

Page 36
Toolbox: saw, screwdriver, wrench, pliers, hammer; Baseball: bat, pitcher, bases, catcher, glove; Horse: pony, donkey, horse, mule, zebra; Water: lake, river, ocean, sea, creek

Page 37
Medicine Chest: aspirin, cough syrup, bandages, eyedrops; Linen Closet: blankets, sheets; pillowcases, quilts; Silverware Drawer: forks, knives, teaspoons, serving spoons; Pantry: cereal, canned soup, crackers, cake mix; Garage Shelves: motor oil, toolbox, fishing tackle, car wax; Bookshelf: dictionary, novels, atlas, encyclopedias

Page 38
Wording of answers may vary:
1. Kinds of Languages; 2. Things That Are Hot; 3. Computer Equipment; 4. Musical Instruments; 5. Kinds of Trees; 6. Holidays; 7. Air Transportation; 8. Careers (or Occupations); 9. Kinds of Flowers

Page 39
1. views; 2. views; 3. news; 4. views; 5. news; 6. news; 7. views; 8. news; 9. views

Page 40
Burgers: O, F; Sports Car: O, F; In-line Skates: O, F; Video Game: F, O; Movie: O, O, F, F, F

Page 41
Facts: 1, 2, 3, 4, 6, 9, 10, 13
Opinions: 5, 7, 8, 11, 12

Page 43
1. Color the picture of Homer in his cage. 2. Homer had many exciting adventures after crawling out of his cage. 3. Answers will vary.

Page 45
1. Underline: The man found the other Mary, his girlfriend, and gave her the ring.; Mary's mom turned the 9 over to make a 6 again and nailed it tight so their apartment number would be correct.; Mark an X on: The man sent Mary a bill because she ate the chocolates.; Nine-year-old Mary sent the man a dozen roses.;
2. "Love Me Always"; 3. a dozen red roses; 4. Answers will vary.; 5. Friday; 6. Mary's apartment

Page 46
1. chicken nuggets; 2. green beans; 3. applesauce; 4. roll; 5. carrots; 6. corn; 7. salad

Page 47

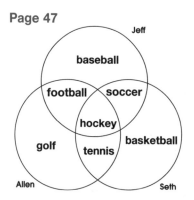

1. hockey; 2. football; 3. soccer; 4. tennis; 5. baseball; 6. golf; 7. basketball

Page 49
1. whale shark; 2. dwarf lantern shark; 3. great white shark; 4. mako shark; 5. all; 6. all; 7. goblin shark; 8. hammerhead shark; 9. all; 10. cookie cutter shark; 11. sawshark; 12. tiger shark

Page 50
1, 3, 4, 6, 8, 9

Page 51
Gravity pulls the swimmer from the **top** of the slide to the **bottom**. Rushing **water** causes the **slide** to be **slippery**.

Page 53

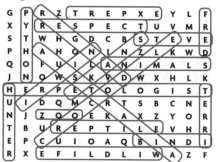

Facts will vary.

Page 54
Answers will vary.

GRAMMAR
Page 102
A. 1. Q; 2. S; 3. S; 4. Q; 5. Q; 6. S; 7. S; 8. Q
B. 1. How did the ant carry the crumb? 2. She carried it herself.

Page 103
A. 1. Can we take a taxi downtown? 2. Where does the bus go? 3. The people on the bus waved to us. 4. We got on the elevator. 5. Should I push the elevator button?
B. 1. Answers will vary. 2. Answers will vary.

Page 104
1. correct as is; 2. help. 3. would not help; 4. The ants; 5. cousins. 6. The man; 7. correct as is; 8. from the ant. 9. strongest. 10. Do you

Page 105
A. 1. E; 2. C; 3. C; 4. E; 5. E; 6. C; 7. E; 8. C
B. Answers will vary.

Page 106
A. 1. There's a Gila monster at the airport! 2. Look at the buffaloes. 3. Pack your toys and games.
B. 1. sentence; 2. sentence; 3. not a sentence; I want to be a subway driver. 4. sentence; 5. not a sentence; I hope there are kids on our street. 6. sentence

Page 107
1. correct as is; 2. excited!; 3. pack.;
4. adorable!; 5. correct as is;
6. Help me find a game.; 7. correct as is; 8. It will be great!; 9. to write to me.; 10. team won the game!

Page 108
A. 1. S; 2. S; 3. P; 4. S; 5. P
B. 1. baby, sisters; 2. nightgown, pockets; 3. hand, fingers;
4. parents, baby; 5. family, girls
C. Singular: train, cow
Plural: fences, gates

Page 109
A. ch, sh, ss, x: Possible answers: beach, fox, box, dress, boss, dish, fish
y: Possible answers: baby, bunny, city, berry, family, diary
f: Possible answers: calf, hoof, shelf, half, wolf
B. 1. cherries; 2. bushes; 3. peaches;
4. boxes; 5. shelves; 6. classes
C. Answers will vary

Page 110
1. boxes; 2. teeth; 3. correct as is;
4. glasses; 5. foxes 6. brushes;
7. groceries; 8. correct as is;
9. mice; 10. stories

Page 111
A. 1. common; 2. common;
3. proper
B. 1. April, brother, sister
2. Julius, May 3. Taiwan, parents 4. April, Saturday, school
5. Mandarin, language
6. May Middle Ages, book
C. Common Nouns: camp, children, picnic; Proper Nouns: August, David, Fourth of July

Page 112
A. 1. Common: doctor; Proper: Pat
2. Common: park; Proper: Atlanta
3. Common: football; Proper: Tangram
B. Answers will vary.

Page 113
1. Fourth of July; 2. correct as is;
3. Tom's apple pie; 4. teacher, Dr. Ruffin; 5. correct as is; 6. Kansas City, Missouri; 7. New Year's Day;
8. school on Monday; 9. pets in North America; 10. the movies on Saturday

Page 114
A. 1. S; 2. S; 3. P; 4. P; 5. S
B. 1. Singular: It; 2. Singular: She;
3. Plural: We; 4. Plural: They
C. 1. he or she; 2. it; 3. they; 4. she

Page 115
A. 1. us, P; 2. him, S; 3. her, S;
4. it, S; 5. me, S; 6. them, P
B. 1. us; 2. me; 3. her; 4. them; 5. him
C. Sample answer: It is inside the house. I will get it.

Page 116
1. us; 2. me; 3. correct as is; 4. It;
5. them; 6. He; 7. correct as is;
8. correct as is; 9. It; 10. I

Page 117
A. 1. cheered; 2. added;
3. give; 4. serves; 5. emptied
B. 1. paraded; 2. whispered;
3. gobbled; 4. skipped; 5. bounced
C. 1. laughed; 2. sighed;
3. whispered

Page 118
A. 1. snatched; 2. cracked;
3. nibbled; 4. scrambled
B. 1. honked; 2. grabbed;
3. shouted; 4. ran; 5. bounced
C. Answers will vary

Page 119
A. 1. arrived; 2. hugged;
3. roasted; 4. ate; 5. cheered
B. 1. chased; 2. dashed;
3. peeked; 4. leaped; 5. grabbed

Page 120
A. 1. past; 2. past; 3. present;
4. past; 5. past; 6. past; 7. present;
8. present; 9. present; 10. past
B. 1. The man crossed the river.
2. He rows his boat.

Page 121
A. 1. fills; 2. watches; 3. takes;
4. leave; 5. go
B. 1. looked; 2. stared; 3. walked;
4. helped
C. 1. Answers will vary.

Page 122
1. correct as is; 2. washes and peels;
3. correct as is; 4. enjoy 5. entered;
6. traveled; 7. arrived; 8. awarded;
9. correct as is; 10. enjoyed

Page 123
A. 1. was; 2. is; 3. are; 4. am;
5. were
B. 1. past; 2. present; 3. present;
4. past; 5. present
C. 1. am; 2. are; 3. is

Page 124
A. 1. is, being; 2. carried, action;
3. were, being; 4. are, being
B. 1. am; 2. are; 3. was; 4. is; 5. were
C. Answers will vary.

Page 125
1. are; 2. correct as is; 3. correct as is;
4. were; 5. am; 6. was; 7. were; 8. were;
9. correct as is; 10. am

Page 126
A. 1. M; 2. H; 3. H; 4. M; 5. H;
6. M; 7. H; 8. M
B. 1. will watch; 2. is going;
3. are reading; 4. have lifted;
5. had climbed

Page 127
A. 1. had built 2. has painted
3. is building 4. will fly 5. will bring
6. am buying
B. 1. is 2. had 3. going 4. using
5. will 6. have
C. Answers will vary.

Page 128
A. 1. reading; 2. playing; 3. walked;
4. come; 5. share
B. 1. has; 2. is; 3. will; 4. will; 5. have

Page 129
A. 1. is; 2. am; 3. was; 4. were;
5. are; 6. will be
B. 1. am, present; 2. was, past;
3. are, present; 4. were, past;
5. is, present
C. 1. am; 2. was; 3. are

Page 130
A. 1. S; 2. S; 3. P; 4. P; 5. S
B. 1. was; 2. were; 3. am; 4. is; 5. are
C. Answers will vary.

Page 131
A. 1. is; 2. am; 3. are; 4. were; 5. was
B. 1. is; 2. was; 3. are; 4. were;
5. will be

Page 132
A. 1. All of the families |
traveled to California.
2. Baby Betsy, Billy, Joe, and Ted |
stayed in the cabin.
3. My father | told us stories.
4. I | baked a pie.
B. 1. Betsy; 2. miners; 3. baby;
4. feet; 5. man
C. 1. made; 2. rolled; 3. added;
4. bakes; 5. loves

Page 133
A. 1. class | took Simple subject: class;
Simple predicate: took
2. paintings | hung Simple subject:
paintings; Simple predicate: hung
3. Maria | saw Simple subject: Maria;
Simple predicate: saw
4. children | looked Simple subject:
children; Simple predicate: looked
5. Paul | pointed Simple subject:
Paul; Simple predicate: pointed
6. friend | liked Simple subject:
friend; Simple predicate: liked
7. Everyone | laughed
Simple subject: Everyone;
Simple predicate: laughed
8. people | visited Simple subject:
people; Simple predicate: visited
9. bus | took Simple subject: bus;
Simple predicate: took
B. Answers will vary.

Page 134
A. 1. complete subject; 2. complete
predicate; 3. complete subject;
4. complete predicate;
5. complete subject
B. 1. simple predicate; 2. simple
subject; 3. simple subject; 4. simple
subject; 5. simple predicate

Page 135
A. 1. big, sweet; 2. many, hot;
3. red, four; 4. ripe, juicy;
5. large, round; 6. delicious, colorful
B. Answers will vary.
C. Answers will vary.

Page 136
A. 1. sparkling; 2. clear; 3. Large;
4. Busy; 5. fresh
B. Answers may include: 1. red;
2. green; 3. sweet; 4. loud; 5. sour

Page 137
A. 1. Several; 2. six; 3. many;
4. blue; 5. colorful
B. 1. delicious; 2. many; 3. some;
4. five; 5. wonderful

Page 138
A. 1. The, the; 2. an; 3. A, a, a;
4. an; 5. The, the, the; 6. The, a;
7. The, an, the; 8. an, the
B. 1. a; 2. the; 3. the; 4. an; 5. an;
6. the; 7. a 8. a

Page 139
A. 1. an; 2. a; 3. an; 4. an; 5. an; 6. a
B. Answers will vary.
C. Answers will vary.

Page 140
A. 1. the; 2. the; 3. an; 4. the; 5. The
B. 1. elephant; 2. airport; 3. umbrella;
4. crab; 5. lobster

Page 141
A. 1. king's; 2. palace's; 3. flowers';
4. trees'; 5. gardener's; 6. birds';
7. singers'; 8. sun's; 9. diamond's;
10. Visitors'
B. 1. king's; 2. palace's; 3. gardener's;
4. sun's; 5. diamond's
C. 1. flowers'; 2. trees'; 3. birds';
4. singers'; 5. Visitors'

Page 142
A. 1. Anna's, S; 2. birds', P;
3. Brad's, S; 4. butterfly's, S;
5. turtle's, S; 6. chipmunks', P;
7. animals', P
B. 1. Carol's; 2. Jim's; 3. sister's;
4. brother's; 5. dad's; 6. sneaker's;
7. dog's

Page 143
A. 1. Kramer's; 2. mother's;
3. brother's; 4. librarian's; 5. Joan's
B. 1. astronomers'; 2. engines';
3. spectators'; 4. scientists';
5. astronauts'

Page 144
A.1. We; 2. It; 3. I; 4. She; 5. He;
6. They; 7. You
B.1. He; 2. She; 3. They; 4. He
5. It; 6. They; 7. We

Page 145
A. 1. us; 2. it; 3. him; 4. you; 5. me;
6. her; 7. them
B. 1. them; 2. her; 3. it; 4. him; 5. us
C. Answers will vary.

Page 146
1. us; 2. It; 3. She; 4. her; 5. them;
6. They; 7. He; 8. We; 9. him; 10. us

Page 147
A.1. I, my; 2. you, your; 3. He, his;
4. She, her; 5. It, its; 6. We, our;
7. They, their
B. 1. their; 2. Her; 3. his; 4. His;
5. My; 6. Your; 7. Its 8. Our

Page 148
A. 1. our; 2. her; 3. my; 4. his; 5. its;
6. your; 7. their
B. 1. his; 2. our; 3. her; 4. its; 5. His;
6. Their
C. Answers will vary.

Page 149
A. 1. her; 2. Its; 3. our; 4. my; 5. his
B. 1. Her; 2. his; 3. Its; 4. Their; 5. our

Page 150
A. 1. Laura (and) Ramona
2. Pa, Ma, (and) Laura
3. dog (and) horses
4. Ma (and) Pa
5. Grass (and) trees
B. 1. swayed (and) creaked
2. hummed (and) sang; 3. twisted (and)
turned; 4. neighed (and) snorted
5. stopped (and) stared
C. Answers will vary.

Page 151
A. 1. Mike and Jody, CS
2. call and e-mail, CP
3. jogs and swims, CP
4. Phil and Jan, CS
5. Juan and Yoshi, CS
6. speak and read, CP
7. Lori, Sam, and Beth, CS
8. practiced and presented, CP
9. clapped and smiled, CP
10. The parents and the principal, CS
B. 1. barked and jumped
2. My dad and sister

Page 152
A. 1. compound subject
2. compound predicate
3. compound subject
4. compound predicate
5. compound subject
B. 1. Paul, Luz, and Annie
2. teacher and students
3. wrote and proofread
4. stamped and mailed
5. ran, skipped, and jumped

Page 153
A. 1. It's; 2. We're; 3. They've;
4. I'm; 5. she'll; 6. They're
B. 1. I've I have; 2. What's What is;
3. It's It is; 4. they're they are;
5. I'm I am
C.1. he'll; 2. they're; 3. who's;
4. I'm; 5. we'll; 6. there's

Page 154
1. What's; 2. it's; 3. I'm; 4. Aren't;
5. can't; 6. doesn't; 7. They're;
8. didn't; 9. I've; 10. don't; 11. there's

Page 155
A.1. We are; 2. You will;
3. We have; 4. I am; 5. It is
B. 1. Who's; 2. There's;
3. she'll; 4. doesn't; 5. Don't

Page 156
A. 1. "I have a strange case,"
2. "What's strange about it?"
3. "Seventeen years ago Mr. Hunt
found an elephant,"
4. "Where did he find it?"
5. The elephant just appeared in his
window," 6. "He must have fainted!"
7. "No, Mr. Hunt brought him,"
B. 1. Huntsville, Alabama; 2. Street,
Huntsville, Alabama; 3. January 8,
2001; 4. January 22, 2001;
5. Peachtree Lane, Farley, Alabama;
6. Redstone Park, Alabama;
7. September 29, 2000; 8. Draper
Road, Newportville, Pennsylvania

Page 157
A. 1. Mrs. Wu's bank is located at
92 Maple Avenue, Inwood, Texas;
2. September 8, 2001; 3. Lakewood,
Texas; 4. weekdays, Saturdays, and;
5. Saturdays, Sundays, and;
6. Ms. Ames, Mr. Pacheco, and Mrs.
Jefferson; 7. checks, bills, and
deposits; 8. May 2, 1974
B. 1. "My favorite author is Jerry
Spinelli," said Rick. 2. Spinelli was born
on February 1, 1941. 3. His home
town is Norristown, Pennsylvania.
4. "What are your favorite books by
him?" asked Teresa. 5. "I like Maniac
Magee, Dump Days, and Fourth Grade
Rats," replied Rick.

Page 158
A. 1. underlining; 2. commas;
3. quotation mark; 4. comma
B. 1. "I have a new baby sister!"
2. April 3, 2002; 3. correct as is;
4. tiny fingers, tiny toes, and a big
scream

Page 159
A. 1. told; 2. was; 3. came; 4. saw;
5. knew; 6. fell; 7. lit; 8. threw
B. 1. knew; 2. saw; 3. threw; 4. fell
C. Answers will vary.

Page 160
A.1. bought 2. ate 3. grew 4. began
5. gave 6. sat
B. 1. came 2. won 3. went 4. was
5. fell 6. said
C. Answers will vary.

WRITING

Page 162
1. S; 2. F; 3. S; 4. S; 5. F; 6. F;
7. S; 8. F; 9. F; 10. F; 11. S; 12. S

Page 163
1. Some of these things are wood,
plants, and nectar. 2. Flower
nectar makes good food for bees.
3. Wasps build nests to store their
food. 4. Termites are wood eaters.
5. A butterfly caterpillar eats leaves.
6. Mosquitoes bite animals and people.

Page 164
1. One type is called igneous.
2. They are formed by layers
of rocks, plants, and animals.
3. Rocks are found everywhere
in our world.

Page 165
1. There are three types of rocks on
our planet. 2. The melted rock inside
the earth is more than 2000°F.
3. Most igneous rocks are formed
inside the earth. 4. Marble is a
metamorphic rock. 5. Fossils are found
in sedimentary rock.

Page 166
1. Why is that car in a tree?
2. Should that monkey be driving a
bus? 3. Did you see feathers on that
crocodile? 4. Can elephants really lay
eggs? 5. Is that my mother covered in
spots?

Page 167
Questions will vary.

Page 168
1. period; 2. question mark;
3. period; 4. exclamation point;
5. question mark; 6. period;
7. question mark; 8. period;
9. question mark; 10. exclamation
point; 11. period; 12. exclamation point;
When reading an exclamation, a voice
shows strong feeling.

Page 169
1. The Sahara Desert is in Africa.
2. Do people live in the Sahara Desert?
3. The Sahara Desert is about the same size as the United States. 4. How high is the temperature in the Sahara Desert? 5. The Sahara Desert is too hot for me!

Page 170
Every sentence begins with a capital letter.; A statement ends with a period.; A question ends with a question mark.; An exclamation ends with an exclamation point.; Sentences will vary.; Did it snow ten inches last night?, It snowed ten inches last night!

Page 171
The kids at Elm School had been waiting for a snowstorm. They knew school would be canceled if the storm brought a lot of snow. Last week their wish came true. It snowed 12 inches! School was canceled, and the kids spent the day sledding, building snowmen, and drinking hot chocolate. It was a great snow day!;
Your child may correct any two of the sentences containing two mistakes.

Page 172
D, B, F, E, A, C

Page 173
Sentences will vary.

Page 174
Sentences will vary.

Page 175
Sentences will vary.

Page 176
1. I ordered a hamburger and a milkshake. 2. I like salt and ketchup on my French fries. 3. My mom makes great pork chops and applesauce.
4. My dad eats two huge helpings of meat loaf and potatoes! 5. My brother helps set the table and clean the dishes. 6. We have cookies and ice cream for dessert.

Page 177
1. We are eating out tonight because Mom worked late. 2. We are going to Joe's Fish Shack although I don't like fish. 3. Dad said I can play outside until it's time to leave. 4. We can play video games while we are waiting for our food. 5. We may stop by Ida's Ice Cream Shop after we leave the restaurant.

Page 178
Lists of words will vary.

Page 179
Possible answers: 1. The melting snow cone sat in the bright sun. 2. Many excited children ran toward the crashing ocean waves. 3. My new friends built a large sandcastle.
4. My younger brother grabbed his favorite beach toys. 5. Our playful dog tried to catch flying beach balls.

Page 180
Words will vary.

Page 181
Words will vary.

Page 182
Dialogue sentences will vary.

Page 183
1. I think it's fun to splash in the puddles. 2. Rain, rain, don't go away!
3. Wow! I should have worn my bathing suit! 4. It's a perfect day to go sailing.

Page 184
Examples: "Somebody turned out the lights!" shouted the cowboy.;
"What makes you think I've been eating cookies?" asked the guilty boy.;
"My parents finally let me get my ears pierced," said the proud girl.

Page 185
Drew woke up early on Saturday. "No school today," he said. He found his mom working in the garden. "What are you doing?" he asked.
"I am planting these flowers," she answered.
Drew looked down. He couldn't believe it. "A four-leaf clover!" he shouted. "This should help us win our big game today," he said.
Drew's entire day was perfect. His sister shared her toys, the ice-cream truck brought his favorite flavor, and his team won the big game. "What a day!" he whispered to himself as he fell asleep that night.

Page 186
Sentences will vary.

Page 187
Paragraphs will vary.

Page 188
Lists of ideas will vary.

Page 189
Sentences that do not belong: My favorite kind of dog is a boxer.; Not much is known about the history of Chinese flags.; Hurricanes have strong, powerful winds.

Page 190
Topic sentences will vary. Examples: Guinea pigs make good pets.; It is easy to make a peanut butter and banana sandwich.; Frogs are different from toads.

Page 191
Topic sentences will vary.

Page 192
The following sentences should be crossed out: My three-year-old brothers both have blonde hair.; Her favorite sport is gymnastics.; I wish I had a fish tank in my room.; The rewritten paragraph should omit the above sentences.

Page 193
Supporting sentences will vary.

Page 194

2, 1, 4, 3; Paragraph sentences will vary but should follow the same order as the numbered sentences.

Page 195

Supporting sentences will vary.

Page 196

1. Of all the seasons, autumn is the best. 2. Though dangerous, the job of an astronaut is exciting. 3. There are many subjects in school, but math is the most difficult. 4. Some gardeners in Florida and Texas can enjoy their flowers all year long. 5. Life would never be the same without computers.

Page 197

Closing sentences will vary.

Page 198

Paragraphs will vary.

Page 199

Paragraph plans and paragraphs will vary.

Page 200

Sentences and paragraph plans will vary.

Page 201

Drawings and paragraph plans will vary.

Page 202

Paragraph plans and paragraphs will vary.

Page 203

Paragraph plans and paragraphs will vary.

Page 204

Letters will vary.

MAPS

Pages 206–207

1. Mill Town; 2. hospital; 3. grass; 4. Sable River; 5. bridge; 6. Doe Avenue; 7. fire house, school, library; 8. Grand Street

Page 208

1. North Pole; 2. South Pole; 3. west; 4. E

Page 209

1. south; 2. north; 3. east; 4. no; 5. clothing shop

Page 210

1. no; 2. North America, South America, Asia, Africa, Australia, Antarctica, Europe; 3. Indian, Arctic, Pacific, Atlantic, Southern; 4. Western and Southern

Page 211

1. Eastern; 2. Arctic; 3. right; 4. top; 5. Hemisphere; Code word: Earth

Page 212

1. southeast; 2. northeast; 3. southeast; 4. northwest; 5. SW

Page 213

1. north; 2. southeast; 3. southwest; 4. north; 5. northwest

Page 214

1. library; 2. D4; 3. A2, B2, C2, D2; 4. D4, D5; 5. yes

Page 215

1. fire department; 2. A5; 3. A5, B5, C5, D5; 4. store; 5. go to the movies
My tour: apartment building; library; store; park; movie theater

Page 216

1. boat house; 2. stable; 3. office; 4. arts and crafts; 5. tennis court

Page 217

1. 25 miles; 2. 45 miles; 3. Luna City; 4. Clark City to Dover to Luna City to Terra View; 81 miles; 5. Far Hills

Page 218

1. 40 feet; 2. 10 feet; 3. 10 feet; 4. 30 feet

Page 219

1. 125 feet; 2. 100 feet; 3. 75 feet; 4. about 150 feet; 5. 200 feet

Pages 220–221

1. 150; 2. 200; 3. 300; 4. shorter; 5. Amarillo; 6. less; 7. kilometers; 8. 500 9. 800; 10. kilometers

Pages 222–223

1. Minnesota; 2. 150 miles; 3. Map 2; 4. 1,000 miles; 5. about 2,500; 6. 1,500 miles; 7. North America; 8. more land is shown on Map 3; 9. Map 1

Pages 224–225

1. Mississippi; 2. Kansas and Nebraska; 3. Lake Erie; 4. Mississippi River; 5. Alaska and Hawaii; 6. Juneau; 7. west; 8. North Carolina, Tennessee, Arkansas, Oklahoma, New Mexico, Arizona, California

Page 226

1. south; 2. Belize, Guatemala; 3. Canada; 4. Alaska; 5. Atlantic; Pacific; 6. Arctic; 7. Ottawa; 8. Rio Grande

Page 228

1. c; 2. b; 3. c; 4. b; 5. c; 6. a; 7. a; 8. c

Page 230

1. mountain, hill, plateau; 2. canyon, valley; 3. Both are low land. A valley doesn't have as high, steep walls as a canyon, and it isn't as narrow as a canyon.

Page 231

1. It is more sheltered; the water might be calmer.
2. Both are partially enclosed by land.
3. peninsula; 4. An island is completely surrounded by water while a peninsula is surrounded except for one side.
5. An island is surrounded by water. A lake is surrounded by land.

Page 232

1. valley; 2. red; 3. plateau; 4. Mississippi River; 5. east and south

Page 233
1. north; 2. Kodiak; 3. Alaska Peninsula;
4. mountains; 5. Yukon

Page 234
1. People use them to make things.
2. roads, sandboxes, concrete
3. because natural gas burns

Page 235
1. true; 2. true; 3. false; 4. false;
5. true; 6. true

Pages 236–237
1. 38 to 40 inches of rain a year;
2. north and west; 3. 40 to 44;
4. Houlton; 5. Lewiston; 6. greater;
7. less than 38

Pages 238–239
1. northwest; 2. Missouri River;
3. Fort Laramie; 4. Rocky Mountains;
5. Snake River; 6. The trail followed
rivers and valleys.; 7. The weather was
better during spring and summer.
Word scramble: Oregon, Idaho,
Nebraska, Kansas

Pages 240–241
1. picnic area; 2. southwest;
3. Take Kinney Road to Bajada Loop
heading northeast. Go right onto
Golden Gate Road. Then turn left on
Picture Rocks Road.; 4. Saguaro cacti;
5. waterhole; to drink; 6. Sandario Road

Pages 242–243
1. Hudson River; East River;
2. east to west; 3. north to south
4. southern; 5. 59th Street;
Fifth Avenue and Central Park West;
6. Fifth Avenue and 42nd Street;
7. east; 8. west; 9. It is easier
to find places.

Pages 244-245
1. Fremont-Daly City Route; 2. blue;
3. Concord-Daly City; 4. yes;
5. Concord, Daly City, Richmond,
Fremont; 6. It's a transfer stop
where people can change trains.
7. Richmond-Fremont;
8. northeast; 9. San Francisco Bay;
10. over bridges, by boat, by plane

Page 246
1. 5 to 10 inches of rain;
2. coasts; 3. 10 to 20 inches;
4. less than 5 inches a year;
5. Canberra; 6. Indian, Pacific;
7. southeast; 8. All are true.

Page 247
1. Map 1; 2. 200; 3. 10; 4. Sacramento;
5. 500; 6. Pacific Ocean; 7. Nevada,
Arizona; 8. national border

Page 248

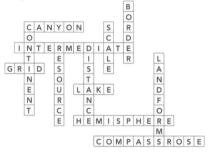

SCIENCE
Pages 252–253

In the fairy tale *The Frog Prince*, an ugly frog kisses a
princess and then turns into a handsome prince. They marry and
live happily ever after. In real life, frogs don't kiss princesses, but
they are otherwise remarkable animals.

Frogs are amphibians. All amphibians are cold-blooded—
their bodies have the same temperature as the air or water
they live in. Amphibians have backbones, no scales, and moist
skin. Frogs begin their lives in calm water as eggs and then as
tadpoles.

But that just defines frogs. What is interesting is that there
are more than 6,300 species of frog! Some are as small as flies,
while others are big enough to eat small snakes, mice, and other
frogs. Some frogs can jump 10 feet. Some live more than 20 years.

Also interesting is how long frogs have been around.
Herpetologists (HUR-puh-tol-oh-jists)—the scientists who study
amphibians and reptiles—know that frogs have existed for at
least 200 million years! They were here along with the dinosaurs.

1. B; Sample answer: Since frogs start
their lives in water, moist must mean
wet, or damp. 2. A; Sample answer:
According to the article, all the other
choices about frogs are true. Plus, it
says that amphibians have no scales.
3. Sample answer: In paragraph 2, it
says that frogs are amphibians, and all
amphibians are cold-blooded.
4. Sample answer: The author did this
to get the reader's attention and to
bring up the idea that real frogs are
fascinating even though they do not
turn into princes.

Pages 254–255

Ponies are not baby horses, though people often think they
are. In fact, horses and ponies are different animals in the same
family. Both are *equines* (E-kwī¯nz). Let's compare them.

All equines are mammals. Horses and ponies are warm-
blooded. They have backbones and skin covered with hair.
Their babies are born live and nurse on the mother's milk. Both
horses and ponies can be used for riding, doing farm work, or
pulling wagons. Both graze to eat a plant-based diet. They
enjoy hay, grass, leaves, fruits, vegetables, and oats.

But these two equines differ in several ways. The key
contrast is in their heights. An equine is a horse if it's 58 or
more inches tall at the shoulder. Ponies rarely get that tall. They
have shorter legs, necks, and heads, and wider bodies than
horses do. Ponies cope with cold weather better than horses do
because they have thicker manes and coats.

Horses and ponies do not behave the same either.
Both can be smart and stubborn, but ponies usually stay
calmer than horses do.

1. C; Sample answer: The writer says
that equines are mammals, which are
warm-blooded. 2. B; In paragraph 3, it
says that the key contrast is in their
heights. 3. Sample answer: Both are
small as babies, but only the horse will
grow to be taller than 58 inches at the
shoulder. Even grown ponies will always
have shorter legs, necks, and heads
than horses have. 4. Sample answer:
The manes and coats of horses are not
as thick as they are on ponies, so they
can't keep as warm as ponies can.

Page 256

G N **M E E R K A T** M K N **A** G K S W **A** R C
A S W D V F R N F P S C N T H F T A H R O
Z Q U E T D S E D I A W T I P A T R B O C
N P A D A X I C H L U M E R L I S D O C C
A L E R K Y B T H A Y E L S E V H V X L U
F L A M I N G O D N E N O **Z E B R A** P D
X A **C O A L A** R T A I T P W E C D R F I
Q Y X C D B **R H I N O C E R O S** I K T L
A D F Y I H I E R T Y H O S G U E T R R
Z L X C O R L F R K D E G P S D N B S M
L I O N D S L P O R A E H **G I R A F F E**
W O **H Y E N A** L O R N T C D R C A S A M
M T D N A G T E N O R A T F P R D S W E
A S D E M **O S T R I C H** U **L E O P A R D**

Answers will vary.

Pages 257–261
Investigation 1: Your child should
notice air bubbles forming in the "Food
and Water" bag. He or she should
come to the conclusion that yeast, like
animals, needs food and water to live.
Investigation 2: Results will vary
depending on foods tested. Sugar
works very well and will likely produce
the most impressive amount of gas.

Page 262
continents, desert, powerful, pouches, webbed

Page 263
1. blue whale; 2. cheetah; 3. Goliath birdeater; 4. sloth; 5. ostrich; 6. sailfish; 7. Komodo dragon; 8. giraffe

Pages 264–265
1. D; Sample answer: The author says that whales spend their entire lives in oceans. 2. C; Sample answer: In the caption about ears, I read that whales "navigate through water by listening to their sounds." That makes me think they are finding their way as they move, so steer seems like the best answer. 3. Sample answer: It helps them make long and deep dives. 4. Sample answer: I read that whales rely more on sounds than on sight to move and hunt. 5. Sample answer: The flukes are the tail at the back of the whale's body. The flippers are on the side of the body. The whale uses its flukes for power when swimming, and maybe to communicate with other whales. It uses its flippers to steer itself as it swims (Flukes and Flippers captions).

Pages 266–267
1. A; Sample answer: The author defines burrs as "prickly, clinging seed cases." 2. B; Sample answer: I picked B because the sticky burrs were an accident that led de Mestral to come up with a useful invention. 3. Sample answer: The tape means the two strips of fabric that will stick together; locking means that they stay stuck until you pull them apart. 4. Sample answer: When he saw how well the burrs clung and how hard they were to pull off, it made him think about a new idea for fastening clothing and other things. 5. Sample answer: I think he was a clever, creative, and hard-working person who used his education to come up with something new and useful.

Page 268
1. bark; 2. leaf; 3. stem; 4. trunk; 5. root

Page 269
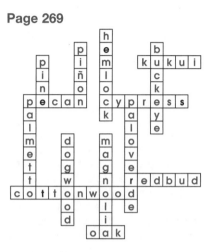

Pages 270–271
1. It persuades the reader to recycle aluminum, glass, plastic, and paper. 2. clean, resources; 3. Answers will vary. Check facts.; Answers will vary but should include two examples of how your child can help keep the planet clean and protect resources.

Pages 272–273
Have you ever watched how snow behaves on a car's windshield? If the temperature stays low, the snow sticks. But if the temperature rises, the snow begins to slide. It moves in chunks down the windshield.

This is a tiny example of an avalanche—a sudden surge of snow and ice down a mountain. A large avalanche might let loose enough snow to cover 20 soccer fields 10-feet deep!

Roaring Snowball Avalanches occur when piled-up layers of snow get too heavy and then weaken. The loosened snow starts to slide down. As it speeds up, it picks up rocks, trees, and even houses, animals, and people in its path. Avalanches grow in size, affecting everything in their way.

Causes Many factors can set off an avalanche. Some are natural causes: heavy rains, warming temperatures, earthquakes, or changes in wind direction. And then there are human causes: snowmobiling, skiing, or explosions.

Danger! Avalanches generally occur in winter or spring. But they can happen any time. And because they start so suddenly, they can be very dangerous.

Page 274 (column 3)
1. C; Sample answer: The dark-print heading of that paragraph is the clue to what factors are. 2. A; Sample answer: It's the only choice not mentioned in the essay. 3. Sample answer: They can happen so suddenly and cause a lot of damage. 4. Sample answer: The author wanted to give an example that readers may know about. Also, it's a simple way to introduce a hard idea.

Page 274
lava, breathe, flattened, ignited, floods

Pages 275–279
Investigation 1: Results will vary depending on materials used to accelerate the melting.
Investigation 2: Results will vary depending on materials used to keep ice from melting.

Page 280

Page 281
Answers will vary.

Pages 282–283
People: People stay in warm houses. People wear heavy coats, gloves, and hats. People eat soup and drink hot chocolate. People go on vacation to places that are warm. People snuggle under the covers and stay in bed a little longer on cold mornings.
Animals: Squirrels, mice, and rabbits find holes in trees and logs and even burrow underground. Animals grow thicker fur. Rabbits and deer eat twigs, bark, and moss. Foxes eat rodents. Some animals migrate to warmer places. Some animals spend part of the winter in a deep sleep called hibernation.

Pages 284–285

Will earthworms wriggle out of the ground prior to a flood? Will sharks swim to deeper waters before a hurricane? Do animals actually have powers beyond those that guide them in their daily lives, powers that enable them to predict natural disasters like earthquakes or hurricanes? The short answer is probably "No." But the long answer is more complex.

Scientists are skeptical that animals have a special sense that enables them to predict the weather. But they know that many animals have more highly developed senses than humans do, and are capable of detecting signals of impending weather change sooner than we can. Some, like dogs, pick up infrasonic sound waves—sounds that are at lower frequencies than we can hear. Others, like the frogs that go silent before a storm, can detect differences in air pressure. However they get their signals, animals learn to associate them with danger. Those signals alert them that it is time to move to a safer area.

All animals have a strong survival instinct, but can they predict weather patterns? Does a groundhog know what kind of spring lies ahead? Will a black bear choose its winter den depending on how cold the upcoming winter promises to be? Not likely, say the scientists. But if you spot a cluster of birds hunkering down outside your window, you'd be wise to take your umbrella.

1. D; Sample answer: The article says that animals can detect change in weather before it happens, so I guessed that impending means approaching, or coming. 2. B; Sample answer: The article mentions each of the other choices but it says in the last paragraph that it's not likely that animals can predict weather patterns. 3. Sample answer: The article explores whether animals can predict natural disasters. Scientists are skeptical of this, but they do acknowledge that animals have superior senses that help them sense weather changes before humans can. 4. Sample answer: I think the author recognizes that, as appealing as it might be to link animal behavior with the power to predict disasters, scientists do not strongly support this idea. There are some apparent connections, but no actual proof of extraordinary powers has been found.

Page 286
Answers will vary.

Pages 287–291
Investigation 1: Results will vary. Your child should be able to determine the direction of the shadow by step 7.
Investigation 2: Your child should determine that Earth turns to make day and night.

Pages 292–293
1. B; Sample answer: I reread the paragraph about rainbows and about the prism. The article says you cannot touch a rainbow, so I picked B. 2. A; Sample answer: I read that refracted means bent. 3. Sample answer: There is no such person. "Roy G. Biv" is a shortcut way to help you remember the colors of the spectrum in order: red, orange, yellow, green, blue, indigo, violet. 4. Sample answer: Newton was a famous scientist who discovered important ideas about light that we still use today. 5. Sample answer: I think the author wanted to get readers interested right away in something that is well known to them. And it is a great way to start talking about rainbows.

Page 294

```
P  Z  B  E  L  H  M  J  U  P  I  T  E  R
Y  X  M  A  R  S  U  G  W  S  Z  L  U  F
I  R  I  M  U  J  A  S  A  T  U  R  N  U
M  E  X  C  L  N  F  M  H  F  X  G  M  F
M  M  L  F  F  E  E  X  K  K  F  S  H  N
E  S  I  H  Y  P  X  M  O  O  N  O  S  Q
R  Z  C  C  S  T  U  L  I  I  C  L  V  D
C  G  Z  Y  E  U  A  Q  M  N  W  C  E  A
U  J  E  S  D  N  Z  N  Q  J  V  X  N  L
R  J  L  G  U  E  C  C  U  R  A  N  U  S
Y  P  W  Y  U  F  U  A  Y  L  L  G  S  B
Y  N  U  E  A  R  T  H  Z  M  G  N  A  L
S  U  N  K  V  V  M  D  T  Y  M  O  Y  I
```

Pages 295–299
Investigation 1: Starting from the top and going counterclockwise the phases should be labeled: full moon, last quarter, new moon, first quarter.
Investigation 2: Going counterclockwise from the full moon, the phases should be in this order: Full Moon, Waning Gibbous, Last Quarter, Waning Crescent, New Moon, Waxing Crescent, First Quarter, Waxing Gibbous.

Page 300
commute, invisible, swimming, scrambled, sponge

Pages 301–305
Investigation 1: Your child should be able to feel that the full bottle gives a bigger push, with more force. Both rolling bottles will give the box a push away from the ramp. The heavier, full bottle will push the box farther.
Investigation 2: Your child may find that the following changes will increase the distance the box moves: a steeper ramp (unless it gets too steep), a longer ramp, a lighter box, a smaller box (assuming its not so small the bottle rolls over it), a heavier bottle, a bigger bottle (assuming it doesn't roll over the box), or a smoother floor surface.

Pages 306–307
Author's purposes: to entertain, to inform

(I) Are you "circus fit"? Big-top performers are. They need to be in peak condition. How else could they perform all those wacky stunts? How do they juggle while balancing on a rope? How do they ride around backwards on a unicycle?

(I) To do all this nutty stuff, circus performers exercise a lot. They must be as strong as they are silly. They must be as fit as they are funny. One major circus now shares its fitness secrets with kids. Clowns, dancers, and acrobats visit schools to teach what they do to stay in shape.

(I) Kids who take part may not learn to prance about in huge flapping shoes. But they will learn how to be strong and flexible. They will get tips for keeping fit and staying safe. Plus, they may learn riddles like this one:

(E) **Q:** Why do lions like to eat high-wire artists?
A: Because they want a well-balanced meal!

(I) When that circus comes to town, the kids get to attend. Some lucky ones may even step into the ring and perform!

1. D; Sample answer: Peak condition means the most fit you can be, and a pro athlete would need to be that fit.
2. C; Sample answer: The article said nothing about those other skills, only that clowns teach kids how to be fit.
3. Sample answer: The riddle is funny because it is a play on words—balancing well on a high wire is different than a well-balanced meal. The author included it to entertain readers.
4. Sample answer: The author does two things. One is to inform readers that circus performers are not just funny—they are strong and in great physical shape. The other is to entertain with a joke and by describing some funny things you see at a circus.

Pages 308–309

Does it matter how much fat, salt, and sugar children eat? Should kids avoid fatty foods like chicken fingers and French fries? Should they steer clear of salty junk foods, like puffed cheese sticks? Should they stay away from foods loaded with chemicals and dyes? Soda has both.

Fat, salt, and sugar make foods taste good. But too much of a good thing can harm you. That's why food scientists strongly support healthy eating. They want to direct children and parents toward wiser food choices. Teachers, school nurses, doctors, and many parents agree. They hope schools will share the responsibility of keeping kids fit and strong.

So, many school communities urge cafeteria lunches to be both tasty and nourishing. They encourage serving wholesome, natural foods. They don't want kids eating foods with unhealthy ingredients in them. And scientists and educators want school lunches to be varied.They suggest that menus celebrate cultural differences.

Teachers and principals care deeply about how kids learn best. Science shows that a healthy diet increases a child's ability to stay alert for learning. That is surely food for thought.

1. A; Sample answer: Junk foods are mentioned in the first paragraph, which describes foods to avoid. 2. C; Sample answer: In the first paragraph, the words avoid, steer clear, and stay away from seem to mean the same thing.
3. Sample answer: The writer worries that kids eat too much junk food—food that has too much salt, sugar, fat, and chemicals, and not enough healthy nutritious food. 4. Sample answer: According to the article, science shows that a healthy diet helps children learn better. Also, teachers believe that schools can share the responsibility for keeping kids alert, fit, and strong.

Pages 310–311

1. D; Sample answer: I read each choice and checked to find it in the text. The only one that isn't there is D.
2. A; Sample answer: Step 2 talks about toasting the seeds in a pan, so I know they are getting heated. Then it says, "Don't let them scorch." So, I think scorch is another word for burn. I know that when toast burns, it gets dark brown. That's why I picked A.
3. Sample answer: You could collect the ingredients and utensils in any order as long as you have them all before you start. But you have to follow the preparation and cooking steps in order.
4. Sample answer: I think it's because you shouldn't even start cooking until you have gathered everything you need.
5. Sample answer: The ingredients list includes butter, sugar, an egg, and flour, which are used to make many kinds of cookies; the first utensil is a cookie sheet; and step 5 talks about a cookie sheet, then says the dough spreads out as it bakes, like a lot of cookies do.

Page 312
Answers will vary.

ADDITION & SUBTRACTION
Page 314
7, 4, 13, 10, 15, 5, 9, 16, 8, 12, 3, 6, 18, 11, 14; Charity, Constance, Edward, Humility, Jasper, Oceanus, Peregrine, Priscilla, Prudence, Remember, Resolve, Samuel, Solomon, Susan, Thomas

Page 315

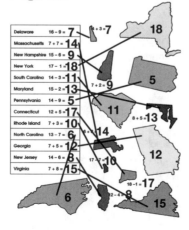

Page 316

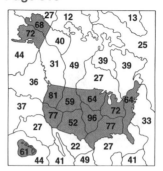

Page 317
Check that your child has circled the correct number of stars.
3 tens, 4 ones, 34; 4 tens, 5 ones, 45; 2 tens, 7 ones, 27; 7 tens, 0 ones, 70; 5 tens, 3 ones, 53; 6 tens, 5 ones 65; 3 tens, 6 ones, 36; 8 tens, 0 ones, 80; 13, 13 + 50 = 63, 6 tens, 3 ones

Page 318

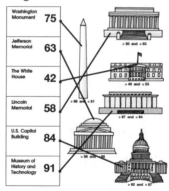

Page 319
52, 53, 82, 61, 96, 52, 82, LINCOLN; 37, 83, 42, 42, 83, 78, 66, 96, 82, JEFFERSON; 98, 72, 64, 65, 53, 82, 45, 47, 96, 82, WASHINGTON

Page 320
37: 3 tens 7 ones, 2 tens 17 ones;
52: 5 tens 2 ones, 4 tens 12 ones;
85: 8 tens 5 ones, 7 tens 15 ones;
43: 4 tens 3 ones, 3 tens 13 ones;
68: 6 tens 8 ones, 5 tens 18 ones;
26: 2 tens 6 ones, 1 ten 16 ones

Page 321

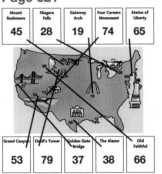

Mount Rushmore	Niagara Falls	Gateway Arch	Four Corners Monument	Statue of Liberty
45	28	19	74	65

Grand Canyon	Devil's Tower	Golden Gate Bridge	The Alamo	Old Faithful
53	79	37	38	66

Page 322

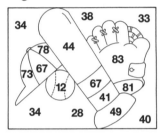

Check your child's coloring.
32, 34, 36, 38, 40, 42, 44, 46, 48, 50

Page 323

16 + 87 = 103, 57 + 11 = 68,
91 + 45 = 136, 39 + 49 = 133,
68 + 29 = 97, 25 + 73 = 98,
83 + 32 = 115, 44 + 58 = 102,
72 + 66 = 138; 87 − 16 = 71,
57 − 11 = 46, 91 − 45 = 46,
94 − 39 = 55, 68 − 29 = 39,
73 − 25 = 48, 83 − 32 = 51,
58 − 44 = 14, 72 − 66 = 6;
A. 41; B. 90; C. 34; D. 58

Page 324

24, 91, 47, 53, 16, 92, 65, 38

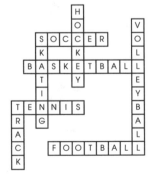

Page 325

56 + 38 = 94, 18 + 24 + 35 = 77,
38 + 34 + 18 = 90, 47 + 24 = 71;
90 − 77 = 13, 94 − 77 = 17, 90 − 71 =
19, 94 − 71 = 23; 47 − 38 = 9;
56 − 18 = 38; 252

Page 326

S. 75; I. 24; A. 65; R. 38; R. 84; W. 57;
H. 58; I. 64; U. 33; O. 72; L. 51; M. 34;
B. 71; L. 80; G. 69; U. 48;
WILLIAM BURROUGHS

Page 327

324 + 632 = 956, 241 + 551 = 792;
155 + 331 = 486, 213 + 313 = 526;
415 + 322 = 737, 143 + 146 = 289,
202 + 216 = 418, 431 + 422 = 853;
142 + 233 = 375, 541 + 134 = 675,
335 + 333 = 668, 712 + 232 = 944;
220 + 314 = 534, 514 + 334 = 848,
224 + 143 = 367, 416 + 132 = 548;
Joe brought $5.40, and Ellie brought
$4.35.

Page 328

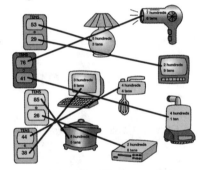

200, 40, 7, 247; 400, 70, 6, 476;
300, 90, 2, 392; 100, 90, 3, 193;
500, 60, 1, 561

Page 329

40, 50, 60; 80, 20, 70; 9 hundreds,
30 tens; 60 tens, 1 hundred;
80 tens, 9 hundreds

Page 330

954	427	554
684	349	364
945	844	472
457	574	942
473	424	842

970	373	872
723	577	884
507	476	397
743	771	712
575	674	974

Page 331

574	534	558
346	506	763
852	523	945
952	524	965
897	563	723

726	622	923
327	288	525
628	824	421
826	842	428
724	725	527

Page 332

534 − 275 = 259; 467 − 278 = 189;
392 − 296 = 96; 625 − 366 = 259;
988 − 589 = 399; 735 − 367 = 368;
854 − 397 = 457; 564 − 498 = 66;
339 − 249 = 90

Page 333

Check your child's coloring.

Page 334

A. 517 + 525 = 1,042;
B. 614 + 478 = 1,092;
C. 709 + 253 = 962;
D. 1,363, 722; E. 709 − 385 = 324,
517 − 463 = 54, 525 − 385 = 140;
253 + 517 + 254 + 614 = 1,638

Page 335

A. 496 − 188 = 308;
B. 956 − 668 = 288;
C. 547 + 239 = 786;
D. 379 + 345 = 724;
E. 723 − 162 = 561;
F. 422 − 215 = 207;
G. 957 − 688 = 269;
H. 884 + 834 = 1,718;
I. 956 − 578 = 378

Page 336

Check labeling.

Page 337

5,063; 3,721; 3,827; 8,749; ALPS;
8,789; 2,429; 3,012; 5,642; 2,351;
ROCKY; 2,429; 5,234; 5,063; 8,789;
5,642; OZARK; 5,063; 6,348; 4,907;
7,483; 8,749; ANDES

Page 338

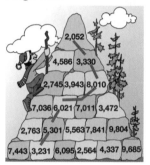

Page 339

F. $39.96; N. $79.96;
N. $99.48; R. $66.99;
K. $86.99; A. $79.77;
L. $88.99; I. $97.00; FRANKLIN;
5, 2, 8, 1, 3, 7, 9, 4, 6

Page 340

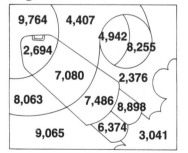

Check your child's coloring.

Page 341

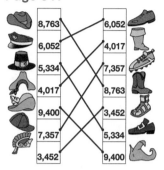

Page 342

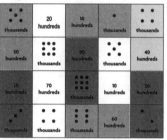

3,167; 5,703; 6,039; 4,584; 9,940

Page 343

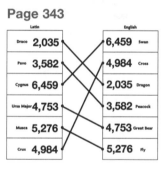

Page 344

MATH is AWESOME!

MATH

Pages 346–347
Scores will vary.

Page 348
Answers will vary.

Page 349
A. thousands; B. tens; C. hundreds;
D. tens; E. hundreds; F. ones; G. tens
The answer to the secret riddle is
"a secret."

Page 350
1. 10; 2. 20; 3. 50; 4. 90; 5. 200;
6. 400; 7. 600; 8. 300; 9. 500;
10. 700
What did the farmer get when he tried
to reach the beehive?
A "buzzy" signal

Page 351
C3: jeweled crown; B1: ruby necklace;
C5: golden cup; D4: X; A4: wooden
treasure chest; E1: silvery sword

Page 352
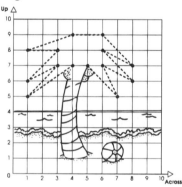

Page 353
1. cheetah; 2. black mamba snake;
3. zebra; 4. lion; 5. 7; 6. yes;
7. speed; 8. no

Page 354
5 pennies equal 5 cents, one nickel
equals 5 cents; 10 pennies equal 10
cents, 2 nickels equal 10 cents, one
dime equals 10 cents; 25 pennies equal
25 cents, 5 nickels equal 25 cents, one
quarter equals 25 cents

Page 355

1. January and December; 2. 80°;
3. June, July, and September;
4. Yes; 10°; 5. No; 6. Warmer; 7. Fall;
8. May; 9. 40 degrees

Page 356

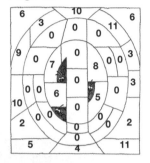

Page 357

A. 6, 16, 22, 14; B. 16, 8, 4, 8; C. 24,
10, 20, 24; D. 18, 2, 20, 14; E. 0, 12, 6,
0; F. 10, 18; G. 12, 2; H. 22, 4;
Rhymes will vary.

Page 358

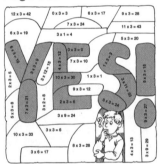

3, 30 letters

Page 359

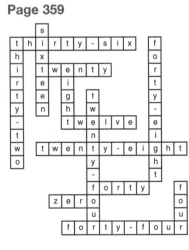

44 buttons

Page 360

A. 10; B. 1; C. 7; D. 50; E. 12; F. 30;
G. 11; H. 15; I. 40; J. 9; K. 5; L. 5;
M. 35; N. 60; O. 4; 60 nuts

Page 361

yellow: 0 + 66 + 12 + 60 = 138; red: 18
+ 30 + 36 + 6 + 24 = 114; orange: 54 +
18 + 66 + 24 + 30 + 48 = 240; blue: 42
+ 72 + 60 + 24 = 198; green: 30 + 42 +
48 + 72 + 0 = 192; purple: 36 + 18 + 12
+ 18 + 6 = 90; 48 fireworks

Page 362

49 times

Page 363

32, 56, 72, 48, 24, 64, 96, 80, 16, 0, 24,
88, 8, 32, 56, 48, 16, 0, 88, 40, 80, 40,
96, 8, 72; 96 seconds

Page 364

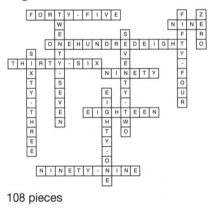

108 pieces

Page 365

Page 366

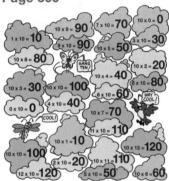

70 clouds

Page 367

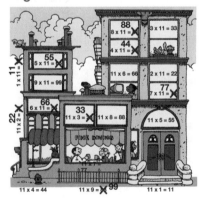

Page 368
A. 12 x 7 = 84, 12 x 0 = 0;
B. 12 x 8 = 96, 12 x 11 = 132,
12 x 6 = 72, 12 x 12 = 144, 12 x 3 = 36;
C. 12 x 1 = 12, 12 x 5 = 60,
7 x 12 = 84, 12 x 9 = 108, 12 x 4 = 48;
D. 12 x 10 = 120, 4 x 12 = 48,
8 x 12 = 96, 11 x 12 = 132, 2 x 12 = 24
72 sentences; Answers will vary.

Page 369

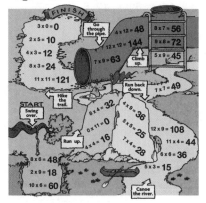

9 x 7 = 63

Page 370
YOUR SMILE
6 x 1 = 6; 6 x 4 = 24; 7 x 7 = 49;
6 x 2 = 12; 7 x 9 = 63; 6 x 3 = 18;
7 x 3 = 21; 7 x 6 = 42; 7 x 4 = 28;
6 x 5 = 30; 6 x 6 = 36; 6 x 9 = 54;
7 x 8 = 56; 7 x 0 = 0; 6 x 7 = 42;
6 x 0 = 0; 7 x 5 = 35; 6 x 8 = 48;
7 x 2 = 14; 7 x 1 = 7

Page 371

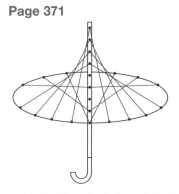

a. 11 b. 10 c. 0 d. 3 e. 4 f. 12

Page 372
6 x 1 = 6; 6 x 4 = 24; 7 x 6 = 42;
11 x 7 = 77; 7 x 8 = 56; 10 x 6 = 60;
8 x 6 = 48; 7 x 7 = 49; 12 x 7 = 84;
6 x 3 = 18; 7 x 5 = 35; 5 x 6 = 30;
6 x 7 = 42; 7 x 1 = 7; 7 x 3 = 21;
10 x 7 = 70 11 x 6 = 66; 7 x 9 = 63;
6 x 9 = 54; 12 x 6 = 72; 7 x 9 = 63;
6 x 6 = 36; 2 x 7 = 14; 4 x 7 = 28
Taking It Further: 8 x 49 = 392

Page 373
1. 9R1; 2. 3R3; 3. 4R0; 4. 5R0; 5. 2R0;
6. 6R1; 7. 3R0; 8. 9R2; 9. 6R0; 10. 4R3

Page 374
35 ÷ 5 = 7; 55 ÷ 5 = 11; 30 ÷ 5 = 6
15 ÷ 5 = 3; 10 ÷ 5 = 2; 45 ÷ 5 = 9
15 ÷ 5 = 3; 5 ÷ 5 = 1; 25 ÷ 5 = 5
20 ÷ 5 = 4; 25 ÷ 5 = 5; 40 ÷ 5 = 8
45 ÷ 5 = 9; 5 ÷ 5 = 1
Taking It Further: 5, 10, 15, 20, 25, 30, 35, 40

Page 375
880 ÷ 2 = 440; 996 ÷ 3 = 332;
576 ÷ 4 = 144; 502 ÷ 2 = 251;
992 ÷2 = 496; 603 ÷3 = 201;
903 ÷ 3 = 301; 392 ÷ 2 = 196;
982 ÷ 2 = 491; 897 ÷ 3 = 299;
738 ÷ 6 = 123; 742 ÷ 2 = 371;
990 ÷ 3 = 330
Taking It Further:

```
      4 3 2
  2 ) 8 6 4
    - 8
      0 6
      - 6
        0 4
        - 4
          0
```

Page 376
1. 20 buttons; 2. 56 buttons;
3. 30 mice; 4. 126 buttons; 5. 8 buttons
Super Challenge: 6 teams

Page 377
1. Here is one way to complete the square. (Child may invert the rows and columns.)

2. 8 dimes, 4 nickels, and 7 pennies
3. Here is one way to "connect the dots":

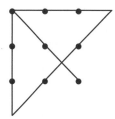

4. SHOES (53045)

Page 378
1. 17 triangles; 2. They show the same time in different ways. 3. Child should complete the shapes. 4. Answers will vary.

Page 379
1. Answers will vary. Child may take an average class size of 30 students and multiply 30 by the number of classes in the school. 2. Answers include 11, 88, 69, and 96. 3. 3 cats
4.

5. three cuts

Page 380
1. 1/4; 2. 1/3; 3. 1/3; 4. 1/2;
5. 1/2; 6. 1/4; 7. 1/3; 8. 1/2;
9. 1/4; 10. 1/2; 11. 1/4; 12. 1/3

Page 381
1. 3/6; 2. 2/4; 3. 3/8; 4. 2/3;
5. 3/4; 6. 4/5; 7. 5/6; 8. 5/8

Page 382
Answers will vary.

Page 383
1. 4 students; 2. 8 students;
3. 6 students

Page 384

3/20 + 2/20 = 1/4; 2/16 + 2/16 = 1/4;
1/14 + 1/14 = 1/7; 1/9 + 2/9 = 1/3;
1/4 + 2/4 = 3/4; 4/9 + 2/9 = 2/3;
4/10 + 2/10 = 3/5; 1/5 + 2/5 = 3/5;
6/12 + 5/12 = 11/12; 4/10 + 5/10 = 9/10;
4/12 + 7/12 = 11/12; 1/10 + 8/10 = 9/10;
4/14 + 6/14 = 5/7; 6/10 + 2/10 = 4/5;
4/8 + 2/8 = 3/4; 4/8 + 3/8 = 7/8;
2/10 + 3/10 = 1/2; 1/6 + 2/6 = 1/2;
1/16 + 1/16 = 1/8; 3/40 + 7/40 = 1/4

Page 385

Check that children have found all of the mistakes and that they have fixed the mistakes with reasonable corrections. Mistakes: 8 days a week should be 7; 8:75 pm is not possible; $10.99 off mountain bikes; bicycle chain is $6.00 a foot; bike helmets are $14.99; you save only $.01, not $1.00, on 2 rolls of tape; free stickers can't be 10 cents each; half-price bicycle seats should be $8.50. The additional mistake—a clock with three hands.

Pages 386–387

apple: 5 pennies
jelly: 2 dimes or 1 dime + 2 nickels
cider: 1 quarter + 1 nickel
corn: 3 dimes + 1 nickel or
2 dimes + 3 nickels
pumpkin: 1 quarter + 2 dimes or
1 quarter + 1 dime + 2 nickels
squash: 1 quarter + 2 dimes + 1 nickel
pie: 1 quarter + 1 dime + 1 nickel
hay ride: 2 dimes + 1 nickel or
2 dimes + 5 pennies

Page 388

Page 389

Answer: "Meet you at noon!"

Page 390

The actual measurements will vary somewhat, but they should be close to the following:
1. 14 1/2 inches; 2. 19 inches
3. 13 1/2 inches; 4. 21 inches

Page 391

Answers will vary.

Page 392

1. ounces; 2. pounds; 3. ounces;
4. pounds; 5. pounds; 6. pounds;
7. ounces; 8. ounces; 9. pounds;
10. ounces; 11. ounces; 12. pounds;
13. pounds; 14. ounces; 15. ounces

Page 393

1. 90°F; 2. 0°C; 3. 30°C; 4. 55°F;
5. 30°F; 6. 40°F; 7. 68°F; 8. 20°C;
9. 75°F; 10. 80°F

Page 394

1. 100; 2. 7; 3. 36; 4. 5280; 5. 60;
6. 12; 7. 12; 8. 4; 9. 26; 10. 20;
11. 16; 12. 52; 13. 5; 14. 2; 15. 24

Page 395

1. 5; 2. 11; 3. 30; 4. 12; 5. 8; 6. 17

Page 396

A. 1F, 2G, 3B, 4C or A, 5E, 6I, 7E, 8H, 9G, 10G, 11C
B. 1B, 2F, 3D, 4I, 5F, 6E, 7A, 8D, 9I, 10F, 11I
C. 1I, 2C, 3C, 4G, 5G, 6C, 7F, 8I, 9B, 10C or A, 11F

Page 397

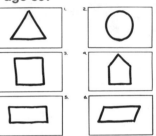

Pages 398–399

Children's tessellate patterns will vary.

Page 400

10; Answers will vary.

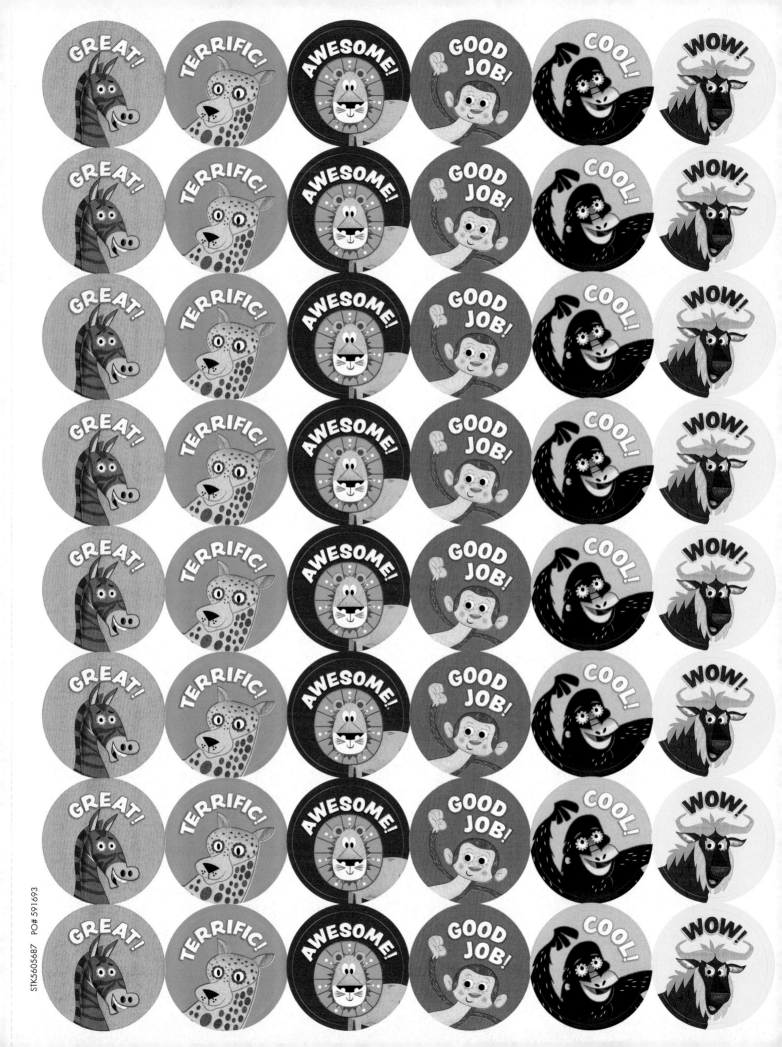